INTO THE BLOODY JAWS OF DEATH

They had reached the last step, and were about to push La into the claws of the lion, when they were arrested by a loud cry from one side of the chamber—a cry that halted the Gomangani and brought the assembled Bolgani to their feet in astonishment and anger, for the sight that met their eyes was well-qualified to arouse the latter within them.

Leaping into the room with raised spear was the almost naked white man of whom they had heard, but whom none of them had as yet seen. And so quick was he that in the very instant of entry—even before they could rise to their feet—he had launched his spear . . .

By Edgar Rice Burroughs
Published by Ballantine Books:

THE TARZAN SERIES
Tarzan of the Apes (#1)
The Return of Tarzan (#2)
The Beasts of Tarzan (#3)
The Son of Tarzan (#4)
Tarzan and the Jewels of Opar (#5)
Jungle Tales of Tarzan (#6)
Tarzan the Untamed (#7)
Tarzan the Terrible (#8)
Tarzan and the Golden Lion (#9)
Tarzan and the Ant Men (#10)
Tarzan, Lord of the Jungle (#11)
Tarzan and the Lost Empire (#12)
Tarzan at the Earth's Core (#13)
Tarzan the Invincible (#14)
Tarzan Triumphant (#15)
Tarzan and the City of Gold (#16)
Tarzan and the Lion Man (#17)
Tarzan and the Leopard Men (#18)
Tarzan's Quest (#19)
Tarzan and the Forbidden City (#20)
Tarzan the Magnificent (#21)
Tarzan and the Foreign Legion (#22)
Tarzan and the Madman (#23)
Tarzan and the Castaways (#24)

By Edgar Rice Burroughs and Joe R. Lansdale:
TARZAN: THE LOST ADVENTURE

COMPLETE AND UNABRIDGED!

And be sure to look for all 11 books of the *Mars* series and all 6 books of the *Pellucidar* series, also published by Ballantine!

TARZAN AND THE GOLDEN LION

Edgar Rice Burroughs

TARZAN AND THE ANT MEN

A Del Rey® Book
BALLANTINE BOOKS • NEW YORK

This book contains an excerpt from the forthcoming edition of *Tarzan: The Lost Adventure* by Edgar Rice Burroughs and Joe R. Lansdale. This excerpt has been set for this edition only and may not reflect the final content of the forthcoming edition.

A Del Rey® Book
Published by Ballantine Books
Excerpt © 1995 by Edgar Rice Burroughs, Inc.

Tarzan and the Golden Lion copyright © 1922, 1923 by Edgar Rice Burroughs, Inc.
Tarzan and the Ant Men copyright © 1924 by Edgar Rice Burroughs, Inc.

This Edgar Rice Burroughs, Inc., Authorized Edition published in the United States by Ballantine Books, a division of Random House, Inc., New York, and simultaneously in Canada by Random House of Canada Limited, Toronto.

Trademark TARZAN® Owned by EDGAR RICE BURROUGHS, INC., and Used by Permission

http://www.randomhouse.com

Library of Congress Catalog Card Number: 96-93070

ISBN 0-345-41348-2

This authorized edition published by arrangement with Edgar Rice Burroughs, Inc.

Manufactured in the United States of America

First Edition: May 1997

10 9 8 7 6 5 4 3 2 1

Contents

TARZAN
AND THE
GOLDEN LION

Contents

1

The Golden Lion

SABOR, THE LIONESS, suckled her young—a single fuzzy ball, spotted like Sheeta, the leopard. She lay in the warm sunshine before the rocky cavern that was her lair, stretched out upon her side with half closed eyes, yet Sabor was alert. There had been three of these little, fuzzy balls at first—two daughters and a son—and Sabor and Numa, their sire, had been proud of them; proud and happy. But kills had not been plentiful, and Sabor, undernourished, had been unable to produce sufficient milk to nourish properly three lusty cubs, and then a cold rain had come, and the little ones had sickened. Only the strongest survived—the two daughters had died. Sabor had mourned, pacing to and fro beside the pitiful bits of bedraggled fur, whining and moaning. Now and again she would nose them with her muzzle as though she would awaken them from the long sleep that knows no waking. At last, however, she abandoned her efforts, and now her whole savage heart was filled with concern for the little male cub that remained to her. That was why Sabor was more alert than usual.

Numa, the lion, was away. Two nights before he had made a kill and dragged it to their lair and last night he had fared forth again, but he had not returned. Sabor was thinking, as she half dozed, of Wappi, the plump antelope, that her splendid mate might this very minute be dragging through the tangled jungle to her. Or perhaps it would be Pacco, the zebra, whose flesh was the best beloved of her kind—juicy, succulent Pacco. Sabor's mouth watered.

5

Ah, what was that? The shadow of a sound had come to those keen ears. She raised her head, cocking it first upon one side and then the other, as with up-pricked ears she sought to catch the faintest repetition of that which had disturbed her. Her nose sniffed the air. There was but the suggestion of a breeze, but what there was moved toward her from the direction of the sound she had heard, and which she still heard in a slightly increasing volume that told her that whatever was making it was approaching her. As it drew closer the beast's nervousness increased and she rolled over on her belly, shutting off the milk supply from the cub, which vented its disapproval in miniature growls until a low, querulous whine from the lioness silenced him, then he stood at her side, looking first at her and then in the direction toward which she looked, cocking his little head first on one side and then on the other.

Evidently there was a disturbing quality in the sound that Sabor heard—something that inspired a certain restlessness, if not actual apprehension—though she could not be sure as yet that it boded ill. It might be her great lord returning, but it did not sound like the movement of a lion, certainly not like a lion dragging a heavy kill. She glanced at her cub, breathing as she did so a plaintive whine. There was always the fear that some danger menaced him—this last of her little family—but she, Sabor the lioness, was there to defend him.

Presently the breeze brought to her nostrils the scent-spoor of the thing that moved toward her through the jungle. Instantly the troubled mother-face was metamorphosed into a bare-fanged, glittering-eyed mask of savage rage, for the scent that had come up to her through the jungle was the hated man-scent. She rose to her feet, her head flattened, her sinuous tail twitching nervously. Through that strange medium by which animals communicate with one another she cautioned her cub to lie down and remain where he was until she returned, then she moved rapidly and silently to meet the intruder.

The cub had heard what its mother heard and now he caught the smell of man—an unfamiliar smell that had never impinged upon his nostrils before, yet a smell that he knew at once for that of an enemy—a smell that brought a reaction as typical as that which marked the attitude of the grown lioness, bringing the hairs along his little spine erect and baring his tiny fangs. As the adult moved quickly and stealthily into the underbrush the small cub, ignoring her injunction, followed after her, his hindquarters wobbling from side to side, after the manner of the very young of his kind, the ridiculous gait comporting ill with the dignified bearing of his forequarters; but the lioness, intent upon that which lay before her, did not know that he followed her.

There was dense jungle before the two for a hundred yards, but through it the lions had worn a tunnel-like path to their lair; and then there was a small clearing through which ran a well-worn jungle trail, out of the jungle at one end of the clearing and into the jungle again at the other. As Sabor reached the clearing she saw the object of her fear and hatred well within it. What if the man-thing were not hunting her or hers? What if he even dreamed not of their presence? These facts were as nothing to Sabor, the lioness, today. Ordinarily she would have let him pass unmolested, so long as he did not come close enough to threaten the safety of her cub; or, cubless, she would have slunk away at the first intimation of his approach. But today the lioness was nervous and fearful—fearful because of the single cub that remained to her—her maternal instinct centered threefold, perhaps, upon this lone and triply loved survivor—and so she did not wait for the man to threaten the safety of her little one; but instead she moved to meet him and to stop him. From the soft mother she had become a terrifying creature of destruction, her brain obsessed by a single thought—to kill.

She did not hesitate an instant at the edge of the clearing, nor did she give the slightest warning. The first intimation that the black warrior had that there was a lion within twenty miles of him, was the terrifying apparition of this devil-faced cat charging across the clearing toward him with the speed of an arrow. The black was not searching for lions. Had he known that there was one near he would have given it a wide berth. He would have fled now had there been anywhere to flee. The nearest tree was farther from him than was the lioness. She could overhaul him before he would have covered a quarter of the distance. There was no hope and there was only one thing to do. The beast was almost upon him and behind her he saw a tiny cub. The man bore a heavy spear. He carried it far back with his right hand and hurled it at the very instant that Sabor rose to seize him. The spear passed through the savage heart and almost simultaneously the giant jaws closed upon the face and skull of the warrior. The momentum of the lioness carried the two heavily to the ground, dead except for a few spasmodic twitchings of their muscles.

The orphaned cub stopped twenty feet away and surveyed the first great catastrophe of his life with questioning eyes. He wanted to approach his dam but a natural fear of the man-scent held him away. Presently he commenced to whine in a tone that always brought his mother to him hurriedly; but this time she did not come—she did not even rise and look toward him. He was puzzled—he could not understand it. He continued to cry, feeling all the while more sad and more lonely. Gradually he crept closer to his mother. He saw that the strange creature she had killed did not move and after a while he felt less terror of it, so that at last he found the courage to come quite close to his mother and sniff at her. He still whined to her, but she did not answer. It dawned on him at last that there was something wrong—that his great, beautiful mother was not as she had been—a change had come over her; yet still he clung to her, crying much until at last he fell asleep, cuddled close to her dead body.

It was thus that Tarzan found him—Tarzan and Jane, his wife, and their son, Korak the Killer, returning from the mysterious land of Pal-ul-don from which the two men had rescued Jane Clayton. At the sound of their approach the cub opened his eyes and rising, flattened his ears and snarled at them, backing close against his dead mother. At sight of him the ape-man smiled.

"Plucky little devil," he commented, taking in the story of the tragedy at a single glance. He approached the spitting cub, expecting it to turn and run away; but it did nothing of the sort. Instead it snarled more ferociously and struck at his extended hand as he stooped and reached for it.

"What a brave little fellow," cried Jane. "Poor little orphan!"

"He's going to make a great lion, or he would have if his dam had lived," said Korak. "Look at that back—as straight and strong as a spear. Too bad the rascal has got to die."

"He doesn't have to die," returned Tarzan.

"There's not much chance for him—he'll need milk for a couple of months more, and who's going to get it for him?"

"I am," replied Tarzan.

"You're going to adopt him?"

Tarzan nodded.

Korak and Jane laughed. "That'll be fine," commented the former.

"Lord Greystoke, foster mother to the son of Numa," laughed Jane.

Tarzan smiled with them, but he did not cease his attentions toward the cub. Reaching out suddenly he caught the little lion by the scruff of its neck and then stroking it gently he talked to it in a low, crooning tone. I do not know what he said; but perhaps the cub did, for presently it ceased its struggles and no longer sought to scratch or bite the caressing hand. After that he picked it up and held it against his breast. It did not seem afraid now, nor did it even bare its fangs against this close proximity to the erstwhile hated man-scent.

"How do you do it?" exclaimed Jane Clayton.

Tarzan shrugged his broad shoulders. "Your kind are not afraid of you—these are really my kind, try to civilize me as you will, and perhaps that is why they are not afraid of me when I give them the signs of friendship. Even this little rascal seems to know it, doesn't he?"

"I can never understand it," commented Korak. "I think I am rather familiar with African animals, yet I haven't the power over them or the understanding that you have. Why is it?"

"There is but one Tarzan," said Lady Greystoke, smiling at her son teasingly, and yet her tone was not without a note of pride.

"Remember that I was born among beasts and raised by beasts," Tarzan reminded him. "Perhaps after all my father was an ape—you know Kala always insisted that he was."

"John! How can you?" exclaimed Jane. "You know perfectly well who your father and mother were."

Tarzan looked solemnly at his son and closed one eye. "Your mother never can learn to appreciate the fine qualities of the anthropoids. One might almost think that she objected to the suggestion that she had mated with one of them."

"John Clayton, I shall never speak to you again if you don't

stop saying such hideous things. I am ashamed of you. It is bad
enough that you are an unregenerate wild-man, without trying
to suggest that you may be an ape into the bargain."

The long journey from Pal-ul-don was almost completed—
inside the week they should be again at the site of their former
home. Whether anything now remained of the ruins the Germans had left was problematical. The barns and outhouses
had all been burned and the interior of the bungalow partially
wrecked. Those of the Waziri, the faithful native retainers of
the Greystokes, who had not been killed by Hauptman Fritz
Schneider's soldiers, had rallied to the beat of the war-drum
and gone to place themselves at the disposal of the English in
whatever capacity they might be found useful to the great
cause of humanity. This much Tarzan had known before he
set out in search of Lady Jane; but how many of his warlike
Waziri had survived the war and what further had befallen his
vast estates he did not know. Wandering tribes of natives, or
raiding bands of Arab slavers might have completed the
demolition inaugurated by the Hun, and it was likely, too, that
the jungle had swept up and reclaimed its own, covering his
clearings and burying amidst its riot of lush verdure every sign
of man's brief trespass upon its world-old preserves.

Following the adoption of the tiny Numa, Tarzan was compelled to an immediate consideration of the needs of his *protégé*
in planning his marches and his halts, for the cub must have sustenance and that sustenance could be naught but milk. Lion's
milk was out of the question, but fortunately they were now in
a comparatively well-peopled country where villages were not
infrequent and where the great Lord of the Jungle was known,
feared, and respected, and so it was that upon the afternoon of
the day he had found the young lion Tarzan approached a village for the purpose of obtaining milk for the cub.

At first the natives appeared sullen and indifferent, looking with contempt upon whites who traveled without a large
safari—with contempt and without fear. With no safari these
strangers could carry no presents for them, nor anything wherewith to repay for the food they would doubtless desire, and
with no askari they could not demand food, or rather they
could not enforce an order, nor could they protect themselves

should it seem worthwhile to molest them. Sullen and indifferent the natives seemed, yet they were scarce unconcerned, their curiosity being aroused by the unusual apparel and ornamentation of these whites. They saw them almost as naked as themselves and armed similarly except that one, the younger man, carried a rifle. All three wore the trappings of Pal-ul-don, primitive and barbaric, and entirely strange to the eyes of the simple blacks.

"Where is your chief?" asked Tarzan as he strode into the village amongst the women, the children, and the yapping dogs.

A few dozing warriors rose from the shadows of the huts where they had been lying and approached the newcomers.

"The chief sleeps," replied one. "Who are you to awaken him? What do you want?"

"I wish to speak to your chief. Go and fetch him!"

The warrior looked at him in wide-eyed amaze, and then broke into a loud laugh.

"The chief must be brought to him," he cried, addressing his fellows, and then, laughing loudly, he slapped his thigh and nudged those nearest him with his elbows.

"Tell him," continued the ape-man, "that Tarzan would speak with him."

Instantly the attitude of his auditors underwent a remarkable transformation—they fell back from him and they ceased laughing—their eyes very wide and round. He who had laughed loudest became suddenly solemn. "Bring mats," he cried, "for Tarzan and his people to sit upon, while I fetch Umanga the chief," and off he ran as fast as he could as though glad of the excuse to escape the presence of the mighty one he feared he had offended.

It made no difference now that they had no safari, no askari, nor any presents. The villagers were vying with one another to do them honor. Even before the chief came many had already brought presents of food and ornaments. Presently Umanga appeared. He was an old man who had been a chief even before Tarzan of the Apes was born. His manner was patriarchal and dignified and he greeted his guest as one great man might greet another, yet he was undeniably pleased that the Lord of the Jungle had honored his village with a visit.

When Tarzan explained his wishes and exhibited the lion cub Umanga assured him that there would be milk a-plenty so long as Tarzan honored them with his presence—warm milk, fresh from the chief's own goats. As they palavered the ape-man's keen eyes took in every detail of the village and its people, and presently they alighted upon a large bitch among the numerous curs that overran the huts and the street. Her udder was swollen with milk and the sight of it suggested a plan to Tarzan. He jerked a thumb in the direction of the animal. "I would buy her," he said to Umanga.

"She is yours, Bwana, without payment," replied the chief. "She whelped two days since and last night her pups were all stolen from her nest, doubtless by a great snake; but if you will accept them I will give you instead as many younger and fatter dogs as you wish, for I am sure that this one would prove poor eating."

"I do not wish to eat her," replied Tarzan. "I will take her along with me to furnish milk for the cub. Have her brought to me."

Some boys then caught the animal and tying a thong about its neck dragged it to the ape-man. Like the lion, the dog was at first afraid, for the scent of the Tarmangani was not as the scent of the blacks, and it snarled and snapped at its new master; but at length he won the animal's confidence so that it lay quietly beside him while he stroked its head. To get the lion close to it was, however, another matter, for here both were terrified by the enemy scent of the other—the lion snarling and spitting and the dog bare-fanged and growling. It required patience—infinite patience—but at last the thing was an accomplished fact and the cur bitch suckled the son of Numa. Hunger had succeeded in overcoming the natural suspicion of the lion, while the firm yet kindly attitude of the ape-man had won the confidence of the canine, which had been accustomed through life to more of cuffs and kicks than kindness.

That night Tarzan had the dog tied in the hut he occupied, and twice before morning he made her lie while the cub fed. The next day they took leave of Umanga and his people and with the dog still upon a leash trotting beside them they set off once more toward home, the young lion cuddled in the hollow of one of Tarzan's arms or carried in a sack slung across his shoulder.

They named the lion Jad-bal-ja, which in the language of the pithecanthropi of Pal-ul-don, means the Golden Lion, because of his color. Every day he became more accustomed to them and to his foster mother, who finally came to accept him as flesh of her flesh. The bitch they called Za, meaning girl. The second day they removed her leash and she followed them willingly through the jungle, nor ever after did she seek to leave them, nor was happy unless she was near one of the three.

As the moment approached when the trail should break from the jungle onto the edge of the rolling plain where their home had been, the three were filled with suppressed excitement, though none uttered a syllable of the hope and fear that was in the heart of each. What would they find? What *could* they find other than the same tangled mass of vegetation that the ape-man had cleared away to build his home when first he had come there with his bride?

At last they stepped from the concealing verdure of the forest to look out across the plain where, in the distance, the outlines of the bungalow had once been clearly discernible nestled amidst the trees and shrubs that had been retained or imported to beautify the grounds.

"Look!" cried Lady Jane. "It is there—it is still there!"

"But what are those other things to the left, beyond it?" asked Korak.

"They are the huts of natives," replied Tarzan.

"The fields are being cultivated!" exclaimed the woman.

"And some of the outbuildings have been rebuilt," said Tarzan. "It can mean but one thing—the Waziri have come back from the war—my faithful Waziri. They have restored what the Hun destroyed and are watching over our home until we return."

2

The Training of Jad-bal-ja

AND SO TARZAN of the Apes, and Jane Clayton, and Korak came home after a long absence and with them came Jad-bal-ja, the golden lion, and Za, the bitch. Among the first to meet them and to welcome them home was old Muviro, father of Wasimbu, who had given his life in defense of the home and wife of the ape-man.

"Ah, Bwana," cried the faithful black, "my old eyes are made young again by the sight of you. It has been long that you have been gone, but though many doubted that you would return, old Muviro knew that the great world held nothing that might overcome his master. And so he knew, too, that his master would return to the home of his love and the land where his faithful Waziri awaited him; but that she, whom we have mourned as dead, should have returned is beyond belief, and great shall be the rejoicing in the huts of the Waziri tonight. And the earth shall tremble to the dancing feet of the warriors and the heavens ring with the glad cries of their women, since the three they love most on earth have come back to them."

And in truth, great indeed was the rejoicing in the huts of the Waziri. And not for one night alone, but for many nights did the dancing and the rejoicing continue until Tarzan was compelled to put a stop to the festivities that he and his family might gain a few hours of unbroken slumber. The ape-man found that not only had his faithful Waziri, under the equally faithful guidance of his English foreman, Jervis, completely rehabilitated his stables, corrals, and outbuildings, as well as

14

the native huts, but had restored the interior of the bungalow, so that in all outward appearances the place was precisely as it had been before the raid of the Germans.

Jervis was at Nairobi on the business of the estate, and it was some days after their arrival that he returned to the ranch. His surprise and happiness were no less genuine than those of the Waziri. With the chief and warriors he sat for hours at the feet of the Big Bwana, listening to an account of the strange land of Pal-ul-don and the adventures that had befallen the three during Lady Greystoke's captivity there, and with the Waziri he marveled at the queer pets the ape-man had brought back with him. That Tarzan might have fancied a mongrel native cur was strange enough, but that he should have adopted a cub of his hereditary enemies, Numa and Sabor, seemed beyond all belief. And equally surprising to them all was the manner of Tarzan's education of the cub.

The golden lion and his foster mother occupied a corner of the ape-man's bedroom, and many was the hour each day that he spent in training and educating the little spotted, yellow ball—all playfulness and affection now, but one day to grow into a great, savage beast of prey.

As the days passed and the golden lion grew, Tarzan taught it many tricks—to fetch and carry, to lie motionless in hiding at his almost inaudible word of command, to move from point to point as he indicated, to hunt for hidden things by scent and to retrieve them, and when meat was added to its diet he fed it always in a way that brought grim smiles to the savage lips of the Waziri warriors, for Tarzan had built for him a dummy in the semblance of a man and the meat that the lion was to eat was fastened always at the throat of the dummy. Never did the manner of feeding vary. At a word from the ape-man the golden lion would crouch, belly to the ground, and then Tarzan would point at the dummy and whisper the single word "kill." However hungry he might be, the lion learned never to move toward his meat until that single word had been uttered by its master; and then with a rush and a savage growl it drove straight for the flesh. While it was little it had difficulty at first in clambering up on the dummy to the savory morsel fastened at the figure's throat, but as it grew older and larger it gained the objective more easily, and finally a simple leap would carry it to its goal and down would go the dummy upon its back with the young lion tearing at its throat.

There was one lesson that, of all the others, was most difficult to learn and it is doubtful that any other than Tarzan of the Apes, reared by beasts, among beasts, could have overcome the savage blood-lust of the carnivore and rendered his natural instinct subservient to the will of his master. It took weeks and months of patient endeavor to accomplish this single item of the lion's education, which consisted in teaching him that at the word "fetch" he must find an indicated object and return with it to his master, even the dummy with raw meat tied at its throat, and that he must not touch the meat nor harm the dummy nor any other article that he was fetching, but place them carefully at the ape-man's feet. Afterward he learned always to be sure of his reward, which usually consisted in a double portion of the meat he loved best.

Lady Greystoke and Korak were often interested spectators of the education of the golden lion, though the former expressed mystification as to the purpose of such elaborate training of the young cub and some misgivings as to the wisdom of the ape-man's program.

"What in the world can you do with such a brute after he is grown?" she asked. "He bids fair to be a mighty Numa. Being accustomed to men he will be utterly fearless of them, and having fed always at the throat of a dummy he will look there at the throat of the living men for his food hereafter."

"He will feed only upon what I tell him to feed," replied the ape-man.

"But you do not expect him to feed always upon men?" she interrogated, laughingly.

"He will never feed upon men."

"But how can you prevent it, having taught him from cubhood always to feed upon men?"

"I am afraid, Jane, that you underestimate the intelligence of a lion, or else I very much overestimate it. If your theory is correct the hardest part of my work is yet before me, but if I am right it is practically complete now. However, we will experiment a bit and see which is right. We shall take Jad-bal-ja out upon the plain with us this afternoon. Game is plentiful and we shall have no difficulty in ascertaining just how much control I have over young Numa after all."

"I'll wager a hundred pounds," said Korak, laughing, "that he does just what he jolly well pleases after he gets a taste of live blood."

"You're on, my son," said the ape-man. "I think I am going to show you and your mother this afternoon what you or anyone else never dreamed could be accomplished."

"Lord Greystoke, the world's premier animal trainer!" cried Lady Greystoke, and Tarzan joined them in their laughter.

"It is not animal training," said the ape-man. "The plan upon which I work would be impossible to anyone but Tarzan of the Apes. Let us take a hypothetical case to illustrate what I mean. There comes to you some creature whom you hate, whom by instinct and heredity you consider a deadly enemy. You are afraid of him. You understand no word that he speaks. Finally, by means sometimes brutal he impresses upon your mind his wishes. You may do the thing he wants, but do you do it with a spirit of unselfish loyalty? You do not—you do it under compulsion, hating the creature that forces his will upon you. At any moment that you felt it was in your power to do so, you would disobey him. You would even go further—you would turn upon him and destroy him. On the other hand, there comes to you one with whom you are familiar; he is a friend, a protector. He understand and speaks the language that you understand and speak. He has fed you, he has gained your confidence by kindness and protection, he asks you to do something for him. Do you refuse? No, you obey willingly. It is thus that the golden lion will obey me."

"As long as it suits his purpose to do so," commented Korak.

"Let me go a step farther then," said the ape-man. "Suppose that this creature, whom you love and obey, has the power to punish, even to kill you, if it is necessary so to do to enforce his commands. How then about your obedience?"

"We'll see," said Korak, "how easily the golden lion will make one hundred pounds for me."

That afternoon they set out across the plain, Jad-bal-ja following Tarzan's horse's heels. They dismounted at a little clump of trees some distance from the bungalow and from there proceeded onward warily toward a swale in which antelopes were usually to be found, moving up which they came cautiously to the heavy brush that bordered the swale upon their side. There was Tarzan, Jane, and Korak, and close beside Tarzan the golden lion—four jungle hunters—and of the four Jad-bal-ja, the lion, was the least accomplished. Stealthily they crawled through the brush, scarce a leaf rustling to their passage, until at last they looked down into the swale upon a small herd of antelope grazing peacefully below. Closest to them was an old buck, and him Tarzan pointed out in some mysterious manner to Jad-bal-ja.

"Fetch him," he whispered, and the golden lion rumbled a scarce audible acknowledgment of the command.

Stealthily he worked his way through the brush. The antelopes fed on, unsuspecting. The distance separating the lion from his prey was over great for a successful charge, and so Jad-bal-ja waited, hiding in the brush, until the antelope should either graze closer to him or turn its back toward him. No sound came from the four watching the grazing herbivora, nor did the latter give any indication of a suspicion of the nearness of danger. The old buck moved closer to Jad-bal-ja. Almost imperceptibly the lion was gathering for the charge. The only noticeable movement was the twitching of his tail's tip, and then, as lightning from the sky, as an arrow from a bow, he shot from immobility to tremendous speed in an instant. He was almost upon the buck before the latter realized the proximity of danger, and then it was too late, for scarcely had the antelope wheeled than the lion rose upon its hind legs and seized it, while the balance of the herd broke into precipitate flight.

"Now," said Korak, "we shall see."

"He will bring the antelope to me," said Tarzan confidently.

The golden lion hesitated a moment, growling over the carcass of his kill. Then he seized it by the back and with his head turned to one side dragged it along the ground beside him, as he made his way slowly back toward Tarzan. Through the brush he dragged the slain antelope until he had dropped it at the feet of his master, where he stood, looking up at the face of the ape-man with an expression that could not have been construed into aught but pride in his achievement and a plea for commendation.

Tarzan stroked his head and spoke to him in a low voice,

praising him, and then, drawing his hunting knife, he cut the jugular of the antelope and let the blood from the carcass. Jane and Korak stood close, watching Jad-bal-ja—what would the lion do with the smell of fresh, hot blood in his nostrils? He sniffed at it and growled, and with bared fangs he eyed the three wickedly. The ape-man pushed him away with his open palm and the lion growled again angrily and snapped at him.

Quick is Numa, quick is Bara, the deer, but Tarzan of the Apes is lightning. So swiftly did he strike, and so heavily, that Jad-bal-ja was falling on his back almost in the very instant that he had growled at his master. Swiftly he came to his feet again and the two stood facing one another.

"Down!" commanded the ape-man. "Lie down, Jad-bal-ja!" His voice was low and firm. The lion hesitated but for an instant, and then lay down as Tarzan of the Apes had taught him to do at the word of command. Tarzan turned and lifted the carcass of the antelope to his shoulder.

"Come," he said to Jad-bal-ja. "Heel!" and without another glance at the carnivore he moved off toward the horses.

"I might have known it," said Korak, with a laugh, "and saved my hundred pounds."

"Of course you might have known it," said his mother.

3

A Meeting of Mystery

A RATHER ATTRACTIVE-LOOKING, though overdressed young woman was dining in a second-rate chop-house in London. She was noticeable, not so much for her fine figure and coarsely beautiful face as for the size and appearance of her companion, a large, well-proportioned man in the mid-twenties, with such a tremendous beard that it gave him the appearance of hiding in ambush. He stood fully three inches over six feet. His shoulders were broad, his chest deep, and his hips narrow. His physique, his carriage, everything about him, suggested indubitably the trained athlete.

The two were in close conversation, a conversation that occasionally gave every evidence of bordering upon heated argument.

"I tell you," said the man, "that I do not see what we need of the others. Why should they share with us—why divide into six portions that which you and I might have alone?"

"It takes money to carry the plan through," she replied, "and neither you nor I have any money. *They* have it and they will back us with it—me for my knowledge and you for your appearance and your strength. They searched for you, Esteban, for two years, and, now that they have found you, I should not care to be in your shoes if you betrayed them. They would just as soon slit your throat as not, Esteban, if they no more than thought they couldn't use you, now that you have all the details of their plan. But if you should try to take all the profit from them—" She paused, shrugging her shoulders. "No, my dear, I love life too well to join you in any such conspiracy as that."

"But I tell you, Flora, we ought to get more out of it than they want to give. You furnish all the knowledge and I take all the risk—why shouldn't we have more than a sixth apiece?"

"Talk to them yourself, then, Esteban," said the girl, with a shrug, "but if you will take my advice you will be satisfied with what you are offered. Not only have I the information, without which they can do nothing, but I found you into the bargain, yet I do not ask it all—I shall be perfectly satisfied with one-sixth, and I can assure you that if you do not muddle the thing, one-sixth of what you bring out will be enough for any one of us for the rest of his natural life."

The man did not seem convinced, and the young woman had a feeling that he would bear watching. Really, she knew very little about him, and had seen him in person only a few times since her first discovery of him some two months before, upon the screen of a London cinema house in a spectacular feature in which he had played the role of a Roman soldier of the Pretorian Guard.

Here his heroic size and perfect physique had alone entitled him to consideration, for his part was a minor one, and doubtless of all the thousands who saw him upon the silver sheet Flora Hawkes was the only one who took more than a passing interest in him, and her interest was aroused, not by his histrionic ability, but rather because for some two years she and her confederates had been searching for such a type as Esteban Miranda so admirably represented. To find him in the flesh bade fair to prove difficult of accomplishment, but after a month of seemingly fruitless searching she finally discovered him among a score of extra men at the studio of one of London's lesser producing companies. She needed no other credentials than her good looks to form his acquaintance, and while that was ripening into intimacy she made no mention to him of the real purpose of her association with him.

That he was a Spaniard and apparently of good family was evident to her, and that he was unscrupulous was to be guessed by the celerity with which he agreed to take part in the shady transaction that had been conceived in the mind of Flora Hawkes, and the details of which had been perfected by her and her four confederates. So, therefore, knowing that he was unscrupulous, she was aware that every precaution must be taken to prevent him taking advantage of the knowledge of their plan that he must one day have in detail, the key to which she, up to the present moment, had kept entirely to herself, not even confiding it to any one of her four other confederates.

They sat for a moment in silence, toying with the empty glasses from which they had been drinking. Presently she looked up to find his gaze fixed upon her and an expression in his eyes that even a less sophisticated woman than Flora Hawkes might readily have interpreted.

"You can make me do anything you want, Flora," he said, "for when I am with you I forget the gold, and think only of that other reward which you continually deny me, but which one day I shall win."

"Love and business do not mix well," replied the girl. "Wait until you have succeeded in this work, Esteban, and then we may talk of love."

"You do not love me," he whispered, hoarsely. "I know—I have seen—that each of the others loves you. That is why I could hate them. And if I thought that you loved one of them, I could cut his heart out. Sometimes I have thought that you did—first one of them and then another. You are too familiar with them, Flora. I have seen John Peebles squeeze your hand when he thought no one was looking, and when you dance with Dick Throck he holds you too close and you dance cheek to cheek. I tell you I do not like it, Flora, and one of these days I shall forget all about the gold and think only of you, and then something will happen and there will not be so many to divide the ingots that I shall bring back from Africa. And Bluber and Kraski are almost as bad; perhaps Kraski is the worst of all, for he is a good-looking devil and I do not like the way in which you cast sheep's eyes at him."

The fire of growing anger was leaping to the girl's eyes. With an angry gesture she silenced him.

"What business is it of yours, *Señor* Miranda, who I choose for my friends, or how I treat them or how they treat me? I will have you understand that I have known these men for years, while I have known you for but a few weeks, and if any has a right to dictate my behavior, which, thank God, none has, it would be one of them rather than you."

His eyes blazed angrily.

"It is as I thought!" he cried. "You love one of them." He half rose from the table and leaned across it toward her, menacingly. "Just let me find out which one it is and I will cut him into pieces!"

He ran his fingers through his long, black hair until it stood up on end like the mane of an angry lion. His eyes were blazing with a light that sent a chill of dread through the girl's heart. He appeared a man temporarily bereft of reason—if he were not a maniac he most certainly looked one, and the girl was afraid and realized that she must placate him.

"Come, come, Esteban," she whispered softly, "there is no need for working yourself into a towering rage over nothing. I have not said that I loved one of these, nor have I said that I do not love you, but I am not used to being wooed in such fashion. Perhaps your Spanish *señoritas* like it, but I am an English girl and if you love me treat me as an English lover would treat me."

"You have not said that you loved one of these others—no, but on the other hand you have not said that you do not love one of them—tell me, Flora, which one of them is it that you love?"

His eyes were still blazing, and his great frame trembling with suppressed passion.

"I do not love any of them, Esteban," she replied, "nor, as yet, do I love you. But I could, Esteban, that much I will tell you. I could love you, Esteban, as I could never love another, but I shall not permit myself to do so until after you have returned and we are free to live where and how we like. Then maybe—but, even so, I do not promise."

"You had better promise," he said, sullenly, though evidently somewhat mollified. "You had better promise, Flora, for I care nothing for the gold if I may not have you also."

"Hush," she cautioned, "here they come now, and it is about time; they are fully a half-hour late."

The man turned his eyes in the direction of her gaze, and the two sat watching the approach of four men who had just entered the chop-house. Two of them were evidently Englishmen—big, meaty fellows of the middle class, who looked what they really were, former pugilists; the third, Adolph Bluber, was a short, fat German, with a round, red face and a bull neck; the other, the youngest of the four, was by far the best looking. His smooth face, clear complexion, and large dark eyes might of themselves have proven sufficient grounds for Miranda's jealousy, but supplementing these were a mop of wavy, brown hair, the figure of a Greek god and the grace of a Russian dancer, which, in truth, was what Carl Kraski was when he chose to be other than a rogue.

The girl greeted the four pleasantly, while the Spaniard vouchsafed them but a single, surly nod, as they found chairs and seated themselves at the table.

"Ale!" cried Peebles, pounding the table to attract the attention of a waiter, "let's 'ave ale."

The suggestion met with unanimous approval, and as they waited for their drink they spoke casually of unimportant things; the heat, the circumstance that had delayed them, the trivial occurrences since they had last met; throughout which Esteban sat in sullen silence, but after the waiter had returned and they drank to Flora, with which ceremony it had long been their custom to signalize each gathering, they got down to business.

"Now," cried Peebles, pounding the table with his meaty fist, " 'ere we are, and that's that! We 'ave everything, Flora—the plans, the money, *Señor* Miranda—and are jolly well ready, old dear, for your part of it."

"How much money have you?" asked Flora. "It is going to take a lot of money, and there is no use starting unless you have plenty to carry on with."

Peebles turned to Bluber. "There," he said, pointing a pudgy finger at him, "is the bloomin' treasurer, 'E can tell you 'ow much we 'ave, the fat rascal of a Dutchman."

Bluber smiled an oily smile and rubbed his fat palms together. "Vell," he said, "how much you t'ink, Miss Flora, ve should have?"

"Not less than two thousand pounds to be on the safe side," she replied quickly.

"Ach, weh!" exclaimed Bluber. "But dat is a lot of money—two t'ousand pounds."

The girl made a gesture of disgust. "I told you in the first place that I wouldn't have anything to do with a bunch of cheap screws, and that until you had enough money to carry the thing out properly I would not give you the maps and directions, without which you cannot hope to reach the vaults, where there is stored enough gold to buy this whole, tight, little island if half that what I have heard them say about it is true. You can go along and spend your own money, but you've got to show me that you have at least two thousand pounds to spend before I give up the information that will make you the richest men in the world."

"The blighter's got the money," growled Throck. "Blime if I know what he's beefin' about."

"He can't help it," growled the Russian, "he's that kind of chap; Bluber would try to bargain with the marriage license clerk if he were going to get married."

"Oh, vell," sighed Bluber, "for vy should we spend more money than is necessary? If ve can do it for von t'ousand pounds so much the better."

"Certainly," snapped the girl, "and if it doesn't take but one thousand, that is all that you will have to spend, but you've got to have the two thousand in case of emergencies, and from what I have seen of that country you are likely to run up against more emergencies than anything else."

"*Ach, weh!*" cried Bluber.

" 'E's got the money all right," said Peebles, "now let's get busy."

"He may have it, but I want to see it first," replied the girl.

"Vat you t'ink; I carry all dat money around in my pocket?" cried Bluber.

"Can't you take our word for it?" grumbled Throck.

"You're a nice bunch of crooks to ask me that," she replied, laughing in the face of the burly ruffians. "I'll take Carl's word for it, though; if he tells me that you have it, and that it is in such shape that it can, and will, be used to pay all the necessary expenses of our expedition, I will believe him."

Peebles and Throck scowled angrily, and Miranda's eyes closed to two narrow, nasty slits, as he directed his gaze upon the Russian. Bluber, on the contrary, was affected not at all; the more he was insulted, the better, apparently, he liked it. Toward one who treated him with consideration or respect he would have become arrogant, while he fawned upon the hand that struck him. Kraski, alone, smiled a self-satisfied smile that set the blood of the Spaniard boiling.

"Bluber has the money, Flora," he said; "each of us has contributed his share. We'll make Bluber treasurer, because we know that he will squeeze the last farthing until it shrieks before he will let it escape him. It is our plan now to set out from London in pairs."

He drew a map from his pocket, and unfolding it, spread it out upon the table before them. With his finger he indicated a point marked X. "Here we will meet and here we will equip our expedition. Bluber and Miranda will go first; then Peebles and Throck. By the time that you and I arrive everything will be in shape for moving immediately into the interior, where we shall establish a permanent camp, off the beaten track and as near our objective as possible. Miranda will disport himself behind his whiskers until he is ready to set out upon the final stage of his long journey. I understand that he is well schooled in the part that he is to play and that he can depict the character to perfection. As he will have only ignorant natives and wild beasts to deceive it should not tax his histrionic ability too greatly." There was a veiled note of sarcasm in the soft, drawling tone that caused the black eyes of the Spaniard to gleam wickedly.

"Do I understand," asked Miranda, his soft tone belying his angry scowl, "that you and Miss Hawkes travel alone to X?"

"You do, unless your understanding is poor," replied the Russian.

The Spaniard half rose from the table and leaned across it menacingly toward Kraski. The girl, who was sitting next to him, seized his coat.

"None of that!" she said, dragging him back into his chair. "There has been too much of it among you already, and if there is any more I shall cut you all and seek more congenial companions for my expedition."

"Yes, cut it out; 'ere we are, and that's that!" exclaimed Peebles belligerently.

"John's right," rumbled Throck, in his deep bass, "and I'm here to back him up. And if there is any more of it, blime if I don't bash a couple of you pretty 'uns," and he looked first at Miranda and then at Kraski.

"Now," soothed Bluber, "let's all shake hands and be good friends."

"Right-o," cried Peebles, "that's the talk. Give 'im your 'and, Esteban. Come, Carl, bury the 'atchet. We can't start in on this thing with no hanimosities, and 'ere we are, and that's that."

The Russian, feeling secure in his position with Flora, and therefore in a magnanimous mood, extended his hand across the table toward the Spaniard. For a moment Esteban hesitated.

"Come, man, shake!" growled Throck, "or you can go back to your job as an extra man, blime, and we'll find someone else to do your work and divvy the swag with."

Suddenly the dark countenance of the Spaniard was lighted by a pleasant smile. He extended his hand quickly and clasped Kraski's. "Forgive me," he said, "I am hot-tempered, but I mean nothing. Miss Hawkes is right, we must all be friends, and here's my hand on it, Kraski, as far as I am concerned."

"Good," said Kraski, "and I am sorry if I offended you." But he forgot that the other was an actor, and if he could have seen into the depths of that dark soul he would have shuddered.

"Und now, dat we are all good friends," said Bluber, rubbing his hands together unctuously, "vy not arrange for vhen ve shall commence starting to finish up everyt'ings? Miss Flora, she gives me the map und der directions und we start commencing immediately."

"Loan me a pencil, Carl," said the girl, and when the man had handed her one she searched out a spot upon the map some distance into the interior from X, where she drew a tiny circle. "This is O," she said. "When we all reach here you shall have the final directions and not before."

Bluber threw up his hands. "*Ach!* Miss Flora, vat you t'ink, ve spend two t'ousand pounds to buy a pig in a poke? *Ach, weh!* you vouldn't ask us to do dat? Ve must see everyt'ing, ve must know everyt'ing before ve spend vun farthing."

"Yes, and 'ere we are, and that's that!" roared John Peebles, striking the table with his fist.

The girl rose leisurely from her seat. "Oh, very well," she said with a shrug. "If you feel that way about it we might as well call it all off."

"Oh, vait, vait, Miss Flora," cried Bluber, rising hurriedly. "Don't be ogcited. But can't you see vere ve are? Two t'ousand pounds is a lot of money, and ve are good businessmen. Ve shouldn't be spending it all vit'out getting not'ings for it."

"I am not asking you to spend it and get nothing for it," replied the girl, tartly; "but if anyone has got to trust anyone else in this outfit, it is you who are going to trust me. If I give you all the information I have, there is nothing in the world that could prevent you from going ahead and leaving me out in the cold, and I don't intend that that shall happen."

"But we are not fools, Miss Flora," insisted Bluber. "Ve vould not t'ink for vun minute of cheating you."

"You're not angels, either, Bluber, any of you," retorted the girl. "If you want to go ahead with this you've got to do it in my way, and I am going to be there at the finish to see that I get what is coming to me. You've taken my word for it, up to the present time, that I had the dope, and now you've got to take it the rest of the way or all bets are off. What good would it do me to go over into a bally jungle and suffer all the hardships that we are bound to suffer, dragging you along with me, if I were not going to be able to deliver the goods when I got there? And I am not such a softy as to think I could get away with it with a bunch of bandits like you if I tried to put anything of that kind over on you. And as long as I do play straight I feel perfectly safe, for I know that either Esteban or Carl will look after me, and I don't know but what the rest of you would, too. Is it a go or isn't it?"

"Vell, John, vot do you und Dick t'ink?" asked Bluber, addressing the two ex-prizefighters. "Carl, I know he vill t'ink vhatever Flora t'inks. Hey? Vat?"

"Blime," said Throck, "I never was much of a hand at trusting nobody unless I had to, but it looks now as though we had to trust Flora."

"Same 'ere," said John Peebles. "If you try any funny work, Flora—" He made a significant movement with his finger across his throat.

"I understand, John," said the girl with a smile, "and I know that you would do it as quickly for two pounds as you would for two thousand. But you are all agreed, then, to carry on according to my plans? You too, Carl?"

The Russian nodded. "Whatever the rest say goes with me," he remarked.

And so the gentle little coterie discussed their plans insofar as they could—each minutest detail that would be necessary to place them all at the O which the girl had drawn upon the map.

4

What the Footprints Told

WHEN JAD-BAL-JA, THE golden lion, was two years old, he was as magnificent a specimen of his kind as the Greystokes had ever looked upon. In size he was far above the average of that attained by mature males; in conformation he was superb, his noble head and his great black mane giving him the appearance of a full-grown male, while in intelligence he far outranked his savage brothers of the forest.

Jad-bal-ja was a never-ending source of pride and delight to the ape-man who had trained him so carefully, and nourished him cunningly for the purpose of developing to the full all the latent powers within him. The lion no longer slept at the foot of his master's bed, but occupied a strong cage that Tarzan had constructed for him at the rear of the bungalow, for who knew better than the ape-man that a lion, wherever he may be or however he may have been raised, is yet a lion—a savage flesh-eater. For the first year he had roamed at will about the house and grounds; after that he went abroad only in the company of Tarzan. Often the two roamed the plain and the jungle hunting together. In a way the lion was almost equally as familiar with Jane and Korak, and neither of them feared or mistrusted him, but toward Tarzan of the Apes did he show the greatest affection. The blacks of Tarzan's household he tolerated, nor did he ever offer to molest any of the domestic animals or fowl, after Tarzan had impressed upon him in his early cubhood that appropriate punishment followed immediately upon any predatory excursion into the corrals or henhouses. The fact that he was never permitted to become ravenously hungry was doubtless the deciding factor in safeguarding the livestock of the farm.

The man and the beast seemed to understand one another perfectly. It is doubtful that the lion understood all that Tarzan said to him, but be that as it may the ease with which he communicated his wishes to the lion bordered upon the uncanny. The obedience that a combination of sternness and affection had elicited from the cub had become largely habit in the grown lion. At Tarzan's command he would go to great distances and bring back antelope or zebra, laying his kill at his master's feet without offering to taste the flesh himself, and he had even retrieved living animals without harming them. Such, then, was the golden lion that roamed the primeval forest with his godlike master.

It was at about this time that there commenced to drift in to the ape-man rumors of a predatory band to the west and south of his estate; ugly stories of ivory-raiding, slave-running and torture, such as had not disturbed the quiet of the ape-man's savage jungle since the days of Sheik Amor Ben Khatour, and there came other tales, too, that caused Tarzan of the Apes to pucker his brows in puzzlement and thought, and then a month elapsed during which Tarzan heard no more of the rumors from the west.

The war had reduced the resources of the Greystokes to but a meager income. They had given practically all to the cause of the Allies, and now what little had remained to them had been all but exhausted in the rehabilitation of Tarzan's African estate.

"It looks very much, Jane," he said to his wife one night, "as though another trip to Opar were on the books."

"I dread to think of it. I do not want you to go," she said. "You have come away from that awful city twice, but barely with your life. The third time you may not be so fortunate. We have enough, John, to permit us to live here in comfort and in happiness. Why jeopardize those two things which are greater than all wealth in another attempt to raid the treasure vaults?"

"There is no danger, Jane," he assured her. "The last time Werper dogged my footsteps, and between him and the earthquake I was nearly done for. But there is no chance of any such combination of circumstances thwarting me again."

"You will not go alone, John?" she asked. "You will take Korak with you?"

"No," he said, "I shall not take him. He must remain here with you, for really my long absences are more dangerous to you than to me. I shall take fifty of the Waziri, as porters, to carry the gold, and thus we should be able to bring out enough to last us for a long time."

"And Jad-bal-ja," she asked, "shall you take him?"

"No, he had better remain here; Korak can look after him and take him out for a hunt occasionally. I am going to travel light and fast and it would be too hard a trip for him—lions don't care to move around too much in the hot sun, and as we shall travel mostly by day I doubt if Jad-bal-ja would last long."

And so it befell that Tarzan of the Apes set out once more upon the long trail that leads to Opar. Behind him marched fifty giant Waziri, the pick of the warlike tribe that had adopted

Tarzan as its Chief. Upon the veranda of the bungalow stood Jane and Korak waving their adieux, while from the rear of the building there came to the ape-man's ears the rumbling roar of Jad-bal-ja, the golden lion. And as they marched away the voice of Numa accompanied them out upon the rolling plain, until at last it trailed off to nothingness in the distance.

His speed determined by that of the slowest of the blacks, Tarzan made but comparatively rapid progress. Opar lay a good twenty-five days' trek from the farm for men traveling light, as were these, but upon the return journey, laden as they would be with the ingots of gold, their progress would be slower. And because of this the ape-man had allotted two months for the venture. His safari, consisting of seasoned warriors only, permitted of really rapid progress. They carried no supplies, for they were all hunters and were moving through a country in which game was abundant—no need then for burdening themselves with the cumbersome impedimenta of white huntsmen.

A thorn boma and a few leaves furnished their shelter for the night, while spears and arrows and the powers of their great white chief insured that their bellies would never go empty. With the picked men that he had brought with him Tarzan expected to make the trip to Opar in twenty-one days, though had he been traveling alone he would have moved two or three times as fast, since, when Tarzan elected to travel with speed, he fairly flew through the jungle, equally at home in it by day or by night and practically tireless.

It was on a midafternoon the third week of the march that Tarzan, ranging far ahead of his blacks in search of game, came suddenly upon the carcass of Bara, the deer, a feathered arrow protruding from its flank. It was evident that Bara had been wounded at some little distance from where it had lain down to die, for the location of the missile indicated that the wound could not have caused immediate death. But what particularly caught the attention of the ape-man, even before he had come close enough to make a minute examination, was the design of the arrow, and immediately he withdrew it from the body of the deer he knew it for what it was, and was filled with such wonderment as might come to you or to me were we to see a native Swazi headdress upon Broadway or the Strand, for the arrow was precisely such as one may purchase in most any sporting-goods house in any large city of the world—such an arrow as is sold and used for archery practice in the parks and suburbs. Nothing could have been more incongruous than this silly toy in the heart of savage Africa, and yet that it had done its work effectively was evident by the dead body of Bara, though the ape-man guessed that the shaft had been sped by no practiced, savage hand.

Tarzan's curiosity was aroused and also his inherent jungle caution. One must know his jungle well to survive long in it, and if one would know it well he must let no unusual occurrence or circumstance go unexplained. And so it was that Tarzan set out upon the back track of Bara for the purpose of ascertaining, if possible, the nature of Bara's slayer. The bloody spoor was easily followed and the ape-man wondered why it was that the hunter had not tracked and overtaken his quarry, which had evidently been dead since the previous day. He found that Bara had traveled far, and the sun was already low in the west before Tarzan came upon the first indications of the slayer of the animal. These were in the nature of footprints that filled him with quite as much surprise as had the arrow. He examined them carefully, and, stooping low, even sniffed at them with his sensitive nostrils. Improbable, nay impossible though it seemed, the naked footprints were those of *a white man*—a large man, probably as large as Tarzan himself. As the foster-son of Kala stood gazing upon the spoor of the mysterious stranger he ran the fingers of one hand through his thick, black hair in a characteristic gesture indicative of deep puzzlement.

What naked white man could there be in Tarzan's jungle who slew Tarzan's game with the pretty arrow of an archery club? It was incredible that there should be such a one, and yet there recurred to the ape-man's mind the vague rumors that he had heard weeks before. Determined to solve the mystery he set out now upon the trail of the stranger—an erratic trail which wound about through the jungle, apparently aimlessly, prompted, Tarzan guessed, by the ignorance of an inexperienced hunter. But night fell before he had arrived at a solution of the riddle, and it was pitch dark as the ape-man turned his steps toward camp.

He knew that his Waziri would be expecting meat and it was not Tarzan's intention to disappoint them, though he then discovered that he was not the only carnivore hunting the district that night. The coughing grunt of a lion close by apprised him of it first, and then, from the distance, the deep roar of another. But of what moment was it to the ape-man that others hunted? It would not be the first time that he had pitted his cunning, his strength, and his agility against the other hunters of his savage world—both man and beast.

And so it was that Tarzan made his kill at last, snatching it almost from under the nose of a disappointed and infuriated lion—a fat antelope that the latter had marked as his own. Throwing his kill to his shoulder almost in the path of the charging Numa, the ape-man swung lightly to the lower terraces and with a taunting laugh for the infuriated cat, vanished noiselessly into the night.

He found the camp and his hungry Waziri without trouble, and so great was their faith in him that they not for a moment doubted but that he would return with meat for them.

Early the following morning Tarzan set out again toward Opar, and directing his Waziri to continue the march in the most direct way, he left them that he might pursue further his investigations of the mysterious presence in his jungle that the arrow and the footsteps had apprised him of. Coming again to the spot at which darkness had forced him to abandon his investigations, he took up the spoor of the stranger. Nor had he followed it far before he came upon further evidence of the presence of this new and malign personality—stretched before him in the trail was the body of a giant ape, one of the tribe of great anthropoids among whom Tarzan had been raised. Protruding from the hairy abdomen of the Mangani was another of the machine-made arrows of civilization. The ape-man's eyes narrowed and a scowl darkened his brow. Who was this who dared invade his sacred preserves and slaughter thus ruthlessly Tarzan's people?

A low growl rumbled in the throat of the ape-man. Sloughed with the habiliments of civilization was the thin veneer of civilization that Tarzan wore among white men. No English lord was this who looked upon the corpse of his hairy cousin, but another jungle beast in whose breast raged the unquenchable fire of suspicion and hatred for the man-thing that is the heritage of the jungle-bred. A beast of prey viewed the bloody work of ruthless man. Nor was there in the consciousness of Tarzan any acknowledgement of his blood relationship to the killer.

Realizing that the trail had been made upon the second day before, Tarzan hastened on in pursuit of the slayer. There was no doubt in his mind but that plain murder had been committed, for he was sufficiently familiar with the traits of the Mangani to know that none of them would provoke assault unless driven to it.

Tarzan was traveling upwind, and some half-hour after he had discovered the body of the ape his keen nostrils caught the scent-spoor of others of its kind. Knowing the timidity of these fierce denizens of the jungle he moved forward now with great wariness, lest, warned of his approach, they take flight before they were aware of his identity. He did not see them often, yet he knew that there were always those among them who recalled him, and that through these he could always establish amicable relations with the balance of the tribe.

Owing to the denseness of the undergrowth Tarzan chose the middle terraces for his advance, and here, swinging freely and swiftly among the leafy boughs, he came presently upon the giant anthropoids. There were about twenty of them in the band, and they were engaged, in a little natural clearing, in their never-ending search for caterpillars and beetles, which formed important items in the diet of the Mangani.

A faint smile overspread the ape-man's face as he paused upon a great branch, himself hidden by the leafy foliage about him, and watched the little band below him. Every action, every movement of the great apes, recalled vividly to Tarzan's mind the long years of his childhood, when, protected by the fierce mother-love of Kala, the she-ape, he had ranged the jungle with the tribe of Kerchak. In the romping young, he saw again Neeta and his other childhood playmates and in the adults all the great, savage brutes he had feared in youth and conquered in manhood. The ways of man may change but the ways of the ape are the same, yesterday, today, and forever.

He watched them in silence for some minutes. How glad they would be to see him when they discovered his identity!

For Tarzan of the Apes was known the length and the breadth of the great jungle as the friend and protector of the Mangani. At first they would growl at him and threaten him, for they would not depend solely on either their eyes or their ears for confirmation of his identity. Not until he had entered the clearing, and bristling bulls with bared fighting fangs had circled him stiffly until they had come close enough for their nostrils to verify the evidence of their eyes and ears, would they finally accept him. Then doubtless there would be great excitement for a few minutes, until, following the instincts of the ape mind, their attention was weaned from him by a blowing leaf, a caterpillar, or a bird's egg, and then they would move about their business, taking no further notice of him more than of any other member of the tribe. But this would not come until after each individual had smelled of him, and perhaps, pawed his flesh with calloused hands.

Now it was that Tarzan made a friendly sound of greeting, and as the apes looked up stepped from his concealment into plain view of them. "I am Tarzan of the Apes," he said, "mighty fighter, friend of the Mangani. Tarzan comes in friendship to his people," and with these words he dropped lightly to the lush green of the clearing.

Instantly pandemonium reigned. Screaming warnings, the shes raced with the young for the opposite side of the clearing, while the bulls, bristling and growling, faced the intruder.

"Come," cried Tarzan, "do you not know me? I am Tarzan of the Apes, friend of the Mangani, son of Kala, and king of the tribe of Kerchak."

"We know you," growled one of the old bulls; "yesterday we saw you when you killed Gobu. Go away or we shall kill you."

"I did not kill Gobu," replied the ape-man. "I found his dead body yesterday and I was following the spoor of his slayer, when I came upon you."

"We saw you," repeated the old bull; "go away or we shall kill you. You are no longer the friend of the Mangani."

The ape-man stood with brows contracted in thought. It was evident that these apes really believed that they had seen him kill their fellow. What was the explanation? How could it be accounted for? Did the naked footprints of the great white man whom he had been following mean more, then, than he had guessed? Tarzan wondered. He raised his eyes and again addressed the bulls.

"It was not I who killed Gobu," he insisted. "Many of you have known me all your lives. You know that only in fair fight, as one bull fights another, have I ever killed a Mangani. You know that, of all the jungle people, the Mangani are my best friends, and that Tarzan of the Apes is the best friend the Mangani have. How, then, could I slay one of my own people?"

"We only know," replied the old bull, "that we saw you kill Gobu. With our own eyes we saw you kill him. Go away quickly, therefore, or we shall kill you. Mighty fighter is Tarzan of the Apes, but mightier even than he are all the great bulls of Pagth. I am Pagth, king of the tribe of Pagth. Go away before we kill you."

Tarzan tried to reason with them but they would not listen, so confident were they that it was he who had slain their fellow, the bull Gobu. Finally, rather than chance a quarrel in which some of them must inevitably be killed, he turned sorrowfully away. But more than ever, now, was he determined to seek out the slayer of Gobu that he might demand an accounting of one who dared thus invade his lifelong domain.

Tarzan trailed the spoor until it mingled with the tracks of many men—barefooted blacks, mostly, but among them the footprints of booted white men, and once he saw the footprints of a woman or a child, which, he could not tell. The trial led apparently toward the rocky hills which protected the barren valley of Opar.

Forgetful now of his original mission and imbued only with a savage desire to wrest from the interlopers a full accounting for their presence in the jungle, and to mete out to the slayer of Gobu his just deserts, Tarzan forged ahead upon the now broad and well-marked trail of the considerable party which could not now be much more than a half-day's march ahead of him, which meant that they were now already upon the rim of the valley of Opar, if this was their ultimate destination. And what other they could have in view Tarzan could not imagine.

He had always kept closely to himself the location of Opar. Insofar as he knew no white person other than Jane, and their son, Korak, knew of the location of the forgotten city of the ancient Atlantians. Yet what else could have drawn these white men, with so large a party, into the savage, unexplored wilderness which hemmed Opar upon all sides?

Such were the thoughts that occupied Tarzan's mind as he followed swiftly the trail that led toward Opar. Darkness fell, but so fresh was the spoor that the ape-man could follow it by scent even when he could not see the imprints upon the ground, and presently, in the distance, he saw the light of a camp ahead of him.

5

The Fatal Drops

At home, the life in the bungalow and at the farm followed its usual routine as it had before the departure of Tarzan. Korak, sometimes on foot and sometimes on horseback, followed the activities of the farm hands and the herders, sometimes alone, but more often in company with the white foreman, Jervis, and often, especially when they rode, Jane accompanied them.

The golden lion Korak exercised upon a leash, since he was not at all confident of his powers of control over the beast, and feared lest, in the absence of his master, Jad-bal-ja might take to the forest and revert to his natural savage state. Such a lion, abroad in the jungle, would be a distinct menace to human life, for Jad-bal-ja, reared among men, lacked the natural timidity of men that is so marked a trait of all wild beasts. Trained as he had been to make his kill at the throat of a human effigy, it required no considerable powers of imagination upon the part of Korak to visualize what might occur should the golden lion, loosed from all restraint, be thrown upon his own resources in the surrounding jungle.

It was during the first week of Tarzan's absence that a runner from Nairobi brought a cable message to Lady Greystoke, announcing the serious illness of her father in London. Mother and son discussed the situation. It would be five or six weeks before Tarzan could return, even if they sent a runner after him, and, were Jane to await him, there would be little likelihood of her reaching her father in time. Even should she depart at once, there seemed only a faint hope that she should see him alive. It was decided, therefore, that she should set out immediately, Korak accompanying her as far as Nairobi, and then returning to the ranch and resuming its general supervision until his father's return.

It is a long trek from Greystoke estate to Nairobi, and Korak had not yet returned when, about three weeks after Tarzan's departure, a black, whose duty it was to feed and care for Jad-bal-ja, carelessly left the door of the cage unfastened while he was cleaning it. The golden lion paced back and forth while the black wielded his broom within the cage. They were old friends, and the Waziri felt no fear of the great lion, with the result that his back was as often turned to him as not. The black was working in the far corner of the cage when Jad-bal-ja paused a moment at the door at the opposite end. The beast saw that the gate hung slightly ajar on its hinges. Silently he raised a great padded paw and inserted it in the opening—a slight pull and the gate swung in. Instantly the golden lion inserted his snout in the widened aperture, and as he swung the barrier aside the horrified black looked up to see his charge drop softly to the ground outside.

"Stop, Jad-bal-ja! Stop!" screamed the frightened black, leaping after him. But the golden lion only increased his pace, and leaping the fence, loped off in the direction of the forest.

The black pursued him with brandishing broom, emitting loud yells that brought the inmates of the Waziri huts into the open, where they joined their fellow in pursuit of the lion. Across the rolling plains they followed him, but might as well have sought to snare the elusive will-o'-the-wisp as this swift and wary fugitive, who heeded neither their blandishments nor their threats. And so it was that they saw the golden lion disappear into the primeval forest and, though they searched diligently until almost dark, they were forced at length to give up their quest and return crestfallen to the farm.

"Ah," cried the unhappy black, who had been responsible for the escape of Jad-bal-ja, "what will the Big Bwana say to me, what will he do to me when he finds that I have permitted the golden lion to get away!"

"You will be banished from the bungalow for a long time, Keewazi," old Muviro assured him. "And doubtless you will be sent to the grazing ground far to the east to guard the herd there, where you will have plenty of lions for company, though they will not be as friendly as was Jad-bal-ja. It is not half what you deserve, and were the heart of the Big Bwana not filled with love for his black children—were he like other white Bwanas old Muviro has seen—you would be lashed until you could not stand, perhaps until you died."

"I am a man," replied Keewazi. "I am a warrior and a Waziri. Whatever punishment the Big Bwana inflicts I will accept as a man should."

It was that same night that Tarzan approached the campfires of the strange party he had been tracking. Unseen by them, he halted in the foliage of a tree directly in the center of their camp, which was surrounded by an enormous thorn boma, and brilliantly lighted by numerous fires which blacks were diligently feeding with branches from an enormous pile of firewood that they had evidently gathered earlier in the day for this purpose. Near the center of the camp were several tents, and before one, in the light of a fire, sat four white men. Two of them were great, bull-necked, red-faced fellows, apparently Englishmen of the lower class, the third appeared to be short, fat, and Teutonic, while the fourth was a tall, slender, handsome fellow, with dark, wavy brown hair and regular features. He and the German were most meticulously garbed for Central African traveling, after the highly idealized standard of motion pictures, in fact either one of them might have stepped directly from a screening of the latest jungle thriller. The young man was evidently not of English descent and Tarzan mentally cataloged him, almost immediately, as a Slav. Shortly after Tarzan's arrival this one arose and entered one of the nearby tents, from which Tarzan immediately heard the sound of voices in low conversation. He could not distinguish the words, but the tones of one seemed quite distinctly feminine. The three remaining at the fire were carrying on a desultory conversation, when suddenly from near at hand beyond the boma wall, a lion's roar broke the silence of the jungle.

With a startled shriek Bluber leaped to his feet, so suddenly that he cleared the ground a good foot, and then, stepping backward, he lost his balance, tripped over his camp-stool, and sprawled upon his back.

"My Gord, Adolph!" roared one of his companions. "If you do that again, damn me if I don't break your neck. 'Ere we are, and that's that."

"Blime if 'e ain't worse'n a bloomin' lion," growled the other.

Bluber crawled to his feet. *"Mein Gott!"* he cried, his voice quavering. "I t'ought sure he vas coming over der fence. S'elp me if I ever get out of diss, neffer again—not for all der gold in Africa vould I go t'rough vat I haf been t'rough dese past t'ree month's. *Ach, weh!* ven I t'ink of it, *Ach, du lieber!* Lions, und leopards, und rhinoceroses, und hippopotamuses."

His companions laughed. "Dick and I tells you right along from the beginning that you 'adn't oughter come into the interior," said one of them.

"But for vy I buy all dese clo's?" wailed the German. *"Mein Gott,* dis suit, it stands me tventy guineas, vot I stand in. Ach, had I know somet'ing, vun guinea vould have bought me my whole vardrobe—tventy guineas for dis und no vun to see it but savages and lions."

"And you look like 'ell in it, besides," commented one of his friends.

"Und look at it, it's all dirty and torn. How should I know it I spoil dis suit? Mit mine own eyes I see it at der Princess Teayter, how der hero spend t'ree mont's in Africa hunting lions und killing cannibals, und ven he comes oud he hasn't even got a greast spot on his pants—how should I know it Africa was so dirty und full of thorns?"

It was at this point that Tarzan of the Apes elected to drop quietly into the circle of their firelight before them. The two Englishmen leaped to their feet, quite evidently startled, and Bluber turned and took a half step as though in flight, but immediately his eyes rested upon the ape-man he halted, a look of relief supplanting that of terror which had overspread his countenance, as Tarzan had dropped upon them apparently from the heavens.

"*Mein Gott,* Esteban," shrilled the German, "vy you come back so soon, and for vy you come back like dot, sudden—don't you suppose ve got nerves?"

Tarzan was angry, angry at these raw intruders, who dared enter without his permission, the wide domain in which he kept peace and order. When Tarzan was angry there flamed upon his forehead the scar that Bolgani, the gorilla, had placed there upon that long-gone day when the boy Tarzan had met the great beast in mortal combat, and first learned the true value of his father's hunting knife—the knife that had placed him, the comparatively weak little Tarmangani, upon an even footing with the great beasts of the jungle.

His gray eyes were narrowed, his voice came cold and level as he addressed them. "Who are you," he demanded, "who dare thus invade the country of the Waziri, the land of Tarzan, without permission from the Lord of the Jungle?"

"Where do you get that stuff, Esteban," demanded one of the Englishmen, "and wat in 'ell are you doin' back 'ere alone and so soon? Where are your porters, and where is the bloomin' gold?"

The ape-man eyed the speaker in silence for a moment. "I am Tarzan of the Apes," he said. "I do not know what you are talking about. I only know that I come in search of him who slew Gobu, the great ape; him who slew Bara, the deer, without my permission."

"Oh, 'ell," exploded the other Englishman, "stow the guff, Esteban—if you're tryin' for to be funny we don't see the joke, 'ere we are, and that's that."

Inside the tent, which the fourth white man had entered while Tarzan was watching the camp from his hiding place in the tree above, a woman, evidently suddenly stirred by terror, touched the arm of her companion frantically, and pointed toward the tall, almost naked figure of the ape-man as he stood revealed in the full light of the beast fires. "God, Carl," she whispered, in trembling tones, "look!"

"What's wrong, Flora?" inquired her companion. "I see only Esteban."

"It is not Esteban," hissed the girl. "It is Lord Greystoke himself—it is Tarzan of the Apes!"

"You are mad, Flora," replied the man, "it cannot be he."

"It is he, though," she insisted. "Do you suppose that I do not know him? Did I not work in his town house for years? Did I not see him nearly every day? Do you suppose that I do not know Tarzan of the Apes? Look at that red scar flaming on his forehead—I have heard the story of that scar and I have seen it burn scarlet when he was aroused to anger. It is scarlet now, and Tarzan of the Apes is angry."

"Well, suppose it *is* Tarzan of the Apes, what can he do?"

"You do not know him," replied the girl. "You do not guess the tremendous power he wields here—the power of life and death over man and beast. If he knew our mission here not one of us would ever reach the coast alive. The very fact that he is here now makes me believe that he may have discovered our purpose, and if he has, God help us—unless—unless——"

"Unless what?" demanded the man.

The girl was silent in thought for a moment. "There is only one way," she said finally. "We dare not kill him. His savage blacks would learn of it, and no power on earth could save us then. There is a way, though, if we act quickly." She turned and searched for a moment in one of her bags, and presently she handed the man a small bottle, containing liquid. "Go out and talk to him," she said, "make friends with him. Lie to him. Tell him anything. Promise anything. But get on friendly enough terms with him so that you can offer him coffee. He does not drink wine or anything with alcohol in it, but I know that he likes coffee. I have often served it to him in his room late at night upon his return from the theater or a ball. Get him to drink coffee and then you will know what to do with this." And she indicated the bottle which the man still held in his hand.

Kraski nodded. "I understand," he said, and, turning, left the tent.

He had taken but a step when the girl recalled him. "Do not let him see me. Do not let him guess that I am here or that you know me."

The man nodded and left her. Approaching the tense figures before the fire he greeted Tarzan with a pleasant smile and a cheery word.

"Welcome," he said, "we are always glad to see a stranger in our camp. Sit down. Hand the gentleman a stool, John," he said to Peebles.

The ape-man eyed Kraski as he had eyed the others. There was no answering friendly light in his eyes responding to the Russian's greeting.

"I have been trying to find out what your party is doing here," he said sharply to the Russian, "but they still insist that I am someone whom I am not. They are either fools or knaves, and I intend to find out which, and deal with them accordingly."

"Come, come," cried Kraski, soothingly. "There must be some mistake, I am sure. But tell me, who are you?"

"I am Tarzan of the Apes," replied the ape-man. "No hunters enter this part of Africa without my permission. That fact is so well known that there is no chance of your having passed the coast without having been so advised. I seek an explanation, and that quickly."

"Ah, you are Tarzan of the Apes," exclaimed Kraski. "Fortunate indeed are we, for now may we be set straight upon our way, and escape from our frightful dilemma is assured. We are lost, sir, inextricably lost, due to the ignorance or knavery of our guide, who deserted us several weeks ago. Surely we knew of you; who does not know of Tarzan of the Apes? But it was not our intention to cross the boundaries of your territory. We were searching farther south for specimens of the fauna of the district, which our good friend and employer, here, Mr. Adolph Bluber, is collecting at great expense for presentation to a museum in his home city in America. Now I am sure that you can tell us where we are and direct us upon our proper course."

Peebles, Throck, and Bluber stood fascinated by Kraski's glib lies, but it was the German who first rose to the occasion. Too thick were the skulls of the English pugs to grasp quickly the clever ruse of the Russian.

"Vy yes," said the oily Bluber, rubbing his palms together, "dot iss it, yust vot I vas going to tell you."

Tarzan turned sharply upon him. "Then what was all this talk about Esteban?" he asked. "Was it not by that name that these others addressed me?"

"Ah," cried Bluber, "John will haf his leetle joke. He iss

ignorant of Africa; he has neffer been here before. He t'ought perhaps dat you vere a native. John he calls all der natives Esteban, und he has great jokes by himself mit dem, because he knows dey cannot onderstand vot he says. Hey John, iss it not so, vot it iss I say?" But the shrewd Bluber did not wait for John to reply. "You see," he went on, "ve are lost, und you take us oud mit dis jungle, ve pay you anyt'ing—you name your own price."

The ape-man only half believed him, yet he was somewhat mollified by their evidently friendly intentions. Perhaps after all they were telling him a half-truth and had, really, wandered into his territory unwittingly. That, however, he would find out definitely from their native carriers, from whom his own Waziri would wean the truth. But the matter of his having been mistaken for Esteban still piqued his curiosity, also he was still desirous of learning the identity of the slayer of Gobu, the great ape.

"Please sit down," urged Kraski. "We were about to have coffee and we should be delighted to have you join us. We meant no wrong in coming here, and I can assure you that we will gladly and willingly make full amends to you, or to whomever else we may have unintentionally wronged."

To take coffee with these men would do no harm. Perhaps he had wronged them, but however that might be a cup of their coffee would place no great obligation upon him. Flora had been right in her assertion that if Tarzan of the Apes had any weakness whatsoever it was for an occasional cup of black coffee late at night. He did not accept the proffered camp stool, but squatted, ape-fashion, before them, the flickering light of the beast fires playing upon his bronzed hide and bringing into relief the gracefully contoured muscles of his godlike frame. Not as the muscles of the blacksmith or the professional strong man were the muscles of Tarzan of the Apes, but rather as those of Mercury or Apollo, so symmetrically balanced were their proportions, suggesting only the great strength that lay in them. Trained to speed and agility were they as well as to strength, and thus, clothing as they did his giant frame, they imparted to him the appearance of a demi-god.

Throck, Peebles, and Bluber sat watching him in spellbound fascination, while Kraski walked over to the cook fire to arrange for the coffee. The two Englishmen were as yet only half awakened to the fact that they had mistaken this newcomer for another, and as it was, Peebles still scratched his head and grumbled to himself in inarticulate half-denial of Kraski's assumption of the new identity of Tarzan. Bluber was inwardly terror-stricken. His keener intelligence had quickly grasped the truth of Kraski's recognition of the man for what he was rather than for what Peebles and Throck thought him to be, and, as Bluber knew nothing of Flora's plan, he was in quite a state of funk as he tried to visualize the outcome of Tarzan's discovery of them at the very threshold of Opar. He did not realize, as did Flora, that their very lives were in danger—that it was Tarzan of the Apes, a beast of the jungle, with whom they had to deal, and not John Clayton, Lord Greystoke, an English peer. Rather was Bluber considering the two thousand pounds that they stood to lose through this deplorable termination of their expedition, for he was sufficiently familiar with the reputation of the ape-man to know that they would never be permitted to take with them the gold that Esteban was very likely, at this moment, pilfering from the vaults of Opar. Really Bluber was almost upon the verge of tears when Kraski returned with the coffee, which he brought himself.

From the dark shadows of the tent's interior Flora Hawkes looked nervously out upon the scene before her. She was terrified at the possibility of discovery by her former employer, for she had been a maid in the Greystokes' London town house as well as at the African bungalow and knew that Lord Greystoke would recognize her instantly should he chance to see her. She entertained for him, now, in his jungle haunts, a fear that was possibly greater than Tarzan's true character warranted, but nonetheless real was it to the girl whose guilty conscience conjured all sorts of possible punishments for her disloyalty to those who had always treated her with uniform kindliness and consideration.

Constant dreaming of the fabulous wealth of the treasure vaults of Opar, concerning which she had heard so much in detail from the conversations of the Greystokes, had aroused within her naturally crafty and unscrupulous mind a desire for possession, and in consequence thereof she had slowly visualized a scheme whereby she might loot the treasure vaults of a sufficient number of the golden ingots to make her independently wealthy for life.

The entire plan had been hers. She had at first interested Kraski, who had in turn enlisted the cooperation of the two Englishmen and Bluber, and these four had raised the necessary money to defray the cost of the expedition. It had been Flora who had searched for a type of man who might successfully impersonate Tarzan in his own jungle, and she had found Esteban Miranda, a handsome, powerful, and unscrupulous Spaniard, whose histrionic ability aided by the art of make-up, of which he was a past master, permitted him to impersonate almost faultlessly the character they desired him to portray, insofar, at least, as outward appearances were concerned.

The Spaniard was not only powerful and active, but physically courageous as well, and since he had shaved his beard and donned the jungle habiliments of a Tarzan, he had lost no opportunity of emulating the ape-man in every way that lay within his ability. Of jungle craft he had none of course, and personal combats with the more savage jungle beasts caution prompted him to eschew, but he hunted the lesser game with spear and arrow and practiced continually with the grass rope that was a part of his make-up.

And now Flora Hawkes saw all her well-laid plans upon the verge of destruction. She trembled as she watched the men before the fire, for her fear of Tarzan was very real, and then she became tense with nervous anticipation as she saw Kraski approaching the group with the coffee pot in one hand and cups in the other. Kraski set the pot and the cups upon the ground a little in the rear of Tarzan, and, as he filled the latter, she saw him pour a portion of the contents of the bottle she had given him into one of the cups. A cold sweat broke out upon her forehead as Kraski lifted this cup and offered it to the ape-man. Would he take it? Would he suspect? If he did suspect what horrible punishment would be meted to them for their temerity? She saw Kraski hand another cup to Peebles, Throck, and Bluber, then return to the circle with the last one for himself. As the Russian raised it before his face and bowed politely to the ape-man, she saw the five men drink. The reaction which ensued left her weak and spent. Turning, she collapsed upon her cot, and lay there trembling, her face buried in her arm. And, outside, Tarzan of the Apes drained his cup to the last drop.

6

Death Steals Behind

DURING THE AFTERNOON of the day that Tarzan discovered the camp of the conspirators, a watcher upon the crumbling outer wall of the ruined city of Opar descried a party of men moving downward into the valley from the summit of the encircling cliff. Tarzan, Jane Clayton, and their black Waziri were the only strangers that the denizens of Opar had even seen within their valley during the lifetime of the oldest among them, and only in half-forgotten legends of a bygone past was there any suggestion that strangers other than these had ever visited Opar. Yet from time immemorial a guard had always remained upon the summit of the outer wall. Now a single knurled and crippled manlike creature was all that recalled the numerous, lithe warriors of lost Atlantis. For down through the long ages the race had deteriorated and finally, through occasional mating with the great apes, the men had become the beastlike things of modern Opar. Strange and inexplicable had been the providence of nature that had confined this deterioration almost solely to the males, leaving the females straight, well-formed, often of comely and even beautiful features, a condition that might be largely attributable to the fact that female infants possessing apelike characteristics were immediately destroyed, while, on the other hand, boy babies who possessed purely human attributes were also done away with.

Typical indeed of the male inhabitants of Opar was the lone watcher upon the outer city wall, a short, stocky man with matted hair and beard, his tangled locks growing low upon a

47

low, receding forehead; small, close-set eyes and fanglike teeth bore evidence of his simian ancestry, as did his short, crooked legs and long, muscular apelike arms, all scantily hair-covered as was his torso.

As his wicked, blood-rimmed eyes watched the progress of the party across the valley toward Opar, evidences of his growing excitement were manifested in the increased rapidity of his breathing, and low, almost inaudible growls that issued from his throat. The strangers were too far distant to be recognizable only as human beings, and their number roughly to be approximated as between two and three score. Having assured himself of these two facts the watcher descended from the outer wall, crossed the space between it and the inner wall, through which he passed, and at a rapid trot crossed the broad avenue beyond and disappeared within the crumbling but still magnificent temple beyond.

Cadj, the High Priest of Opar, squatted beneath the shade of the giant trees which now overgrew what had once been one of the gardens of the ancient temple. With him were a dozen members of the lesser priesthood, the intimate cronies of the High Priest, who were startled by the sudden advent of one of the inferior members of the clan of Opar. The fellow hurried breathlessly to Cadj.

"Cadj," he cried, "strange men descend upon Opar! From the northwest they have come into the valley from beyond the barrier cliffs—fifty of them at least, perhaps half again that number. I saw them as I watched from the summit of the outer wall, but further than they are men I cannot say, for they are still a great distance away. Not since the great Tarmangani came among us last have there been strangers within Opar."

"It has been many moons since the great Tarmangani who called himself Tarzan of the Apes was among us," said Cadj. "He promised us to return before the rain to see that no harm had befallen La, but he did not come back and La has always insisted that he is dead. Have you told any other of what you have seen?" he demanded, turning suddenly upon the messenger.

"No," replied the latter.

"Good!" exclaimed Cadj. "Come, we will all go to the outer wall and see who it is who dares enter forbidden Opar, and let no one breathe a word of what Blagh has told us until I give permission."

"The word of Cadj is law until La speaks," murmured one of the priests.

Cadj turned a scowling face upon the speaker. "I am High Priest of Opar," he growled. "Who dares disobey me?"

"But La is High Priestess," said one, "and the High Priestess is the queen of Opar."

"But the High Priest can offer whom he will as sacrifice in the Chamber of the Dead or to the Flaming God," Cadj reminded the other meaningly.

"We shall keep silence, Cadj," replied the priest, cringing.

"Good!" growled the High Priest and led the way from the garden through the corridors of the temple back toward the outer wall of Opar. From here they watched the approaching party that was in plain view of them, far out across the valley. The watchers conversed in low gutturals in the language of the great apes, interspersed with which were occasional words and phrases of a strange tongue that were doubtless corrupted forms of the ancient language of Atlantis handed down through count-less generations from their human progenitors—that now extinct race whose cities and civilization lie buried deep beneath the tossing waves of the Atlantic, and whose adven-turous spirit had, in remote ages, caused them to penetrate into the heart of Africa in search of gold and to build there, in dupli-cation of their far homes cities, the magnificent city of Opar.

As Cadj and his followers watched from beneath shaggy brows the strangers plodding laboriously beneath the now declining equatorial sun across the rocky, barren valley, a gray little monkey eyed them from amidst the foliage of one of the giant trees that had forced its way through the pavement of the ancient avenue behind them. A solemn, sad-faced little monkey it was, but like all his kind overcome by curiosity, and finally to such an extent that his fear of the fierce males of Opar was so considerably overcome that he at last swung lightly from the tree to the pavement, made his way through the inner wall and up the inside of the outer wall to a position in their rear where he could hide behind one of the massive granite blocks of the crumbling wall in comparative safety from detection, the while he might overhear the conversation of the Oparians, all of which that was carried on in the language of the great apes he could understand perfectly.

The afternoon was drawing to a close before the slowly moving company approaching Opar was close enough for individuals to be recognizable in any way, and then presently one of the younger priests exclaimed excitedly:

"It is he, Cadj. It is the great Tarmangani who calls himself Tarzan of the Apes. I can see him plainly; the others are all black men. He is urging them on, prodding them with his spear. They act as though they were afraid and very tired, but he is forcing them forward."

"You are sure," demanded Cadj, "you are sure that it is Tarzan of the Apes?"

"I am positive," replied the speaker, and then another of the priests joined his assurances to that of his fellow. At last they were close enough so that Cadj himself, whose eyesight was not as good as that of the younger members of the company, realized that it was indeed Tarzan of the Apes who was returning to Opar. The High Priest scowled angrily in thought. Suddenly he turned upon the others.

"He must not come," he cried; "he must not enter Opar. Hasten and fetch a hundred fighting men. We will meet them as they come through the outer wall and slay them one by one."

"But La," cried he who had aroused Cadj's anger in the garden, "I distinctly recall that La offered the friendship of Opar to Tarzan of the Apes upon that time, many moons ago, that he saved her from the tusks of infuriated Tantor."

"Silence," growled Cadj, "he shall not enter; we shall slay them all, though we need not know their identity until it is too late. Do you understand? And know, too, that whosoever attempts to thwart my purpose shall die—and he die not as a sacrifice, he shall die at my hands, but die he shall. You hear me?" And he pointed an unclean finger at the trembling priest.

Manu, the monkey, hearing all this, was almost bursting with excitement. He knew Tarzan of the Apes—as all the migratory monkeys the length and breadth of Africa knew him—he knew him for a friend and protector. To Manu the males of Opar were neither beast, nor man, nor friend. He knew them as cruel and surly creatures who ate the flesh of his kind, and he hated them accordingly. He was therefore greatly exercised at the plot that he had heard discussed which was aimed at the life of the great Tarmangani. He scratched his little gray head, and the root of his tail, and his belly, as he attempted mentally to digest what he had heard, and bring forth from the dim recesses of his little brain a plan to foil the priests and save Tarzan of the Apes. He made grotesque grimaces that were aimed at the unsuspecting Cadj and his followers, but which failed to perturb them, possibly because a huge granite block hid the little monkey from them. This was quite the most momentous thing that had occurred in the life of Manu. He wanted to jump up and down and dance and screech and jabber—to scold and threaten the hated Oparians, but something told him that nothing would be gained by this, other than, perhaps, to launch in his direction a shower of granite missiles, which the priests knew only too well how to throw with accuracy. Now Manu is not a deep thinker, but upon this occasion he quite outdid himself, and managed to concentrate his mind upon the thing at hand rather than permit its being distracted by each falling leaf or buzzing insect. He even permitted a succulent caterpillar to crawl within his reach and out again with impunity.

Just before darkness fell, Cadj saw a little gray money disappear over the summit of the outer wall fifty paces from where he crouched with his fellows, waiting for the coming of the fighting men. But so numerous were the monkeys about the ruins of Opar that the occurrence left Cadj's mind almost as quickly as the monkey disappeared from his view, and in the gathering gloom he did not see the little gray figure scampering off across the valley toward the band of intruders who now appeared to have stopped to rest at the foot of a large kopje that stood alone out in the valley, about a mile from the city.

Little Manu was very much afraid out there alone in the growing dusk, and he scampered very fast with his tail bowed up and out behind him. All the time he cast affrighted glances to the right and left. The moment he reached the kopje he scampered up its face as fast as he could. It was really a huge, precipitous granite rock with almost perpendicular sides, but sufficiently weather-worn to make its ascent easy to little Manu. He paused a moment at the summit to get his breath and still the beatings of his frightened little heart, and then he made his way around to a point where he could look down upon the party beneath.

There, indeed, was the great Tarmangani Tarzan, and with him were some fifty Gomangani. The latter were splicing together a number of long, straight poles, which they had laid upon the ground in two parallel lines. Across these two, at intervals of a foot or more, they were lashing smaller straight branches about eighteen inches in length, the whole forming a crude but substantial ladder. The purpose of all this Manu, of course, did not understand, nor did he know that it had been evolved from the fertile brain of Flora Hawkes as a means of scaling the precipitous kopje, at the summit of which lay the outer entrance to the treasure vaults of Opar. Nor did Manu know that the party had no intention of entering the city of Opar and were therefore in no danger of becoming victims of Cadj's hidden assassins. To him the danger to Tarzan of the Apes was very real, and so, having regained his breath, he lost no time in delivering his warning to the friend of his people.

"Tarzan," he cried, in the language that was common to both.

The white man and the blacks looked up at the sound of his chattering voice.

"It is Manu, Tarzan," continued the little monkey, "who has come to tell you not to go to Opar. Cadj and his people await within the outer wall to slay you."

The blacks, having discovered that the author of the disturbance was nothing but a little gray monkey, returned immediately to their work, while the white man similarly ignored his words of warning. Manu was not surprised at the lack of interest displayed by the blacks, for he knew that they did not understand his language, but he could not comprehend why Tarzan failed to pay any attention whatsoever to him. Again and again he called Tarzan by name. Again and again he shrieked his warning to the ape-man, but without eliciting any reply or any information that the great Tarmangani had either heard or understood him. Manu was mystified. What had occurred to render Tarzan of the Apes so indifferent to the warnings of his old friend?

At last the little monkey gave it up and looked longingly back in the direction of the trees within the walled city of Opar. It was now very dark and he trembled at the thought of recrossing the valley, where he knew enemies might prowl by night. He scratched his head and he hugged his knees, then sat there whimpering, a very forlorn and unhappy little ball of a monkey. But however uncomfortable he was upon the high kopje, he was comparatively safe, and so he decided to remain there during the night rather than venture the terrifying return trip through the darkness. Thus it was that he saw the ladder completed and erected against the side of the kopje; and when the moon rose at last and lighted the scene, he saw Tarzan of the Apes urging his men to mount the ladder. He had never seen Tarzan thus rough and cruel with the blacks who accompanied him. Manu knew how ferocious the great Tarmangani could be with an enemy, whether man or beast, but he had never seen him accord such treatment to the blacks who were his friends.

One by one and with evident reluctance the blacks ascended the ladder, continually urged forward to greater speed by the sharp spear of the white man; when they had all ascended Tarzan followed, and Manu saw them disappear apparently into the heart of the great rock.

It was only a short time later that they commenced to reappear, and now each was burdened by two heavy objects which appeared to Manu to be very similar to some of the smaller stone blocks that had been used in the construction of the buildings in Opar. He saw them take the blocks to the edge of the kopje and cast them over to the ground beneath, and when the last of the blacks had emerged with his load and cast it to the valley below, one by one the party descended the ladder to the foot of the kopje. But this time Tarzan of the Apes went first. Then they lowered the ladder and took it apart and laid its pieces close to the foot of the cliff, after which they took up the blocks which they had brought from the heart of the kopje, and following Tarzan, who set out in the lead, they commenced to retrace their steps toward the rim of the valley.

Manu would have been very much mystified had he been a man, but being only a monkey he saw only what he saw without attempting to reason very much about it. He knew that the ways of men were peculiar, and oftentimes unaccountable. For example, the Gomangani who could not travel through the jungle and the forest with the ease of any other of the animals which frequented them, added to their difficulty by loading themselves down with additional weights in the form of metal anklets and armlets, with necklaces and girdles, and with skins of animals, which did nothing more than impede their progress and render life much more complicated than that which the untrammeled beasts enjoyed. Manu, whenever he gave the matter a thought, congratulated himself that he was not a man—he pitied the foolish, unreasonable creatures.

Manu must have slept. He thought that he had only closed his eyes a moment, but when he opened them the rosy light of dawn had overspread the desolate valley. Just disappearing over the cliffs to the northeast he could see the last of Tarzan's party commencing the descent of the barrier, then Manu turned his face toward Opar and prepared to descend from the kopje, and scamper back to the safety of his trees within the walls of Opar. But first he would reconnoiter—Sheeta, the panther, might be still abroad, and so he scampered around the edge of the kopje to a point where he could see the entire valley floor between himself and Opar. And there it was that he saw again that which filled him with greatest excitement. For, debouching from the ruined outer wall of Opar was a large company of Opar's frightful men—fully a hundred of them Manu could have counted had Manu been able to count.

They seemed to be coming toward the kopje, and he sat and watched them as they approached, deciding to defer his return to the city until after the path was cleared of hated Oparians. It occurred to him that they were coming after him, for the egotism of the lower animals is inordinate. Because he was a monkey, the idea did not seem at all ridiculous and so he hid behind a jutting rock, with only one little, bright eye exposed to the enemy. He saw them come closer and he grew very much excited, though he was not at all afraid, for he knew that if they ascended one side of the kopje he could descend the other and be halfway to Opar before they could possibly locate him again.

On and on they came, but they did not stop at the kopje—as a matter of fact they did not come very close to it, but continued on beyond it. Then it was that the truth of the matter flashed into the little brain of the monkey—Cadj and his people were pursuing Tarzan of the Apes to slay him. If Manu has been offended by Tarzan's indifference to him upon the night before, he had evidently forgotten it, for now he was quite as excited about the danger which he saw menace the ape-man as he had been upon the afternoon previous. At first he thought of running ahead, and again warning Tarzan, but he feared to venture so far from the trees of Opar, even if the thought of having to pass the hated Oparians had not been sufficient to deter him from carrying out this plan. For a few minutes he sat watching them, until they had all passed the kopje, and then it became quite clear to him that they were heading directly for the spot at which the last of Tarzan's party had disappeared from the valley—there could be no doubt that they were in pursuit of the ape-man.

Manu scanned the valley once more toward Opar. There was nothing in sight to deter him from an attempted return, and so, with the agility of his kind, he scampered down the vertical face of the kopje and was off at great speed toward the city's wall. Just when he formulated the plan that he eventually followed it is difficult to say. Perhaps he thought it all out as he sat upon the kopje, watching Cadj and his people upon the trail of the ape-man, or perhaps it occurred to him while he was scampering across the barren waste toward Opar. It may just have popped into his mind from a clear sky after he had regained the leafy sanctuary of his own trees. Be that however as it may, the fact remains that as La, High Priestess and princess of Opar, in company with several of her priestesses, was bathing in a pool in one of the temple gardens, she was startled by the screaming of a monkey, swinging frantically by his tail from the branch of a great tree which overspread the pool—it was a little gray monkey with the face so wise and serious that one might easily have imagined that the fate of nations lay constantly upon the shoulders of its owner.

"La, La," it screamed, "they have gone to kill Tarzan. They have gone to kill Tarzan."

At the sound of that name La was instantly all attention. Standing waist deep in the pool she looked up at the little monkey questioningly. "What do you mean, Manu?" she asked.

"It has been many moons since Tarzan was in Opar. He is not here now. What are you talking about?"

"I saw him," screamed Manu, "I saw him last night with many Gomangani. He came to the great rock that lies in the valley before Opar; with all his men he climbed to the top of it, went into the heart of it, and came out with stones which they threw down into the valley. Afterward they descended from the rock, and picked up the stones again and left the valley—there," and Manu pointed toward the northeast with one of his hairy little fingers.

"How do you know it was Tarzan of the Apes?" asked La.

"Does Manu not know his cousin and his friend?" demanded the monkey. "With my eyes I saw him—it was Tarzan of the Apes."

La of Opar puckered her brows in thought. Deep in her heart smoldered the fires of her great love for Tarzan. Fires that had been quenched by the necessity that had compelled her marriage with Cadj since last she had seen the ape-man. For it is written among the laws of Opar that the High Priestess of the Flaming God must take a mate within a certain number of years after her consecration. For many moons La longed to make Tarzan that mate. The ape-man had not loved her, and finally she had come to a realization that he could never love her. Afterward she had bowed to the frightful fate that had placed her in the arms of Cadj.

As month after month had passed and Tarzan had not returned to Opar, as he had promised he would do, to see that no harm befell La, she had come to accept the opinion of Cadj that the ape-man was dead, and though she hated the repulsive Cadj nonetheless, her love for Tarzan had gradually become little more than a sorrowful memory. Now to learn that he was alive and had been so near was like reopening an old wound. At first she comprehended little else than that Tarzan had been close to Opar, but presently the cries of Manu aroused her to a realization that the ape-man was in danger—just what the danger was, she did not know.

"Who has gone to kill Tarzan of the Apes?" she demanded suddenly.

"Cadj, Cadj!" shrieked Manu. "He has gone with many, many men, and is following upon the spoor of Tarzan."

La sprang quickly from the pool, seized her girdle and ornaments from her attendant and adjusting them hurriedly, sped through the garden and into the temple.

7

"You Must Sacrifice Him"

WARILY CADJ AND his hundred frightful followers, armed with their bludgeons and knives, crept stealthily down the face of the barrier into the valley below, upon the trail of the white man and his black companions. They made no haste, for they had noted from the summit of Opar's outer wall, that the party they were pursuing moved very slowly, though why, they did not know, for they had been at too great a distance to see the burden that each of the blacks carried. Nor was it Cadj's desire to overtake his quarry by daylight, his plans contemplating a stealthy night attack, the suddenness of which, together with the great number of his followers, might easily confuse and overwhelm a sleeping camp.

The spoor they followed was well marked. There could be no mistaking it, and they moved slowly down the now gentle declivity, toward the bottom of the valley. It was close to noon that they were brought to a sudden halt by the discovery of a thorn boma recently constructed in a small clearing just ahead of them. From the center of the boma arose the thin smoke of a dying fire. Here, then, was the camp of the ape-man.

Cadj drew his followers into the concealment of the thick bushes that bordered the trail, and from there he sent ahead a single man to reconnoiter. It was but a few moments later that the latter returned to say that the camp was deserted, and once again Cadj moved forward with his men. Entering the boma they examined it in an effort to estimate the size of the party that accompanied Tarzan. As they were thus occupied Cadj saw something lying half concealed by bushes at the far end of the boma. Very warily he approached it, for there was that about it which not only aroused his curiosity but prompted him to caution, for it resembled indistinctly the figure of a man, lying huddled upon the ground.

With ready bludgeons a dozen of them approached the thing that had aroused Cadj's curiosity, and when they had come close to it they saw lying before them the lifeless figure of Tarzan of the Apes.

"The Flaming God has reached forth to avenge his desecrated altar," cried the High Priest, his eyes glowing with the maniacal fires of fanaticism. But another priest, more practical, perhaps, or at least more cautious, kneeled beside the figure of the ape-man and placed his ear against the latter's heart.

"He is not dead," he whispered; "perhaps he only sleeps."

"Seize him, then, quickly," cried Cadj, and an instant later Tarzan's body was covered by the hairy forms of as many of the frightful men as could pile upon him. He offered no resistance—he did not even open his eyes, and presently his arms were securely bound behind him.

"Drag him forth where the eye of the Flaming God may rest upon him," cried Cadj. They dragged Tarzan out into the center of the boma into the full light of the sun, and Cadj, the High Priest, drawing his knife from his loincloth, raised it above his head and stood over the prostrate form of his intended victim. Cadj's followers formed a rough circle about the ape-man and some of them pressed close behind their leader. They appeared uneasy, looking alternately at Tarzan and their High Priest, and then casting furtive glances at the sun, riding high in a cloud-mottled sky. But whatever the thoughts that troubled their half-savage brains, there was only one who dared voice his, and he was the same priest who, upon the preceding day, had questioned Cadj's proposal to slay the ape-man.

"Cadj," he said now, "who are you to offer up a sacrifice to the Flaming God? It is the privilege alone of La, our High Priestess and our queen, and indeed will she be angry when she learns what you have done."

"Silence, Dooth!" cried Cadj, "I, Cadj, am the High Priest of Opar. I, Cadj, am the mate of La, the queen. My word, too, is law in Opar. And you would remain a priest, and you would remain alive, keep silence."

"Your word is not law," replied Dooth, angrily, "and if you anger La, the High Priestess, or if you anger the Flaming God, you may be punished as another. If you make this sacrifice both will be angry."

"Enough," cried Cadj, "the Flaming God has spoken to me and has demanded that I offer up as sacrifice this defiler of his temple."

He knelt beside the ape-man and touched his breast above the heart with the point of his sharp blade, and then he raised the weapon high above him, preparatory to the fatal plunge into the living heart. At that instant a cloud passed before the face of the sun and a shadow rested upon them. A murmur rose from the surrounding priests.

"Look," cried Dooth, "the Flaming God is angry. He has hidden his face from the people of Opar."

Cadj paused. He cast a half-defiant, half-frightened look at the cloud obscuring the face of the sun. Then he rose slowly to his feet, and extending his arms upward toward the hidden god of day, he remained for a moment silent in apparently attentive and listening attitude. Then, suddenly, he turned upon his followers.

"Priests of Opar," he cried, "the Flaming God has spoken to his High Priest, Cadj. He is not angered. He but wishes to speak to me alone, and he directs that you go away into the jungle and wait until he has come and spoken to Cadj, after which I shall call you to return. Go!"

For the most part they seemed to accept the word of Cadj as law, but Dooth and a few others, doubtless prompted by a certain skepticism, hesitated.

"Be gone!" commanded Cadj. And so powerful is the habit of obedience that the doubters finally turned away and melted into the jungle with the others. A crafty smile lighted the cruel face of the High Priest as the last of them disappeared from sight, and then he once again turned his attention to the ape-man. That, deep within his breast however, lurked an inherent fear of his deity, was evidenced by the fact that he turned questioning glances toward the sky. He had determined to slay the ape-man while Dooth and the others were absent, yet the fear of his god restrained his hand until the light of his deity should shine forth upon him once more and assure him that the thing he contemplated might meet with favor.

It was a large cloud that overcast the sun, and while Cadj waited his nervousness increased. Six times he raised his knife for the fatal blow, yet in each instance his superstition prevented the consummation of the act. Five, ten, fifteen minutes passed, and still the sun remained obscured. But now at last Cadj could see that it was nearing the edge of the cloud, and once again he took his position kneeling beside the ape-man with his blade ready for the moment that the sunlight should flood again, for the last time, the living Tarzan. He saw it sweeping slowly across the boma toward him, and as it came a look of demoniacal hatred shone in his close-set, wicked eyes. Another instant and the Flaming God would have set the seal of his approval upon the sacrifice. Cadj trembled in anticipation. He raised the knife a trifle higher, his muscles tensed for the downward plunge, and then the silence of the jungle was broken by a woman's voice, raised almost to a scream.

"Cadj!" came the single word, but with all the suddenness and all the surprising effect of lightning from a clear sky.

His knife still poised on high, the High Priest turned in the direction of the interruption to see at the clearing's edge the figure of La, the High Priestess, and behind her Dooth and a score of the lesser priests.

"What means this, Cadj?" demanded La, angrily, approaching rapidly toward him across the clearing. Sullenly the High Priest rose.

"The Flaming God demanded the life of this unbeliever," he cried.

"Speaker of lies," retorted La, "the Flaming God communicates with men through the lips of his High Priestess only. Too often already have you attempted to thwart the will of your queen. Know, then, Cadj, that the power of life and death which your queen holds is as potent over you as another. During the long ages that Opar has endured, our legends tell us that more than one High Priest has been offered upon the altar to the Flaming God. And it is not unlikely that yet another may go the way of the presumptuous. Curb, therefore, your vanity and your lust for power, lest they prove your undoing."

Cadj sheathed his knife and turned sullenly away, casting a venomous look at Dooth, to whom he evidently attributed his undoing. That he was temporarily abashed by the presence of his queen was evident, but to those who knew Cadj there was little doubt that he still harbored his intention to despatch the ape-man, and if the opportunity ever presented itself that he would do so, for Cadj had a strong following among the people and priests of Opar. There were many who doubted that La would ever dare to incur the displeasure and anger of so important a portion of her followers as to cause the death or degradation of their High Priest, who occupied his office by virtue of laws and customs so old that their origin had been long lost in antiquity.

For years she had found first one excuse and then another to delay the ceremonies that would unite her in marriage to the High Priest. She had further aroused the antagonism of her people by palpable proofs of her infatuation for the ape-man, and even though at last she had been compelled to mate with Cadj, she had made no effort whatsoever to conceal her hatred and loathing for the man. How much further she could go with impunity was a question that often troubled those whose position in Opar depended upon her favor, and, knowing all these conditions as he did, it was not strange that Cadj should entertain treasonable thoughts toward his queen. Leagued with him in his treachery was Oah, a priestess who aspired to the power and offices of La. If La could be done away with, then Cadj had the influence to see that Oah became High Priestess. He also had Oah's promise to mate with him and permit him to rule as king, but as yet both were bound by the superstitious fear of their flaming deity, and because of this fact was the life of La temporarily made safe. It required, however, but the slightest spark to ignite the flames of treason that were smoldering about her.

So far, she was well within her rights in forbidding the sacrifice of Tarzan by the High Priest. But her fate, her very life, perhaps, depended upon her future treatment of the prisoner. Should she spare him, should she evidence in any way a return of the great love she had once almost publicly avowed for him, it was likely that her doom would be sealed. It was even questionable whether or not she might with impunity spare his life and set him at liberty.

Cadj and the others watched her closely now as she crossed to the side of Tarzan. Standing there silently for several moments she looked down upon him.

"He is already dead?" she asked.

"He was not dead when Cadj sent us away," volunteered Dooth. "If he is dead now it is because Cadj killed him while we were away."

"I did not kill him," said Cadj. "That remains, as La, our queen, has told you, for her to do. The eye of the Flaming God looks down upon you, High Priestess of Opar. The knife is at your hip, the sacrifice lies before you."

La ignored the man's words and turned toward Dooth. "If he still lives," she said, "construct a litter and bear him back to Opar."

Thus, once more, came Tarzan of the Apes into the ancient colonial city of Atlantians. The effects of the narcotic that Kraski had administered to him did not wear off for many hours. It was night when he opened his eyes, and for a moment he was bewildered by the darkness and the silence that surrounded him. All that he could scent at first was that he lay upon a pile of furs and that he was uninjured; for he felt no pain. Slowly there broke through the fog of his drugged brain recollection of the last moment before unconsciousness had overcome him, and presently he realized the trick that had been played upon him. For how long he had been unconscious and where he then was he could not imagine. Slowly he arose to his feet, finding that except for a slight dizziness he was quite himself. Cautiously he felt around in the darkness, moving with care, a hand outstretched, and always feeling carefully with his feet for secure footing. Almost immediately a stone wall stopped his progress, and this he followed around four sides of what he soon realized was a small room in which there were but two openings, a door upon each of the opposite sides. Only his senses of touch and smell were of value to him here. These told him only at first that he was imprisoned in a subterranean chamber, but as the effects of the narcotic diminished, the keenness of the latter returned, and with its return there was borne in upon Tarzan's brain an insistent impression of familiarity in certain fragrant odors that impinged upon his olfactory organs—a haunting suggestion that he had known them before under similar circumstances. Presently from above, through earth and masonry, came the shadow of an uncanny scream—just the faintest suggestion of it reached the keen ears of the ape-man, but it was sufficient to flood his mind with vivid recollections, and, by association of ideas, to fix the identity of the familiar odors about him. He knew at last that he was in the dark pit beneath Opar.

Above him, in her chamber in the temple, La, the High Priestess, tossed upon a sleepless couch. She knew all too well the temper of her people and the treachery of the High Priest, Cadj. She knew the religious fanaticism which prompted the ofttime maniacal actions of her bestial and ignorant followers, and she guessed truly that Cadj would inflame them against her should she fail this time in sacrificing the ape-man to the Flaming God. And it was the effort to find an escape from her dilemma that left her sleepless, for it was not in the heart of La to sacrifice Tarzan of the Apes. High Priestess of a horrid cult though she was, the queen of a race of half-beasts, yet she was a woman, too, a woman who had loved but once and given that love to the godlike ape-man who was again within her power. Twice before had he escaped her sacrificial knife; in the final instance love had at last triumphed over jealousy and fanaticism, and La, the woman, had realized that never again could she place in jeopardy the life of the man she loved, however hopeless she knew that love to be.

Tonight she was faced with a problem that she felt almost beyond her powers of solution. The fact that she was mated with Cadj removed the last vestige of hope that she had ever had of becoming the wife of the ape-man. Yet she was no less determined to save Tarzan if it were possible. Twice had he saved her life, once from a mad priest, and once from Tantor in *must*. Then, too, she had given her word that when Tarzan came again to Opar he came in friendship and would be received in friendship. But the influence of Cadj was great, and she knew that that influence had been directed unremittingly against the ape-man—she had seen it in the attitude of her followers from the very moment that they had placed Tarzan upon a litter to bear him back to Opar—she had seen it in the evil glances that had been cast at her. Sooner or later they would dare denounce her—all that they needed was some slight, new excuse, that, she knew, they eagerly awaited in her forthcoming attitude toward Tarzan. It was well after midnight when there came to her one of the priestesses who remained always upon guard outside her chamber door.

"Dooth would speak to you," whispered the handmaiden.

"It is late," replied La, "and men are not permitted in this part of the temple. How came he here, and why?"

"He says that he comes in the service of La, who is in great danger," replied the girl.

"Fetch him here then," said La, "and as you value your life see that you tell no one."

"I shall be as voiceless as the stones of the altar," replied the girl, as she turned and left the chamber.

A moment later she returned bringing Dooth, who halted a few feet from the High Priestess and saluted her. La signaled to the girl who had brought him to depart, and then she turned questioningly to the man.

"Speak, Dooth!" she commanded.

"We all know," he said, "of La's love for the strange ape-man, and it is not for me, a lesser priest, to question the thoughts or acts of my High Priestess. It is only for me to serve, as those would do better to serve who now plot against you."

"What do you mean, Dooth? Who plots against me?"

"Even at this minute are Cadj and Oah and several of the priests and priestesses carrying out a plan for your undoing. They are setting spies to watch you, knowing that you would liberate the ape-man, because there will come to you one who will tell you that to permit him to escape will be the easiest solution of your problem. This one will be sent by Cadj, and then those who watch you will report to the people and to the priests that they have seen you lead the sacrifice to liberty. But even that will avail you nothing, for Cadj and Oah and the others have placed upon the trail from Opar many men in hiding, who will fall upon the ape-man and slay him before the Flaming God has descended twice into the western forest. In but one way only may you save yourself, La of Opar."

"And what is that way?" she asked.

"You must, with your own hands, upon the altar of our temple, sacrifice the ape-man to the Flaming God."

8

Mystery of the Past

LA HAD BREAKFASTED the following morning, and had sent Dooth with food for Tarzan, when there came to her a young priestess, who was the sister of Oah. Even before the girl had spoken La knew that she was the emissary from Cadj, and that the treachery of which Dooth had warned her was already under way. The girl was ill at ease and quite evidently frightened, for she was young and held in high revere the queen whom she had good reason to know was all-powerful, and who might even inflict death upon her if she so wished. La, who had already determined upon a plan of action that she knew would be most embarrassing to Cadj and his conspirators, waited in silence for the girl to speak. But it was some time before the girl could muster up her courage or find a proper opening. Instead, she spoke of many things that had no bearing whatsoever upon her subject, and La, the High Priestess, was amused at her discomfiture.

"It is not often," said La, "that the sister of Oah comes to the apartments of her queen unless she is bidden. I am glad to see that she at last realizes the service that she owes to the High Priestess of the Flaming God."

"I come," said the girl, at last, speaking almost as one who has learned a part, "to tell you that I have overheard that which may be of interest to you, and which I am sure that you will be glad to hear."

"Yes?" interrogated La, raising her arched eyebrows.

"I overheard Cadj speaking with the lesser priests," the girl continued, "and I distinctly heard him say that he would be glad if the ape-man escaped, as that would relieve you, and Cadj as well, of much embarrassment. I thought that La, the queen, would be glad to know this, for it is known by all of us that La has promised friendship to the ape-man and therefore does not wish to sacrifice him upon the altar of the Flaming God."

"My duty is plain to me," replied La, in a haughty voice, "and I do not need Cadj nor any handmaiden to interpret it to me. I also know the prerogatives of a High Priestess, and that the right of sacrifice is one of them. For this reason I prevented Cadj from sacrificing the stranger. No other hand than mine may offer his heart's blood to the Flaming God, and upon the third day he shall die beneath my knife upon the altar of our temple."

The effect of these words upon the girl were precisely what La had anticipated. She saw disappointment and chagrin written upon the face of Cadj's messenger, who now had no answer, for her instructions had not foreseen this attitude upon the part of La. Presently the girl found some lame pretext upon which to withdraw, and when she had left the presence of the High Priestess, La could scarcely restrain a smile. She had no intention of sacrificing Tarzan, but this, of course, the sister of Oah did not know. So she returned to Cadj and repeated as nearly as she could recall it, all that La had said to her. The High Priest was much chagrined, for his plan had been now, not so much to encompass the destruction of Tarzan as to lead La into the commission of an act that would bring upon her the wrath of the priests and people of Opar, who, properly instigated, would demand her life in expiation. Oah, who was present when her sister returned, bit her lips, for great was her disappointment. Never before had she seen so close at hand the longed-for possibility of becoming High Priestess. For several minutes she paced to and fro in deep thought, and then, suddenly, she halted before Cadj.

"La loves this ape-man," she said, "and even though she may sacrifice him, it is only because of fear of her people. She loves him still—loves him better, Cadj, than she has ever loved you. The ape-man knows it, and trusts her, and because he knows it there is a way. Listen, Cadj, to Oah. We will send one to the ape-man who shall tell him that she comes from La, and that La has instructed her to lead him out of Opar and set him free. This one shall lead him into our ambush and when he is killed we shall go, many of us, before La, and accuse her of treachery. The one who led the ape-man from Opar shall say that La ordered her to do it, and the priests and the people will be very angry, and then you shall demand the life of La. It will be very easy and we shall be rid of both of them."

"Good!" exclaimed Cadj. "We shall do this thing at dawn upon the morrow, and before the Flaming God goes to his rest at night he shall look upon a new High Priestess in Opar."

That night Tarzan was aroused from his sleep by a sound at one of the doors of his prison cell. He heard the bolt slipped back and the door creak slowly open upon its ancient hinges. In the inky darkness he could discern no presence, but he heard the stealthy movement of sandaled feet upon the concrete floor, and then, out of the darkness, his name was whispered, in a woman's voice.

"I am here," he replied. "Who are you and what do you want of Tarzan of the Apes?"

"Your life is in danger," replied the voice. "Come, follow me."

"Who sent you?" demanded the ape-man, his sensitive nostrils searching for a clue to the identity of the nocturnal visitor, but so heavily was the air laden with the pungent odor of some pungent perfume with which the body of the woman seemed to have been anointed, that there was no distinguishing clue which he might judge as to whether she was one of the priestesses he had known upon the occasion of his former visits to Opar, or an entire stranger to him.

"La sent me," she said, "to lead you from the pits of Opar to the freedom of the outside world beyond the city's walls." Groping in the darkness she finally found him. "Here are your weapons," she said, handing them to him, and then she took his hand, turned and led him from the dungeon, through a long, winding, and equally black corridor, down flights of age-old concrete steps, through passages and corridors, opening and closing door after door that creaked and groaned upon rusty hinges. How far they traveled thus, and in what direction, Tarzan could not guess. He had gleaned enough from Dooth, when the latter brought him his food, to believe that in La he had a friend who would aid him, for Dooth had told him that she had saved him from Cadj when the latter had discovered him unconscious in the deserted boma of the Europeans who had drugged and left him. And so, the woman having said that she came from La, Tarzan followed her willingly. He could not but recall Jane's prophecy of the evils that he might expect to befall him should he persist in undertaking this third trip to Opar, and he wondered if, after all, his wife were right, that he should never again escape from the toils of the fanatical priests of the Flaming God. He had not, of course, expected to enter Opar, but there seemed to hang over the accursed city a guardian demon that threatened the life of whosoever dared approach the forbidden spot or wrest from the forgotten treasure vaults a portion of their great horde.

For more than an hour his guide led him through the Stygian darkness of underground passages, until ascending a flight of steps they emerged into the center of a clump of bushes, through which the pale light of the moon was barely discernible. The fresh air, however, told him that they had reached the surface of the ground, and now the woman, who had not spoken a word since she had led him from his cell, continued on in silence, following a devious trail that wound hither and thither in an erratic fashion through a heavy forest choked with undergrowth, and always upward.

From the location of the stars and moon, and from the upward trend of the trail, Tarzan knew that he was being led into the mountains that lie behind Opar—a place he had never thought of visiting, since the country appeared rough and uninviting, and not likely to harbor game such as Tarzan cared most to hunt. He was already surprised by the nature of the vegetation, for he had thought the hills barren except for stunted trees and scraggy bush. As they continued upon their way, climbing ever upward, the moon rose higher in the heavens, until its soft light revealed more clearly to the keen eyes of the ape-man the topography of the country they were traversing, and then it was that he saw they were ascending a narrow, thickly wooded gorge, and he understood why the heavy vegetation had been invisible from the plain before Opar. Himself naturally uncommunicative, the woman's silence made no particular impression upon Tarzan. Had he had anything to say he should have said it, and likewise he assumed that there was no necessity for her speaking unless there was some good reason for speaking, for those who travel far and fast have no breath to waste upon conversation.

The eastern stars were fading at the first hint of coming dawn when the two scrambled up a precipitous bank that formed the upper end of the ravine, and came out upon comparatively level ground. As they advanced the sky lightened, and presently the woman halted at the edge of a declivity, and as the day broke Tarzan saw below him a wooded basin in the heart of the mountain, and, showing through the trees at what appeared to be some two or three miles distant, the outlines of a building that glistened and sparkled and scintillated in the light of the new sun. Then he turned and looked at his companion, and surprise and consternation were writ upon his face, for standing before him was La, the High Priestess of Opar.

"You?" he exclaimed. "Now indeed will Cadj have the excuse that Dooth said he sought to put you out of the way."

"He will never have the opportunity to put me out of the way," replied La, "for I shall never return to Opar."

"Never return to Opar!" he exclaimed, "then where are you going? Where can you go?"

"I am going with you," she replied. "I do not ask that you love me. I only ask that you take me away from Opar and from the enemies who would slay me. There was no other way. Manu, the monkey, overheard them plotting, and he came to me and told me all that they would do. Whether I saved you or sacrificed you, it had all been the same with me. They were determined to do away with me, that Oah might be High Priestess and Cadj king of Opar. But I should not have sacrificed you, Tarzan, under any circumstances, and this, then, seemed the only way in which we might both be saved. We could not go to the north or the west across the plain of Opar for there Cadj has placed warriors in ambush to waylay you, and though you be Tarzan and a mighty fighter, they would overwhelm you by their very numbers and slay you."

"But where are you leading me?" asked Tarzan.

"I have chosen the lesser of two evils; in this direction lies an unknown country, filled for us Oparians with legends of grim monsters and strange people. Never has an Oparian ventured here and returned again to Opar. But if there lives in all the world a creature who could win through this unknown valley, it be you, Tarzan of the Apes."

"But if you know nothing of this country, of its inhabitants," demanded Tarzan, "how is it that you so well know the trail that leads to it?"

"We well know the trail to the summit, but that is as far as I have ever been before. The great apes and the lions use this trail when they come down into Opar. The lions, of course, cannot tell us where it leads, and the great apes will not, for usually we are at war with them. Along this trail they come down into Opar to steal our people, and upon this trail we await to capture them, for often we offer a great ape in sacrifice to the Flaming God, or rather that was our former custom, but for many years they have been too wary for us, the toll being upon the other side, though we do not know for what purpose they steal our people, unless it be that they eat them. They are a very powerful race, standing higher than Bolgani, the gorilla, and infinitely more cunning, for, as there is ape blood in our veins, so is there human blood in the veins of these great apes that dwell in the valley above Opar."

"Why is it, La, that we must past through this valley in order to escape from Opar? There must be some other way."

"There is no other way, Tarzan of the Apes," she replied. "The avenues across the valley are guarded by Cadj's people. Our only chance of escape lies in this direction, and I have brought you along the only trail that pierces the precipitous cliffs that guard Opar upon the south. Across or around this valley we must go in an attempt to find an avenue across the mountain and down upon the other side."

The ape-man stood gazing down into the wooded basin below them, his mind occupied with the problems of the moment. Had he been alone he would not have come this way, for he was sufficiently confident of his own prowess to believe that he might easily have crossed the valley of Opar in comparative safety, regardless of Cadj's plans to the contrary. But he was not alone. He had now to think of La, and he realized that in her efforts to save him she had placed him under a moral obligation which he might not disregard.

To skirt the basin, keeping as far as possible from the building, which he could see in the distance, seemed the wisest course to pursue, since, of course, his sole purpose was to find a way across the mountain and out of this inhospitable country. But the glimpses he caught of the edifice, half concealed as it was amid the foliage of great trees, piqued his curiosity to such an extent that he felt an almost irresistible urge to investigate. He did not believe that the basin was inhabited by other than wild beasts, and he attributed the building which he saw to the handiwork of an extinct or departed people, either contemporaneous with the ancient Atlantians who had built Opar or, perhaps, built by the original Oparians themselves, but now forgotten by their descendants. The glimpses which he caught of the building suggested such size and magnificence as might belong to a palace.

The ape-man knew no fear, though he possessed to a reasonable extent that caution which is inherent in all wild beasts. He would not have hesitated to pit his cunning and his prowess against the lower orders, however ferocious they might be, for, unlike man, they could not band together to his undoing. But should men elect to hunt him in numbers he knew that a real danger would confront him, and that, in the face of their combined strength and intelligence, his own might not avail him. There was little likelihood, however, he reasoned, that the basin was inhabited by human beings. Doubtless closer investigation of the building he saw would reveal that it was but a deserted ruin, and that the most formidable foes he would encounter would be the great apes and the lions. Of neither of these had he any fear; with the former it was even reasonable to imagine that he might establish amicable relations. Believing as he did that he must look for egress from the basin upon its opposite side, it was only natural that he should wish to choose the most direct route across the basin. Therefore his inclinations to explore the valley were seconded by considerations of speed and expediency.

"Come," he said to La, and started down the declivity which led into the basin in the direction of the building ahead of them.

"You are not going that way?" she cried in astonishment.

"Why not?" he said. "It is the shortest way across the valley, and insofar as I can judge our trail over the mountains is more likely to lie in that direction than elsewhere."

"But I am afraid," she said. "The Flaming God alone knows what hideous dangers lurk in the depths of that forest below us."

"Only Numa and the Mangani," he said. "Of these we need have no fear."

"You fear nothing," she said, "but I am only a woman."

"We can die but once," replied Tarzan, "and that once we must die. To be always fearing, then, would not avert it, and would make life miserable. We shall go the short way, then, and perhaps we shall see enough to make the risk well worthwhile."

They followed a well-worn trail downward among the brush, the trees increasing in both size and number as they approached the floor of the basin, until at last they were walking beneath the foliage of a great forest. What wind there was at their back, and the ape-man, though he moved at a swinging walk, was constantly on the alert. Upon the hard-packed earth of the trail there were few signs to indicate the nature of the animals that had passed to and fro, but here and there the spoor of a lion was in evidence. Several times Tarzan stopped and listened, often he raised his head and his sensitive nostrils dilated as he sought for whatever the surrounding air might hold for him.

"I think there are men in this valley," he said presently. "For some time I have been almost positive that we are being watched. But whoever is stalking us is clever beyond words, for it is only the barest suggestion of another presence that I can scent."

La looked about apprehensively and drew close to his side. "I see no one," she said, in a low voice.

"Nor I," he replied. "Nor can I catch any well-defined scent spoor, yet I am positive that someone is following us. Someone or something that trails by scent, and is clever enough to keep its scent from us. It is more than likely that, whatever it is, it is passing through the trees, at a sufficient height to keep its scent spoor always above us. The air is right for that, and even if he were upwind from us we might not catch his scent at all. Wait here, I will make sure," and he swung lightly into the branches of a nearby tree and swarmed upward with the agility of Manu, the monkey. A moment later he descended to the girl's side.

"I was right," he said, "there is someone, or something, not far off. But whether it is man or Mangani I cannot say, for the odor is a strange one to me, suggesting neither, yet both. But two can play at that game. Come!" And he swung the girl to his shoulder and a moment later had carried her high into the trees. "Unless he is close enough to watch us, which I doubt," he said, "our spoor will be carried over his head and it will be some time before he can pick it up again, unless he is wise enough to rise to a higher level."

La marveled at the strength of the ape-man as he carried her easily from tree to tree, and at the speed with which he traversed the swaying, leafy trail. For half an hour he continued onward, and then quite suddenly he stopped, poised high upon a swaying bough.

"Look!" he said, pointing ahead and below them. Looking in the direction that he indicated the girl saw through the leafy foliage a small, heavily stockaded compound, in which were some dozen huts that immediately riveted her surprised attention, nor no less was the ape-man's curiosity piqued by what he glimpsed vaguely through the foliage. Huts they evidently were, but they seemed to be moving to and fro in the air, some moving gently backward and forward, while others jumped up and down in more or less violent agitation. Tarzan swung to a nearer tree and descended to a sturdy branch, to which he lowered La from his shoulder. Then he crept forward stealthily, the girl following, for she was, in common with the other Oparians, slightly arboreal. Presently they reached a point where they could see plainly the village below them, and immediately the seeming mystery of the dancing huts was explained.

They were of the beehive type, common in many African tribes, and were about seven feet in diameter by six or seven in height, but instead of resting on the ground, each hut was suspended by a heavy hawserlike grass rope to a branch of one of the several giant trees that grew within the stockade. From the center of the bottom of each hut trailed another lighter rope. From his position above them Tarzan saw no openings in any of the huts large enough to admit the body of a man, though there were several openings four or five inches in diameter in the sides of each hut about three feet above the floor. Upon the ground, inside the compound, were several of the inhabitants of the village, if the little collection of swinging houses could be dignified by such a name. Nor were the people any less strange to Tarzan than their peculiar domiciles. That they were negroes was evident, but of a type entirely unfamiliar to the ape-man. All were naked, and without any ornamentation whatsoever other than a few daubs of color, placed apparently at random upon their bodies. They were tall, and very muscular appearing, though their legs seemed much too short and their arms too long for perfect symmetry, while their faces were almost bestial in contour, their jaws being exaggeratedly prognathous while above their beetling brows there was no forehead, the skull running back in an almost horizontal plane to a point.

As Tarzan stood looking at them he saw another descend one of the ropes that dangled from the bottom of a hut, and immediately he understood the purpose of the ropes and the location of the entrances to the dwellings. The creatures squatting about upon their haunches were engaged in feeding. Several had bones from which they were tearing the uncooked flesh with their great teeth, while others ate fruit and tubers. There were individuals of both sexes and of various ages, from childhood to maturity, but there was none that seemed very old. They were practically hairless, except for scraggy, reddish brown locks upon their heads. They spoke but seldom and then in tones which resembled the growling of beasts, nor once, while Tarzan watched them, did he see one laugh or even smile, which, of all their traits, rendered them most unlike the average native of Africa. Though Tarzan's eyes searched the compound carefully he saw no indication of cooking utensils or of any fire. Upon the ground about them lay their weapons, short javelinlike spears and a sort of battle-ax with a sharpened, metal blade. Tarzan of the Apes was glad that he had come this way, for it had permitted him to see such a type of native as he had not dreamed existed—a type that bordered closely upon the brute. Even the Waz-dons and Hodons of Pal-ul-don were far advanced in the scale of evolution compared to these.

As he looked at them he could not but wonder that they were sufficiently intelligent to manufacture the weapons they possessed, which he could see, even at a distance, were of fine workmanship and design. Their huts, too, seemed well and ingeniously made, while the stockade which surrounded the little compound was tall, strong, and well-built, evidently for the purpose of safeguarding them against the lions which infested the basin.

As Tarzan and La watched these people they became presently aware of the approach of some creature from their left, and a moment later they saw a man similar to those of the compound swing from a tree that overhung the stockade and drop within. The others acknowledged his coming with scarce more than indifferent glances. He came forward and, squatting among them, appeared to be telling them of something, and though Tarzan could not hear his words he judged from his gestures and the sign language which he used to supplement his meager speech, that he was telling his fellows of the strange creatures he had seen in the forest a short time before, and the ape-man immediately judged that this was the same whom he had been aware was following them and whom he had successfully put off the scent. The narration evidently excited them, for some of them arose, and leaping up and down with bent knees, slapped their arms against their sides grotesquely. The expressions upon their faces scarcely changed, however, and after a moment each squatted down again as he had been before.

It was while they were thus engaged that there echoed through the forest a loud scream that awakened in the mind of the ape-man many savage memories.

"Bolgani," he whispered to La.

"It is one of the great apes," she said, and shuddered.

Presently they saw him, swinging down the jungle trail toward the compound. A huge gorilla, but such a gorilla as Tarzan of the Apes had never looked on before. Of almost gigantic stature, the creature was walking erect with the stride of a man, not ever once touching his knuckles to the ground. His head and face were almost those of a gorilla, and yet there was a difference, as Tarzan could note as the creature came nearer—it was Bolgani, with the soul and brain of a man—nor was this all that rendered the creature startling and unique. Stranger perhaps than aught else was the fact that it wore ornaments—and such ornaments! Gold and diamonds sparkling against its shaggy coat, above its elbows were numerous armlets and there were anklets upon its legs, while from a girdle about its middle there depended before and behind a long narrow strip that almost touched the ground and which seemed to be entirely constructed of golden spangles set with small diamonds. Never before had John Clayton, Lord Greystoke, seen such a display of barbaric finery, nor even amidst the jewels of Opar such a wealth of priceless stones.

Immediately the hideous scream had first broken the comparative silence of the forest, Tarzan had noticed its effects upon the inmates of the compound. Instantly they had arisen to their feet. The women and children scurried behind the boles of the trees or clambered up the ropes into their swinging cages, while some of the men advanced to what Tarzan now saw was the gate of the compound. Outside this gate the gorilla halted and again raised his voice, but this time in speech rather than his hideous scream.

9

The Shaft of Death

As THE HUGE, manlike gorilla entered the compound the warriors closed the gate, and fell back respectfully as he advanced to the center of the village where he stood for a moment, looking about.

"Where are the shes and the balus?" he asked, tersely. "Call them."

The women and the children must have heard the command, but they did not emerge from their hiding places. The warriors moved about uneasily, evidently torn by the conflicting emotions of fear of the creature who had issued the order, and reluctance to fulfill his commands.

"Call them," he repeated, "or go and fetch them." But at last one of the warriors mustered the courage to address him.

"This village has already furnished one woman within the moon," he said. "It is the turn of another village."

"Silence!" roared the gorilla-man, advancing threateningly toward him. "You are a rash Gomangani to threaten the will of a Bolgani—I speak with the voice of Numa, the Emperor; obey or die."

Trembling, the black turned and called the women and children, but none responded to his summons. The Bolgani gestured impatiently.

"Go and fetch them," he demanded. And the blacks, cringing, moved sullenly across the compound toward the hiding places of their women and children. Presently they returned, dragging them with them, by the arms sometimes, but usually by the hair. Although they had seemed loath to give them up, they showed no gentleness toward them, nor any indication of affection. Their attitude toward them, however, was presently explained to Tarzan by the next words of the warriors who had spoken previously.

"Great Bolgani," he said, addressing the gorilla-man, "if Numa takes always from this village, there will soon be not enough women for the warriors here, and there will be too few children, and in a little time there will be none of us left."

"What of that?" growled the gorilla-man. "There are already too many Gomangani in the world. For what other purpose were you created than to serve Numa, the emperor, and his chosen people, the Bolgani?" As he spoke he was examining the women and children, pinching their flesh and pounding upon their chests and backs. Presently he returned to a comparatively young woman, straddling whose hip was a small child.

"This one will do," he said, snatching the child from its mother and hurling it roughly across the compound, where it lay against the face of the palisade, moaning pitifully, and perchance broken and dying. The poor, stupid mother, apparently more beast than human, stood for a moment trembling in dumb anguish, and then she started to rush forward to her child. But the gorilla-man seized her with one of his great hands and hurled her to the ground. Simultaneously there arose from the silent foliage above them the fierce and terrible scream of the challenging bull ape. In terror the simple blacks cast affrighted glances upward, while the gorilla-man raised his hideous face in snarling anger toward the author of the bestial cry.

Swaying upon a leafy bough they beheld such a creature as none of them had ever looked upon before—a white man, a Tarmangani, with hide as hairless as the body of Histah, the snake. In the instant that they looked they saw the spear hand of the stranger drive forward, and the shaft, speeding with the swiftness of thought, bury itself in the breast of the Bolgani. With a single scream of rage and pain, the gorilla-man crumpled to the earth, where he struggled spasmodically for a moment and then lay still, in death.

The ape-man held no great love for the Gomangani as a race, but inherent in his English brain and heart was the spirit of fair play, which prompted him to spontaneous espousal of the cause of the weak. On the other hand Bolgani was his hereditary enemy. His first battle had been with Bolgani, and his first kill.

The poor blacks were still standing in stupefied wonderment when he dropped from the tree to the ground among them. They stepped back in terror, and simultaneously they raised their spears menacingly against him.

"I am a friend," he said. "I am Tarzan of the Apes. Lower your spears." And then he turned and withdrew his own weapon from the carcass of Bolgani. "Who is this creature, that may come into your village and slay your balus and steal your shes? Who is he, that you dare not drive your spears through him?"

"He is one of the great Bolgani," said the warrior, who seemed to be spokesman, and the leader in the village. "He is one of the chosen people of Numa, the Emperor, and when Numa learns that he has been killed in our village we shall all die for what you have done."

"Who is Numa?" demanded the ape-man, to whom Numa, in the language of the great apes, meant only lion.

"Numa is the Emperor," replied the black, "who lives with the Bolgani in the Palace of Diamonds."

He did not express himself in just these words, for the meager language of the great apes, even though amplified by the higher intelligence and greater development of the Opar-

ians, is still primitive in the extreme. What he had really said
was more nearly "Numa, the king of kings, who lives in the
king's hut of glittering stones," which carried to the ape-man's
mind the faithful impression of the fact. Numa, evidently, was
the name adopted by the king of the Bolgani, and the title
emperor, indicated merely his preeminence among the chiefs.

The instant that Bolgani had fallen the bereaved mother
rushed forward and gathered her injured infant into her arms.
She squatted now against the palisade, cuddling it to her breast,
and crooning softly to pacify its cries, which Tarzan suddenly
discovered were more the result of fright than injury. At first
the mother had been frightened when he had attempted to
examine the child, drawing away and baring her fighting fangs,
much after the manner of a wild beast. But presently there had
seemed to come to her dull brain a realization that this creature
had saved her from Bolgani, that he had permitted her to
recover her infant and that he was making no effort to harm
either of them. Convinced at last that the child was only
bruised, Tarzan turned again toward the warriors, who were
talking together in an excited little group a few paces away. As
they saw him advancing, they spread into a semicircle and
stood facing him.

"The Bolgani will send and slay us all," they said, "when
they learn what has happened in our village, unless we can take
to them the creature that cast the spear. Therefore, Tarmangani,
you shall go with us to the Palace of Diamonds, and there we
shall give you over to the Bolgani and perhaps Numa will forgive us."

The ape-man smiled. What kind of creature did the simple
blacks think him, to believe that he would permit himself to be
easily led into the avenging hands of Numa, the Emperor of the
Bolgani. Although he was fully aware of the risk that he had
taken in entering the village, he knew too that because he was
Tarzan of the Apes there was a greater chance that he would be
able to escape than that they could hold him. He had faced
savage spearmen before and knew precisely what to expect in
the event of hostilities. He preferred, however, to make peace
with these people, for it had been in his mind to find some
means of questioning them the moment that he had discovered
their village hidden away in this wild forest.

"Wait," he said, therefore. "Would you betray a friend who enters your village to protect you from an enemy?"

"We will not slay you, Tarmangani. We will take you to the Bolgani for Numa, the Emperor."

"But that would amount to the same thing," returned Tarzan, "for you well know that Numa, the Emperor, will have me slain."

"That we cannot help," replied the spokesman. "If we could save you we would, but when the Bolgani discover what has happened in our village, it is we who must suffer, unless, perhaps, they are satisfied to punish you instead."

"But why need they know that the Bolgani has been slain in your village?" asked Tarzan.

"Will they not see his body next time they come?" asked the spokesman.

"Not if you remove his body," replied Tarzan.

The blacks scratched their heads. Into their dull, ignorant minds had crept no such suggestion of a solution of their problem. What the stranger said was true. None but they and he knew that Bolgani had been slain within their palisade. To remove the body, then, would be to remove all suspicion from their village. But where were they to take it? They put the question to Tarzan.

"I will dispose of him for you," replied the Tarmangani. "Answer my questions truthfully and I will promise to take him away and dispose of him in such a manner that no one will know how he died, or where."

"What are you questions," asked the spokesman.

"I am a stranger in your country. I am lost here," replied the ape-man. "And I would find a way out of the valley in that direction." And he pointed toward the southeast.

The black shook his head. "There may be a way out of the valley in that direction," he said, "but what lies beyond no man knows, nor do I know whether there be a way out or whether there be anything beyond. It is said that all is fire beyond the mountain, and no one dares to go and see. As for myself, I have never been far from my village—at most only a day's march to hunt for game for the Bolgani, and to gather fruit and nuts and plantains for them. If there is a way out I do not know, nor would any man dare take it if there were."

"Does no one ever leave the valley?" asked Tarzan.

"I know not what others do," replied the spokesman, "but those of this village never leave the valley."

"What lies in that direction?" asked Tarzan, pointing toward Opar.

"I do not know," replied the black, "only that sometimes the Bolgani come from that way, bringing with them strange creatures; little men with white skins and much hair, with short, crooked legs and long arms, and sometimes white shes, who do not look at all like the strange little Tarmangani. But where they get them I do not know, nor do they ever tell us. Are these all the questions that you wish to ask?"

"Yes, that is all," replied Tarzan, seeing that he could gain no information whatsoever from these ignorant villagers. Realizing that he must find his own way out of the valley, and knowing that he could do so much more quickly and safely if he were alone, he decided to sound the blacks in relation to a plan that had entered his mind.

"If I take the Bolgani away, so that the others will not know that he was slain in your village, will you treat me as a friend?" he asked.

"Yes," replied the spokesman.

"Then," said Tarzan, "will you keep here for me my white she until I return again to your village? You can hide her in one of your huts if a Bolgani comes, and no one need ever know that she is among you. What do you say?"

The blacks looked around. "We do not see her," said the spokesman. "Where is she?"

"If you will promise to protect her and hide her, I will bring her here," replied the ape-man.

"I will not harm her," said the head man, "but I do not know about the others."

Tarzan turned toward the others who were clustered about, listening. "I am going to bring my mate into your village," he said, "and you are going to hide her, and feed her, and protect her until I return. I shall take away the body of Bolgani, so that no suspicion shall fall upon you, and when I come back I shall expect to find my mate safe and unharmed."

He had thought it best to describe La as his mate, since thus they might understand that she was under his protection, and if they felt either gratitude or fear toward him, La would be safer. Raising his face toward the tree where she was hidden, he called to La to descend, and a moment later she clambered down to the lower branches of one of the trees in the compound and dropped into Tarzan's arms.

"This is she," he said to the assembled blacks, "guard her well and hide her from the Bolgani. If, upon my return, I find that any harm has befallen her, I shall take word to the Bolgani that it was you who did this," and he pointed to the corpse of the gorilla-man.

La turned appealingly toward him, fear showing in her eyes. "You are not going to leave me here?" she asked.

"Temporarily only," replied Tarzan. "These poor people are afraid that if the death of this creature is traced to their village they shall all suffer the wrath of his fellows, and so I have promised that I will remove the evidence in such a way as to direct suspicion elsewhere. If they are sufficiently high in the scale of evolution to harbor sentiments of gratitude, which I doubt, they will feel obligated to me for having slain this beast, as well as for preventing suspicion falling upon them. For these reasons they should protect you, but to make assurance doubly sure I have appealed also to their fear of the Bolgani—a characteristic which I know they possess. I am sure that you will be as safe here as with me until I return, otherwise I would not leave you. But alone I can travel much faster, and while I am gone I intend to find a way out of this valley, then I shall return for you and together we may make our escape easily, or at least with greater assurance of success than were we to blunder slowly about together."

"You will come back?" she asked, a note of fear, longing, and appeal in her voice.

"I will come back," he replied, and then turning to the blacks: "Clear out one of these huts for my mate, and see that she is not molested, and that she is furnished with food and water. And remember what I said, upon her safety your lives depend."

Stooping, Tarzan lifted the dead gorilla-man to his shoulder, and the simple blacks marveled at his prowess. Of great physical strength themselves, there was not one of them but would have staggered under the weight of Bolgani, yet this strange Tarmangani walked easily beneath his burden, and when they had opened the gate in the palisade he trotted down the jungle trail as though he carried nothing but his own frame. A moment later he disappeared at a turn and was swallowed by the forest.

La turned to the blacks: "Prepare my hut," she said, for she was very tired and longed to rest. They eyed her askance and whispered among themselves. It was evident to her that there was a difference of opinion among them, and presently from snatches of conversation which she overheard she realized that while some of the blacks were in favor of obeying Tarzan's injunctions implicitly, there were others who objected strenuously and who wished to rid their village of her, lest she be discovered there by the Bolgani, and the villagers be punished accordingly.

"It would be better," she heard one of the blacks say, "to turn her over to the Bolgani at once and tell them that we saw her mate slay the messenger of Numa. We will say that we tried to capture the Tarmangani but that he escaped, and that we were only able to seize his mate. Thus will we win the favor of Numa, and perhaps then he will not take so many of our women and children."

"But the Tarmangani is great," replied one of the others. "He is more powerful even than Bolgani. He would make a terrible enemy, and, as the chances are that the Bolgani would not believe us we should then have not only them but the Tarmangani to fear."

"You are right," cried La, "the Tarmangani is great. Far better will it be for you to have him for friend than enemy. Single-handed he grapples with Numa, the lion, and slays him. You saw with what ease he lifted the body of the mighty Bolgani to his shoulder. You saw him trot lightly down the jungle trail beneath his burden. With equal ease will he carry the corpse through the trees of the forest, far above the ground. In all the world there is no other like him, no other like Tarzan of the Apes. If you are wise, Gomangani, you will have Tarzan for a friend."

The blacks listened to her, their dull faces revealing nothing of what was passing in their stupid brains. For a few moments they stood thus in silence, the hulking, ignorant blacks upon one side, the slender, beautiful white woman upon the other. Then La spoke.

"Go," she cried imperiously, "and prepare my hut." It was the High Priestess of the Flaming God; La, the queen of Opar, addressing slaves. Her regal mien, her commanding tones, wrought an instant change in the villagers, and La knew then that Tarzan was right in his assumption that they could be moved only through fear, for now they turned quickly, cowering like whipped dogs, and hastened to a nearby hut, which they quickly prepared for her, fetching fresh leaves and grasses for its floor, and fruit and nuts and plantains for her meal.

When all was ready, La clambered up the rope and through the circular opening in the floor of the hanging hut, which she found large and airy, and now reasonably clean. She drew the rope up after her and threw herself upon the soft bed they had prepared for her, and soon the gentle swaying of the swinging hut, the soft murmur of the leaves above her, the voices of the birds and insects combined with her own physical exhaustion to lull her into deep slumber.

10

Mad Treachery

To THE NORTHWEST of the valley of Opar the smoke rose from the cook fires of a camp in which some hundred blacks and six whites were eating their evening meal. The negroes squatted sullen and morose, mumbling together in low tones over their meager fare, the whites, scowling and apprehensive, kept their firearms close at hand. One of them, a girl, and the only member of her sex in the party, was addressing her fellows:

"We have Adolph's stinginess and Esteban's braggadocio to thank for the condition in which we are," she said.

The fat Bluber shrugged his shoulder, the big Spaniard scowled.

"For vy," asked Adolph, "am I to blame?"

"You were too stingy to employ carriers. I told you at the time that we ought to have had two hundred blacks in our party, but you wanted to save a little money, and now what is the result? Fifty men carrying eighty pounds of gold apiece and the other carriers are overburdened with camp equipment, while there are scarce enough left for askari to guard us properly. We have to drive them like beasts to make any progress and to keep them from throwing away their loads, and they are fagged out and angry. They don't require much of an excuse to kill us all on the spot. On top of all this they are underfed. If we could keep their bellies filled we could probably keep them happy and reasonably contented, but I have learned enough about natives to know that if they are hungry they are neither happy nor contented, even in idleness. If Esteban had not bragged so much about his prowess as a hunter we should have brought enough provisions to last us through, but now, though we are barely started upon our return journey, we are upon less than half rations."

"I can't kill game when there isn't any game," growled the Spaniard.

"There is plenty of game," said Kraski, the Russian. "We see the tracks of it every day."

The Spaniard eyed him venomously. "If there is so much game," he said, "go out and get it yourself."

"I never claimed to be a hunter," replied Kraski, "though I could go out with a sling shot and a pea shooter and do as well as you have."

The Spaniard leaped to his feet menacingly, and instantly the Russian covered him with a heavy service revolver.

"Cut that business," cried the girl, sharply, leaping between them.

"Let the blighters fight," growled John Peebles. "If one of 'em kills the hother there'll be fewer to split the swag, and 'ere we are 'n that's that."

"For vy should ve quarrel?" demanded Bluber. "Dere is

enough for all—over forty-tree t'ousand pounds apiece. Ven you get mad at me you call me names und say dat I am stingy, but *Mein Gott!* you English are vorser. You vould kill vun of your friends to get more money. *Ja wohl,* tank *Gott* dat I am not an Englisher."

"Shut up," growled Throck, "or we'll have forty-three thousand pounds more to divide."

Bluber eyed the big Englishman fearfully. "Come, come, Dick," he oozed, in his oiliest tones, "you vouldn't get mad at a leedle choke vould you, und me your best friend?"

"I'm sick of all this grousin'," said Throck. "I ain't no high-brow, I ain't nothin' but a pug. But I got sense enough to know that Flora's the only one in the bloomin' bunch whose brains wouldn't rattle around in a peanut shell. John, Bluber, Kraski and me, we're here because we could raise the money to carry out Flora's plan. The actor there"—and he indicated Esteban—"because his face and his figure filled the bill. There don't any of us need no brains for this work, and there ain't any of us got any more brains than we need. Flora's the brains of this outfit, and the sooner everyone understands that and takes orders from her, the better off we'll all be. She's been to Africa with this Lord Greystoke feller before— you wuz his wife's maid, wasn't you, Flora? And she knows somethin' about the country and the natives and the animals, and there don't none of us know nuttin'."

"Throck is right," said Kraski, quickly, "we've been muddling long enough. We haven't had a boss, and the thing to do is to make Flora boss from now on. If anyone can get us out of this, she can, and from the way those fellows over there are acting," and he nodded toward the blacks, "we'll be lucky if we ever get out with our skins, let alone taking any of the gold with us."

"*Ach, nein!* You don't mean to leave der gold?" almost shrieked Bluber.

"I mean that we do whatever Flora thinks best," replied Kraski. "If she says to leave the gold, we'll leave it."

"That we do," seconded Throck.

"I'm for it," said Peebles. "Whatever Flora says goes."

The Spaniard nodded his assent sullenly.

"The rest of us are all for it, Bluber. How about you?" asked Kraski.

"O vell—sure—if you say so," said Bluber, "und as John says 'und here ve ain't und vat's dat.' "

"And now, Flora," said Peebles, "you're the big 'un. What you say goes. What'll we do next?"

"Very well," said the girl, "we shall camp here until these men are rested, and early tomorrow we'll start out intelligently and systematically, and get meat for them. With their help we can do it. When they are rested and well fed we will start on again for the coast, moving very slowly, so as not to tire them too much. This is my first plan, but it hinges upon our ability to get meat. If we do not find it I shall bury the gold here, and we will do our best to reach the coast as quickly as possible. There we shall recruit new porters—twice as many as we have now—and purchase enough provisions to carry us in and out again. As we come back in, we will cache provisions at every camping place for our return trip, thus saving the necessity of carrying heavy loads all the way in and out again. In this way we can come out light, with twice as many porters as we actually need. And by working them in shifts we will travel much faster and there will be no grumbling. These are my two plans. I am not asking you what you think of them, because I do not care. You have made me chief, and I am going to run this from now on as I think best."

"Bully for you," roared Peebles; "that's the kind of talk I likes to hear."

"Tell the head man I want to see him, Carl," said the girl, turning to Kraski, and a moment later the Russian returned with a burly native.

"Owaza," said the girl, as the black halted before her, "we are short of food and the men are burdened with loads twice as heavy as they should carry. Tell them that we shall wait here until they are rested and that tomorrow we shall all go out and hunt for meat. You will send your boys out under three good men, and they will act as beaters and drive the game in to us. In this way we should get plenty of meat, and when the men are rested and well fed we will move on slowly. Where game is plentiful we will hunt and rest. Tell them that if they do this and we reach the coast in safety and with all our loads, I shall pay them twice what they agreed to come for."

"*Himmel!*" spluttered Bluber, "twice vat dey agreed to

come for! Oh, Flora, vy not offer dem ten percent? Dat would be fine interest on their money."

"Shut up, you fool," snapped Kraski, and Bluber subsided, though he rocked back and forth, shaking his head in disapproval.

The black, who had presented himself for the interview with sullen and scowling demeanor, brightened visibly now. "I will tell them," he said, "and I think that you will have no more trouble."

"Good," said Flora, "go and tell them now," and the black turned and left.

"There," said the girl, with a sigh of relief, "I believe that we can see light ahead at last."

"Twice vat ve promised to pay them!" bawled Bluber.

Early the following morning they prepared to set out upon the hunt. The blacks were now smiling and happy in anticipation of plenty of meat, and as they tramped off into the jungle they were singing gayly. Flora had divided them into three parties, each under a head man, with explicit directions for the position each party was to take in the line of beaters. Others had been detailed to the whites as gun-bearers, while a small party of the askari were left behind to guard the camp. The whites, with the exception of Esteban, were armed with rifles. He alone seemed inclined to question Flora's authority, insisting that he preferred to hunt with spear and arrows in keeping with the part he was playing. The fact that, though he had hunted assiduously for weeks, yet had never brought in a single kill, was not sufficient to dampen his egotism. So genuinely had he entered his part that he really thought he was Tarzan of the Apes, and with such fidelity had he equipped himself in every detail, and such a master of the art of makeup was he, that, in conjunction with his splendid figure and his handsome face that were almost a counterpart of Tarzan's, it was scarcely to be wondered at that he almost fooled himself as successfully as he had fooled others, for there were men among the carriers who had known the great ape-man, and even these were deceived, though they wondered at the change in him, since in little things he did not deport himself as Tarzan, and in the matter of kills he was disappointing.

Flora Hawkes, who was endowed with more than a fair

share of intelligence, realized that it would not be well to cross any of her companions unnecessarily, and so she permitted Esteban to hunt that morning in his own way, though some of the others grumbled a little at her decision.

"What is the difference?" she asked them, after the Spaniard had set out alone. "The chances are that he could use a rifle no better than he uses his spear and arrows. Carl and Dick are really the only shots among us, and it is upon them we depend principally for the success of our hunt today. Esteban's egotism has been so badly bumped that it is possible that he will go to the last extremity to make a kill today—let us hope that he is successful."

"I hope he breaks his fool neck," said Kraski. "He has served our purpose and we would be better off if we were rid of him."

The girl shook her head negatively. "No," she said, "we must not think or speak of anything of that kind. We went into this thing together, let us stick together until the end. If you are wishing that one of us is dead, how do you know that others are not wishing that you were dead?"

"I haven't any doubt but that Miranda wishes I were dead," replied Kraski. "I never go to bed at night without thinking that the damned greaser may try to stick a knife into me before morning. And it don't make me feel any kinder toward him to hear you defending him, Flora. You've been a bit soft on him from the start."

"If I have, it's none of your business," retorted the girl.

And so they started out upon their hunt, the Russian scowling and angry, harboring thoughts of vengeance or worse against Esteban, and Esteban, hunting through the jungle, was occupied with his hatred and his jealousy. His dark mind was open to every chance suggestion of a means for putting the other men of the party out of the way, and taking the woman and the gold for himself. He hated them all; in each he saw a possible rival for the affections of Flora, and in the death of each he saw not only one less suitor for the girl's affections, but forty-three thousand additional pounds to be divided among fewer people. His mind was thus occupied to the exclusion of the business of hunting, which should have occupied him solely, when he came through a patch of heavy underbrush, and stepped into the glaring sunlight of a large clearing, face to face with a party of some fifty magnificent ebon warriors. For just an instant Esteban stood frozen in a paralysis of terror, forgetting momentarily the part he was playing—thinking of himself only as a lone white man in the heart of savage Africa facing a large band of warlike natives—cannibals, perhaps. It was that moment of utter silence and inaction that saved him, for, as he stood thus before them, the Waziri saw in the silent, majestic figure their beloved lord in a characteristic pose.

"O Bwana, Bwana," cried one of the warriors, rushing forward, "it is indeed you, Tarzan of the Apes, Lord of the Jungle, whom we had given up as lost. We, your faithful Waziri, have been searching for you, and even now we were about to dare the dangers of Opar, fearing that you might have ventured there without us and had been captured."

The black, who had at one time accompanied Tarzan to London as a body servant, spoke broken English, an accomplishment of which he was inordinately proud, losing no opportunity to air his attainment before his less fortunate fellows. The fact that it had been he whom fate had chosen to act as spokesman was indeed a fortunate circumstance to Miranda. Although the latter had applied himself assiduously to mastering the dialect of the west coast carriers, he would have been hard put to it to carry on a conversation with one of them, while he understood nothing of the Waziri tongue. Flora had schooled him carefully and well in the lore of Tarzan, so that he realized now that he was in the presence of a band of the ape-man's faithful Waziri. Never before had he seen such magnificent blacks—clean-cut, powerful men, with intelligent faces and well molded features, appearing as much higher in the scale of evolution as were the west coast blacks above the apes. Lucky indeed was Esteban Miranda that he was quick-witted and a consummate actor. Otherwise must he have betrayed his terror and his chagrin upon learning that this band of Tarzan's fierce and faithful followers was in this part of the country. For a moment longer he stood in silence before them, gathering his wits, and then he spoke, realizing that his very life depended upon his plausibility. And as he thought a great light broke upon the shrewd brain of the unscrupulous Spaniard.

"Since I last saw you," he said, "I discovered that a party of white men had entered the country for the purpose of robbing the treasure vaults of Opar. I followed them until I found their camp, and then I came in search of you, for there are many of them and they have many ingots of gold, for they have already been to Opar. Follow me, and we will raid their camp and take the gold from them. Come!" and he turned back toward the camp that he had just quitted.

As they made their way along the jungle trail, Usula, the Waziri who had spoken English to him, walked at Esteban's side. Behind them the Spaniard could hear the other warriors speaking in their native tongue, no word of which he understood, and it occurred to him that his position would be most embarrassing should he be addressed in the Waziri language, which of course, Tarzan must have understood perfectly. As he listened to the chatter of Usula his mind was working rapidly, and presently, as though it were an inspiration, there recurred to him the memory of an accident that had befallen Tarzan, which had been narrated to him by Flora—the story of the injury he had received in the treasure vaults of Opar upon the occasion that he had lost his memory because of a blow upon the head. Esteban wondered if he had committed himself too deeply at first to attribute to amnesia any shortcomings in the portrayal of the role he was acting. At its worst, however, it seemed to him the best that he could do. He turned suddenly upon Usula.

"Do you remember," he asked, "the accident that befell me in the treasure vaults of Opar, depriving me of my memory?"

"Yes, Bwana, I remember it well," replied the black.

"A similar accident has befallen me," said Esteban. "A great tree fell in my path, and in falling a branch struck me upon the head. It has not caused me to lose my memory entirely, but since then it is with difficulty that I recall many things, and there are other things which I must have forgotten entirely, for I do not know your name, nor do I understand the words that my other Waziri are speaking about me."

Usula looked at him compassionately. "Ah, Bwana, sad indeed is the heart of Usula to hear that this accident has befallen you. Doubtless it will soon pass away as did the other, and in the meantime I, Usula will be your memory for you."

"Good," said Esteban, "tell the others that they may under-stand, and tell them also that I have lost my memory of other things besides. I could not now find my way home without you, and my other senses are dull as well. But as you say, Usula, it will soon pass off, and I shall be myself again."

"Your faithful Waziri will rejoice indeed with the coming of that moment," said Usula.

As they approached the camp, Miranda cautioned Usula to warn his followers to silence, and presently he halted them at the outskirts of the clearing where they could attain a view of the boma and the tents, guarding which was a little band of a half-dozen askari.

"When they see our greater numbers they will make no resis-tance," said Esteban. "Let us surround the camp, therefore, and at a signal from me we will advance together, when you shall address them, saying that Tarzan of the Apes comes with his Waziri for the gold they have stolen, but that he will spare them if they will leave the country at once and never return."

Had it fulfilled his purpose as well, the Spaniard would have willingly ordered his Waziri to fall upon the men guarding the camp and destroy them all, but to his cunning brain had been born a cleverer scheme. He wanted these men to see him with the Waziri and live to tell the others that they had seen him, and to repeat to Flora and her followers the thing that Esteban had in his mind to tell one of the askari, while the Waziri were gath-ering up the gold ingots from the camp.

In directing Usula to station his men about the camp, Esteban had to warn them that they were not to show them-selves until he had crept out into the clearing and attracted the attention of the askari on guard. Fifteen minutes, perhaps, were consumed in stationing his men, and then Usula returned to Esteban to report that all was ready.

"When I raise my hand then you will know that they have recognized me and that you are to advance," Esteban cautioned him, and stepped forward slowly into the clearing. One of the askari saw him and recognized him as Esteban. The Spaniard took a few steps closer to the boma and then halted.

"I am Tarzan of the Apes," he said; "your camp is entirely surrounded by my warriors. Make no move against us and we shall not hurt you."

He waved his hand. Fifty stalwart Waziri stepped into view from the concealing verdure of the surrounding jungle. The askari eyed them in ill-concealed terror, fingering their rifles nervously.

"Do not shoot," cautioned Esteban, "or we shall slay you all." He approached more closely and his Waziri closed in about him, entirely surrounding the boma.

"Speak to them, Usula," said Esteban. The black stepped forward.

"We are the Waziri," he cried, "and this is Tarzan of the Apes, Lord of the Jungle, our master. We have come to recover the gold of Tarzan that you have stolen from the treasure vaults of Opar. This time we shall spare you on condition that you leave the country and never return. Tell this word to your masters; tell them that Tarzan watches, and that his Waziri watch with him. Lay down your rifles."

The askari, glad to escape so easily, complied with the demands of Usula, and a moment later the Waziri had entered the boma, and at Esteban's direction were gathering up the golden ingots. As they worked, Esteban approached one of the askari, whom he knew spoke broken English.

"Tell your master," he said, "to give thanks for the mercy of Tarzan who has exacted a toll of but one life for this invasion of his country and theft of his treasure. The creature who presumes to pose as Tarzan I have slain, and his body I shall take away with me and feed to the lions. Tell them that Tarzan forgives even their attempt to poison him upon the occasion that he visited their camp, but only upon the condition that they never return to Africa, and that they divulge the secret of Opar to no others. Tarzan watches and his Waziri watch, and no man may enter Africa without Tarzan's knowledge. Even before they left London I knew that they were coming. Tell them that."

It took but a few minutes for the Waziri to gather up the golden ingots, and before the askari had recovered from the surprise of their appearance, they had gone again into the jungle, with Tarzan, their master.

It was late in the afternoon before Flora and the four white men returned from their hunt, surrounded by happy, laughing blacks, bearing the fruits of a successful chase.

"Now that you are in charge, Flora," Kraski was saying,

"fortune is smiling upon us indeed. We have enough meat here for several days, and with plenty of meat in their bellies they ought to make good progress."

"I vill say it myself dot tings look brighter," said Bluber.

"Blime, they do that," said Throck. "I'm tellin' you Flora's a bright one."

"What the devil is this?" demanded Peebles, "what's wrong with them beggars?" And he pointed toward the boma which was now in sight, and from which the askari were issuing at a run, jabbering excitedly as they raced toward them.

"Tarzan of the Apes has been here," they cried excitedly. "He has been here with all his Waziri—a thousand great warriors—and though we fought, they overcame us, and taking the gold they went away. Tarzan of the Apes spoke strange words to me before they left. He said that he had killed one of your number who had dared to call himself Tarzan of the Apes. We do not understand it. He went away alone to hunt when you went in the morning, and he came back shortly with a thousand warriors, and he took all the gold and he threatened to kill us and you if you ever return to this country again."

"Vot, vot?" cried Bluber, "der gold iss gone? *Ach! Ach!*" And then they all commenced to ask questions at once until Flora silenced them.

"Come," she said to the leader of the askari, "we will return to the boma and then you shall tell me slowly and carefully all that has happened since we left."

She listened intently to his narrative, and then questioned him carefully upon various points several times. At last she dismissed him. Then she turned to her confederates.

"It is all clear to me," she said. "Tarzan recovered from the effects of the drug we administered. Then he followed us with his Waziri, caught Esteban and killed him and, finding the camp, has taken the gold away. We shall be fortunate indeed if we escape from Africa with our lives."

"*Ach, weh!*" almost shrieked Bluber, "der dirty crook. He steals all our gold, und ve lose our two t'ousand pounds into der bargain."

"Shut up, you coward," growled Throck. "If it hadn't 'a' been for you and the actor there 'ere thing would never 'a' 'appened. With 'im abraggin' about 'is 'unting and not bein' able to kill anything, and you a-squeezin' every bloomin' hapenny, we're in a rotten mess—that we are. This 'ere Tarzan bounder he bumped off Esteban, which is the best work what 'e ever done. Too bloody bad you weren't 'ere to get it too, and what I got a good mind to do is to slit your throat meself."

"Stow the guff, Dick," roared Peebles, "it wasn't nobody's fault, as far as I can see. Instead of talkin' what we oughter do is to go after this 'ere Tarzan feller and take the bloomin' gold away from 'im."

Flora Hawkes laughed. "We haven't a chance in the world," she said. "I know this Tarzan bloke. If he was all alone we wouldn't be a match for him, but he's got a bunch of his Waziri with him, and there are no finer warriors in Africa than they. And they'd fight for him to the last man. You just tell Owaza that you're thinking of going after Tarzan of the Apes and his Waziri to take the gold away from them, and see how long it'd be before we wouldn't have a single porter with us. The very name of Tarzan scares these west coast blacks out of a year's growth. They would sooner face the devil. No, sir, we've lost, and all we can do is to get out of the country, and thank our lucky stars if we manage to get out alive. The ape-man will watch us. I should not be surprised if he were watching us this minute." Her companions looked around apprehensively at this, casting nervous glances toward the jungle. "And he'd never let us get back to Opar for another load, even if we could prevail upon our blacks to return there."

"Two t'ousand pounds, two t'ousand pounds!" wailed Bluber. "Und all dis suit, vat it cost me tventy guineas vat I can't vear it again in England unless I go to a fancy dress ball, vich I never do."

Kraski had not spoken, but had sat with eyes upon the ground, listening to the others. Now he raised his head. "We have lost our gold," he said, "and before we get back to England we stand to spend the balance of our two thousand pounds—in other words our expedition is a total loss. The rest of you may be satisfied to go back broke, but I am not. There are other things in Africa besides the gold of Opar, and when we leave the country there is no reason why we shouldn't take something with us that will repay us for our time and investment."

"What do you mean?" asked Peebles.

"I have spent a lot of time with Owaza," replied Kraski, "trying to learn their crazy language, and I have come to find out a lot about the old villain. He's as crooked as they make 'em, and if he were to be hanged for all his murders, he'd have to have more lives than a cat, but notwithstanding all that, he's a shrewd old fellow, and I've learned a lot more from him than just his monkey talk—I have learned enough, in fact, so that I feel safe in saying that if we stick together we can go out of Africa with a pretty good-sized stake. Personally, I haven't given up the gold of Opar yet. What we've lost, we've lost, but there's plenty left where that came from, and someday after this blows over, I'm coming back to get my share."

"But how about this other thing?" asked Flora. "How can Owaza help us?"

"There's a little bunch of Arabs down here," explained Kraski, "stealing slaves and ivory. Owaza knows where they are working and where their main camp is. There are only a few of them, and their blacks are nearly all slaves who would turn on them in a minute. Now the idea is this: we have a big enough party to overpower them and take their ivory away from them if we can get their slaves to take our side. We don't want the slaves; we couldn't do anything with them if we had them, so we can promise them their freedom for their help, and give Owaza and his gang a share in the ivory."

"How do you know Owaza will help us?" asked Flora.

"The idea is his; that's the reason I know," replied Kraski.

"It sounds good to me," said Peebles, "I ain't fer goin' 'ome empty 'anded." And in turn the others signified their approval of the scheme.

11

Strange Incense Burns

As Tarzan carried the dead Bolgani from the village of
the Gomangani, he set his steps in the direction of the building
he had seen from the rim of the valley, the curiosity of the man
overcoming the natural caution of the beast. He was traveling
upwind and the odors wafted down to his nostrils told him that
he was approaching the habitat of the Bolgani. Intermingled
with the scent spoor of the gorilla-men was that of Gomangani
and the odor of cooked food, and the suggestion of a heavily
sweet scent, which the ape-man could connect only with
burning incense, though it seemed impossible that such a fragrance could emanate from the dwellings of the Bolgani. Perhaps it came from the great edifice he had seen—a building
which must have been constructed by human beings, and in
which human beings might still dwell, though never among the
multitudinous odors that assailed his nostrils did he once catch
the faintest suggestion of the man scent of whites.

When he perceived from the increasing strength of their odor,
that he was approaching close to the Bolgani, Tarzan took to the
trees with his burden, that he might thus stand a better chance of
avoiding discovery, and presently, through the foliage ahead, he
saw a lofty wall, and, beyond, the outlines of the weird architecture of a strange and mysterious pile—outlines that suggested a
building of another world, so unearthly were they, and from
beyond the wall came the odor of the Bolgani and the fragrance
of the incense, intermingled with the scent spoor of Numa, the
lion. The jungle was cleared away for fifty feet outside the wall

surrounding the building, so that there was no tree overhanging the wall, but Tarzan approached as closely as he could, while still remaining reasonably well-concealed by the foliage. He had chosen a point at a sufficient height above the ground to permit him to see over the top of the wall.

The building within the enclosure was of great size, its different parts appearing to have been constructed at various periods, and each with utter disregard to uniformity, resulting in a conglomeration of connecting buildings and towers, no two of which were alike, though the whole presented a rather pleasing, if somewhat bizarre appearance. The building stood upon an artificial elevation about ten feet high, surrounded by a retaining wall of granite, a wide staircase leading to the ground level below. About the building were shrubbery and trees, some of the latter appearing to be of great antiquity, while one enormous tower was almost entirely covered by ivy. By far the most remarkable feature of the building, however, lay in its rich and barbaric ornamentation. Set into the polished granite of which it was composed was an intricate mosaic of gold and diamonds; glittering stones in countless thousands scintillated from façades, minarets, domes, and towers.

The enclosure, which comprised some fifteen or twenty acres, was occupied for the most part by the building. The terrace upon which it stood was devoted to walks, flowers, shrubs, and ornamental trees, while that part of the area below, which was within the range of Tarzan's vision, seemed to be given over to the raising of garden truck. In the garden and upon the terrace were naked blacks, such as he had seen in the village where he had left La. There were both men and women, and these were occupied with the care of growing things within the enclosure. Among them were several of the gorillalike creatures such as Tarzan had slain in the village, but these performed no labor, devoting themselves rather, it seemed, to directing the work of the blacks, toward whom their manner was haughty and domineering, sometimes even brutal. These gorilla-men were trapped in rich ornaments, similar to those upon the body which now rested in a crotch of the tree behind the ape-man.

As Tarzan watched with interest the scene below him, two

Bolgani emerged from the main entrance, a huge portal, some thirty feet in width, and perhaps fifteen feet high. The two wore headbands, supporting tall, white feathers. As they emerged they took post on either side of the entrance, and cupping their hands before their mouths gave voice to a series of shrill cries that bore a marked resemblance to trumpet calls. Immediately the blacks ceased work and hastened to the foot of the stairs descending from the terrace to the garden. Here they formed lines on either side of the stairway, and similarly the Bolgani formed two lines upon the terrace from the main portal to the stairway, forming a living aisle from one to the other. Presently from the interior of the building came other trumpetlike calls, and a moment later Tarzan saw the head of a procession emerging. First came four Bolgani abreast, each bedecked with an ornate feather headdress, and each carrying a huge bludgeon erect before him. Behind these came two trumpeters, and twenty feet behind the trumpeters paced a huge, black-maned lion, held in leash by four sturdy blacks, two upon either side, holding what appeared to be golden chains that ran to a scintillant diamond collar about the beast's neck. Behind the lion marched twenty more Bolgani, four abreast. These carried spears, but whether they were for the purpose of protecting the lion from the people or the people from the lion Tarzan was at a loss to know.

The attitude of the Bolgani lining either side of the way between the portal and the stairway indicated extreme deference, for they bent their bodies from their waists in a profound bow while Numa was passing between their lines. When the beast reached the top of the stairway the procession halted, and immediately the Gomangani ranged below prostrated themselves and placed their foreheads on the ground. Numa, who was evidently an old lion, stood with lordly mien surveying the prostrate humans before him. His evil eyes glared glassily, the while he bared his tusks in a savage grimace, and from his deep lungs rumbled forth an ominous roar, at the sound of which the Gomangani trembled in unfeigned terror. The ape-man knit his brows in thought. Never before had he been called upon to witness so remarkable a scene of the abasement of man before a beast. Presently the procession continued upon its way descending the staircase and turning to the right along a path through the garden, and when it had passed them the Gomangani and the Bolgani arose and resumed their interrupted duties.

Tarzan remained in his concealment watching them, trying to discover some explanation for the strange, paradoxical conditions that he had witnessed. The lion, with his retinue, had turned the far corner of the palace and disappeared from sight. What was he to these people, to these strange creatures? What did he represent? Why this topsy-turvy arrangement of species? Here man ranked lower than the half-beast, and above all, from the deference that had been accorded him, stood a true beast—a savage carnivore.

He had been occupied with his thoughts and his observations for some fifteen minutes following the disappearance of Numa around the eastern end of the palace, when his attention was attracted to the opposite end of the structure by the sound of other shrill trumpet calls. Turning his eyes in that direction, he saw the procession emerging again into view, and proceeding toward the staircase down which they had entered the garden. Immediately the notes of the shrill call sounded upon their ears the Gomangani and the Bolgani resumed their original positions from below the foot of the staircase to the entrance to the palace, and once again was homage paid to Numa as he made his triumphal entry into the building.

Tarzan of the Apes ran his fingers through his mass of tousled hair, but finally he was forced to shake his head in defeat—he could find no explanation whatsoever for all that he had witnessed. His curiosity, however, was so keenly piqued that he determined to investigate the palace and surrounding grounds further before continuing on his way in search of a trail out of the valley.

Leaving the body of Bolgani where he had cached it, he started slowly to circle the building that he might examine it from all sides from the concealing foliage of the surrounding forest. He found the architecture equally unique upon all sides, and that the garden extended entirely around the building, though a portion upon the south side of the palace was given over to corrals and pens in which were kept numerous goats and a considerable flock of chickens. Upon this side, also, were several hundred swinging, beehive huts, such as he had seen in the native village of the Gomangani. These he took to be the quarters of the black slaves, who performed all the arduous and menial labor connected with the palace.

The lofty granite wall which surrounded the entire enclosure was pierced by but a single gate which opened opposite the east end of the palace. This gate was large and of massive construction, appearing to have been built to withstand the assault of numerous and well-armed forces. So strong did it appear that the ape-man could not but harbor the opinion that it had been constructed to protect the interior against forces equipped with heavy battering rams. That such a force had ever existed within the vicinity in historic times seemed most unlikely, and Tarzan conjectured, therefore, that the wall and the gate were of almost unthinkable antiquity, dating, doubtless, from the forgotten age of the Atlantians, and constructed, perhaps, to protect the builders of the Palace of Diamonds from the well-armed forces that had come from Atlantis to work the gold mines of Opar and to colonize central Africa.

While the wall, the gate, and the palace itself, suggested in many ways almost unbelievable age, yet they were in such an excellent state of repair that it was evident that they were still inhabited by rational and intelligent creatures; while upon the south side Tarzan had seen a new tower in process of construction, where a number of blacks working under the direction of Bolgani were cutting and shaping granite blocks and putting them in place.

Tarzan had halted in a tree near the east gate to watch the life passing in and out of the palace grounds beneath the ancient portal, and as he watched, a long cavalcade of powerful Gomangani emerged from the forest and entered the enclosure. Swung in hides between two poles, this party was carrying rough-hewn blocks of granite, four men to a block. Two or three Bolgani accompanied the long line of carriers, which was preceded and followed by a detachment of black warriors, armed with battle-axes and spears. The demeanor and attitude of the black porters, as well as of the Bolgani, suggested to the ape-man nothing more nor less than a caravan of donkeys, plodding their stupid way at the behest of their drivers. If one lagged he was prodded with the point of a spear or struck with its haft. There was no greater brutality shown than in the ordinary handling of beasts of burden the world around, nor in the demeanor of the blacks was there any more indication of objection or revolt than you see depicted upon the faces of a long line of burden-bearing mules; to all intents and purposes they were dumb, driven cattle. Slowly they filed through the gateway and disappeared from sight.

A few moments later another party came out of the forest and passed into the palace grounds. This consisted of fully fifty armed Bolgani and twice as many black warriors with spears and axes. Entirely surrounded by these armed creatures were four brawny porters, carrying a small litter, upon which was fastened an ornate chest about two feet wide by four feet long, with a depth of approximately two feet. The chest itself was of some dark, weather-worn wood, and was reinforced by bands and corners of what appeared to be virgin gold in which were set many diamonds. What the chest contained Tarzan could not, of course, conceive, but that it was considered of great value was evidenced by the precautions for safety with which it had been surrounded. The chest was borne directly into the huge, ivy-covered tower at the northeast corner of the palace, the entrance to which, Tarzan now first observed, was secured by doors as large and heavy as the east gate itself.

At the first opportunity that he could seize to accomplish it undiscovered, Tarzan swung across the jungle trail and continued through the trees to that one in which he had left the body of the Bolgani. Throwing this across his shoulder he returned to a point close above the trail near the east gate, and seizing upon a moment when there was a lull in the traffic he hurled the body as close to the portal as possible.

"Now," thought the ape-man, "let them guess who slew their fellow if they can."

Making his way toward the southeast, Tarzan approached the mountains which lie back of the Valley of the Palace of Diamonds. He had often to make detours to avoid native villages and to keep out of sight of the numerous parties of Bolgani that seemed to be moving in all directions through the forest. Late in the afternoon he came out of the hulls into full view of the mountains beyond—rough, granite hills they were, whose precipitous peaks rose far above the timber line. Directly before him a well-marked trail led into a canyon,

which he could see wound far upward toward the summit.
This, then, would be as good a place to commence his investigations as another. And so, seeing that the coast was clear, the ape-man descended from the trees, and taking advantage of the underbrush bordering the trail, made his way silently, yet swiftly, into the hills. For the most part he was compelled to worm his way through thickets, for the trail was in constant use by Gomangani and Bolgani, parties passing up it empty-handed and, returning, bearing blocks of granite. As he advanced more deeply into the hills the heavy underbrush gave way to a lighter growth of scrub, through which he could pass with far greater ease though with considerable more risk of discovery. However, the instinct of the beast that dominated Tarzan's jungle craft permitted him to find cover where another would have been in full view of every enemy. Half way up the mountain the trail passed through a narrow gorge, not more than twenty feet wide and eroded from solid granite cliffs. Here there was no concealment whatsoever, and the ape-man realized that to enter it would mean almost immediate discovery. Glancing about, he saw that by making a slight detour he could reach the summit of the gorge, where, amid tumbled, granite boulders and stunted trees and shrubs, he knew that he could find sufficient concealment, and perhaps a plainer view of the trail beyond.

Nor was he mistaken, for, when he had reached a vantage point far above the trail, he saw ahead an open pocket in the mountain, the cliffs surrounding which were honeycombed with numerous openings, which, it seemed to Tarzan, could be naught else than the mouths of tunnels. Rough wooden ladders reached to some of them, closer to the base of the cliffs, while from others knotted ropes dangled to the ground below. Out of these tunnels emerged men carrying little sacks of earth, which they dumped in a common pile beside a rivulet which ran through the gorge. Here other blacks, supervised by Bolgani, were engaged in washing the dirt, but what they hoped to find or what they did find, Tarzan could not guess.

Along one side of the rocky basin many other blacks were engaged in quarrying the granite from the cliffs, which had been cut away through similar operations into a series of terraces running from the floor of the basin to the summit of the cliff. Here naked blacks toiled with primitive tools under the supervision of savage Bolgani. The activities of the quarrymen were obvious enough, but what the others were bringing from the mouths of the tunnels Tarzan could not be positive, though the natural assumption was that it was gold. Where, then, did they obtain their diamonds? Certainly not from these solid granite cliffs.

A few minutes' observation convinced Tarzan that the trail he had followed from the forest ended in this little cul-de-sac, and so he sought a way upward and around it, in search of a pass across the range.

The balance of that day and nearly all the next he devoted to his efforts in this direction, only in the end to be forced to admit that there was no egress from the valley upon this side. To points far above the timber line he made his way, but there, always, he came face to face with sheer, perpendicular cliffs of granite towering high above him, upon the face of which not even the ape-man could find foothold. Along the southern and eastern sides of the basin he carried his investigation, but with similar disappointing results, and then at last he turned his steps back toward the forest with the intention of seeking a way out through the valley of Opar with La, after darkness had fallen.

The sun had just risen when Tarzan arrived at the native village in which he had left La, and no sooner did his eyes rest upon it than he became apprehensive that something was amiss, for not only was the gate wide open but there was no sign of life within the palisade, nor was there any movement of the swinging huts that would indicate that they were occupied. Always wary of ambush, Tarzan reconnoitered carefully before descending into the village. To his trained observation it became evident that the village had been deserted for at least twenty-four hours. Running to the hut in which La had been hidden he hastily ascended the rope and examined the interior—it was vacant, nor was there any sign of the High Priestess. Descending to the ground, the ape-man started to make a thorough investigation of the village in search of clues to the fate of its inhabitants and of La. He had examined the interiors of several huts when his keen eyes noted a slight movement of one of the swinging, cagelike habitations some distance from him. Quickly he crossed the intervening space, and as he approached the hut he saw that no rope trailed from its doorway. Halting beneath, Tarzan raised his face to the aperture, through which nothing but the roof of the hut was visible.

"Gomangani," he cried, "it is I, Tarzan of the Apes. Come to the opening and tell me what has become of your fellows and of my mate, whom I left here under the protection of your warriors."

There was no answer, and again Tarzan called, for he was positive that someone was hiding in the hut.

"Come down," he called again, "or I will come up after you."

Still there was no reply. A grim smile touched the ape-man's lips as he drew his hunting knife from its sheath and placed it between his teeth, and then, with a catlike spring, leaped for the opening, and catching its sides, drew his body up into the interior of the hut.

If he had expected opposition, he met with none, nor in the dimly lighted interior could he at first distinguish any presence, though, when his eyes became accustomed to the semi-darkness, he descried a bundle of leaves and grasses lying against the opposite wall of the structure. Crossing to these he tore them aside revealing the huddled form of a terrified woman. Seizing her by a shoulder he drew her to a sitting position.

"What has happened?" he demanded. "Where are the villagers? Where is my mate?"

"Do not kill me! Do not kill me!" she cried. "It was not I. It was not my fault."

"I do not intend to kill you," replied Tarzan. "Tell me the truth and you shall be safe."

"The Bolgani have taken them away," cried the woman. "They came when the sun was low upon the day that you arrived, and they were very angry, for they had found the body of their fellow outside the gate of the Palace of Diamonds. They knew that he had come here to our village, and no one had seen him alive since he had departed from the palace. They came, then, and threatened and tortured our people, until at last the warriors told them all. I hid. I do not know why they did not find me. But at last they went away, taking all the others with them; taking your mate, too. They will never come back."

"You think that the Bolgani will kill them?" asked Tarzan.

"Yes," she replied, "they kill all who displease them."

Alone, now, and relieved of the responsibility of La, Tarzan might easily make his way by night through the valley of Opar and to safety beyond the barrier. But perhaps such a thought never entered his head. Gratitude and loyalty were marked characteristics of the ape-man. La had saved him from the fanaticism and intrigue of her people. She had saved him at a cost of all that was most dear to her, power and position, peace and safety. She had jeopardized her life for him, and became an exile from her own country. The mere fact then that the Bolgani had taken her with the possible intention of slaying her, was not sufficient for the ape-man. He must know whether or not she lived, and if she lived he must devote his every energy to winning her release and her eventual escape from the dangers of this valley.

Tarzan spent the day reconnoitering outside the palace grounds, seeking an opportunity of gaining entrance without detection, but this he found impossible inasmuch as there was never a moment that there were not Gomangani or Bolgani in the outer garden. But with the approach of darkness the great east gate was closed, and the inmates of the huts and palace withdrew within their walls, leaving not even a single sentinel without—a fact that indicated clearly that the Bolgani had no reason to apprehend an attack. The subjugation of the Gomangani, then, was apparently complete, and so the towering wall surrounding their palace, which was more than sufficient to protect them from the inroads of lions, was but the reminder of an ancient day when a once-powerful, but now vanished, enemy threatened their peace and safety.

When darkness had finally settled Tarzan approached the gate, and throwing the noose of his grass rope over one of the carved lions that capped the gate posts, ascended quickly to the summit of the wall, from where he dropped lightly into the garden below. To insure an avenue for quick escape in the event that he found La, he unlatched the heavy gates and swung them open. Then he crept stealthily toward the ivy-covered east tower, which he had chosen after a day of investigation as offering easiest ingress to the palace. The success of his plan hinged largely upon the age and strength of the ivy which grew almost to the summit of the tower, and, to his immense relief, he found that it would easily support his weight.

Far above the ground, near the summit of the tower, he had seen from the trees surrounding the palace an open window, which, unlike the balance of those in this part of the palace, was without bars. Dim lights shone from several of the tower windows, as from those of other parts of the palace. Avoiding these lighted apertures, Tarzan ascended quickly, though carefully, toward the unbarred window above, and as he reached it and cautiously raised his eyes above the level of the sill, he was delighted to find that it opened into an unlighted chamber, the interior of which, however, was so shrouded in darkness that he could discern nothing within. Drawing himself carefully to the level of the sill he crept quietly into the apartment beyond. Groping through the blackness, he cautiously made the rounds of the room, which he found to contain a carved bedstead of peculiar design, a table, and a couple of benches. Upon the bedstead were stuffs of woven material, thrown over the softly tanned pelts of antelopes and leopards.

Opposite the window through which he had entered was a closed door. This he opened slowly and silently, until, through a tiny aperture he could look out upon a dimly lighted corridor or circular hallway, in the center of which was an opening about four feet in diameter, passing through which and disappearing beyond a similar opening in the ceiling directly above was a straight pole with short crosspieces fastened to it at intervals of about a foot—quite evidently the primitive staircase which gave communication between the various floors of the tower. Three upright columns, set at equal intervals about the circumference of the circular opening in the center of the floor helped to support the ceiling above. Around the outside of this circular hallway there were other doors, similar to that opening into the apartment in which he was.

Hearing no noise and seeing no evidence of another than himself, Tarzan opened the door and stepped into the hallway. His nostrils were now assailed strongly by the same heavy fragrance of incense that had first greeted him upon his approach to the palace several days before. In the interior of the tower, however, it was much more powerful, practically obliterating all other odors, and placing upon the ape-man an almost prohibitive handicap in his search for La. In fact as he viewed the doors upon this single stage of the tower, he was filled with consternation at the prospect of the well-nigh impossible task that confronted him. To search this great tower alone, without any assistance whatever from his keen sense of scent, seemed impossible of accomplishment, if he were to take even the most ordinary precautions against detection.

The ape-man's self-confidence was in no measure blundering egotism. Knowing his limitations, he knew that he would have little or no chance against even a few Bolgani were he to be discovered within their palace, where all was familiar to them and strange to him. Behind him was the open window, and the silent jungle night, and freedom. Ahead danger, predestined failure; and, quite likely, death. Which would he choose? For a moment he stood in silent thought, and then, raising his head and squaring his great shoulders, he shook his black locks defiantly and stepped boldly toward the nearest door. Room after room he had investigated until he had made the entire circle of the landing, but insofar as La or any clue to her were concerned his search was fruitless. He found quaint furniture and rugs and tapestries, and ornaments of gold and diamonds, and in one dimly lighted chamber he came upon a sleeping Bolgani, but so silent were the movements of the ape-man that the sleeper slept on undisturbed, even though Tarzan passed entirely around his bed, which was set in the center of the chamber, and investigated a curtained alcove beyond.

Having completed the rounds of this floor, Tarzan determined to work upward first and then, returning, investigate the lower stages later. Pursuant to this plan, therefore, he ascended the strange stairway. Three landings he passed before he reached the upper floor of the tower. Circling each floor was a ring of doors, all of which were closed, while dimly lighting each landing were feebly burning cressets—shallow, golden bowls—containing what appeared to be tallow, in which floated a towlike wick.

Upon the upper landing there were but three doors, all of which were closed. The ceiling of this hallway was the dome-like roof of the tower, in the center of which was another circular opening, through which the stairway protruded into the darkness of the night above.

As Tarzan opened the door nearest him it creaked upon its hinges, giving forth the first audible sound that had resulted from his investigations up to this point. The interior of the apartment before him was unlighted, and as Tarzan stood there in the entrance in statuesque silence for a few seconds following the creaking of the hinge, he was suddenly aware of movement—of the faintest shadow of a sound—behind him. Wheeling quickly he saw the figure of a man standing in an open doorway upon the opposite site of the landing.

12

The Golden Ingots

ESTEBAN MIRANDA HAD played the role of Tarzan of the Apes with the Waziri as his audience for less than twenty-four hours when he began to realize that, even with the lee-way that his supposedly injured brain gave him, it was going to be a very difficult thing to carry on the deception indefinitely. In the first place Usula did not seem at all pleased at the idea of merely taking the gold away from the intruders and then running from them. Nor did his fellow warriors seem any more enthusiastic over the plan than he. As a matter of fact they could not conceive that any number of bumps upon the head could render their Tarzan of the Apes a coward, and to run away from these west coast blacks and a handful of inexperienced whites seemed nothing less than cowardly.

Following all this, there had occurred in the afternoon that which finally decided the Spaniard that he was building for himself anything other than a bed of roses, and that the sooner he found an excuse for quitting the company of the Waziri the greater would be his life expectancy.

They were passing through rather open jungle at the time. The brush was not particularly heavy and the trees were at considerable distances apart, when suddenly, without warning, a rhinoceros charged them. To the consternation of the Waziri, Tarzan of the Apes turned and fled for the nearest tree the instant his eyes alighted upon the charging Buto. In his haste Esteban tripped and fell, and when at last he reached the tree instead of leaping agilely into the lower branches, he attempted to shin up the huge bole as a schoolboy shins up a telegraph pole, only to slip and fall back again to the ground.

In the meantime Buto, who charges either by scent or hearing, rather than by eyesight, his powers of which are extremely poor, had been distracted from his original direction by one of the Waziri, and after missing the fellow had gone blundering on to disappear in the underbrush beyond.

When Esteban finally arose and discovered that the rhinoceros was gone, he saw surrounding him a semicircle of huge blacks, upon whose faces were written expressions of pity and sorrow, not unmingled, in some instances, with a tinge of contempt. The Spaniard saw that he had been terrified into a practically irreparable blunder, yet he seized despairingly upon the only excuse he could conjure up.

"My poor head," he cried, pressing both palms to his temples.

"The blow was upon your *head*, Bwana," said Usula, "and your faithful Waziri thought that it was the *heart* of their master that knew no fear."

Esteban made no reply, and in silence they resumed their march. In silence they continued until they made camp before dark upon the bank of the river just above a waterfall. During the afternoon Esteban had evolved a plan of escape from his dilemma, and no sooner had he made camp than he ordered the Waziri to bury the treasure.

"We shall leave it here," he said, "and tomorrow we shall set forth in search of the thieves, for I have decided to punish them. They must be taught that they may not come into the jungle of Tarzan with impunity. It was only the injury to my head that prevented me from slaying them immediately I discovered their perfidy."

This attitude pleased the Waziri better. They commenced to see a ray of hope. Once again was Tarzan of the Apes becoming

Tarzan. And so it was that with lighter hearts and a new cheerfulness they set forth the next morning in search of the camp of the Englishmen, and by shrewd guessing on Usula's part they cut across the jungle to intercept the probable march of the Europeans to such advantage that they came upon them just as they were making camp that night. Long before they reached them they smelled the smoke of their fires and heard the songs and chatter of the west coast carriers.

Then it was that Esteban gathered the Waziri about him. "My children," he said, addressing Usula in English, "these strangers have come here to wrong Tarzan. To Tarzan, then, belongs the vengeance. Go, therefore, and leave me to punish my enemies alone and in my own way. Return home, leave the gold where it is, for it will be a long time before I shall need it."

The Waziri were disappointed, for this new plan did not at all accord with their desires, which contemplated a cheerful massacre of the west coast blacks. But as yet the man before them was Tarzan, their big Bwana, to whom they had never failed in implicit obedience. For a few moments following Esteban's declaration of his intention, they stood in silence shifting uneasily, and then at last they commenced to speak to one another in Waziri. What they said the Spaniard did not know, but evidently they were urging something upon Usula, who presently turned toward him.

"Oh, Bwana," cried the black. "How can we return home to the Lady Jane and tell her that we left you injured and alone to face the rifles of the white men and their askari? Do not ask us to do it, Bwana. If you were yourself we should not fear for your safety, but since the injury to your head you have not been the same, and we fear to leave you alone in the jungle. Let us, then, your faithful Waziri, punish these people, after which we will take you home in safety, where you may be cured of the evils that have fallen upon you."

The Spaniard laughed. "I am entirely recovered," he said, "and I am in no more danger alone than I would be with you," which he knew, even better than they, was but a mild statement of the facts. "You will obey my wishes," he continued sternly. "Go back at once the way that we have come. After you have gone at least two miles you may make camp for the night, and in the morning start out again for home. Make no noise, I do not want them to know that I am here. Do not worry about me. I am all right, and I shall probably overtake you before you reach home. Go!"

Sorrowfully the Waziri turned back upon the trail they had just covered and a moment later the last of them disappeared from the sight of the Spaniard.

With a sigh of relief Esteban Miranda turned toward the camp of his own people. Fearing that to surprise them suddenly might invite a volley of shots from the askari he whistled, and then called aloud as he approached.

"It is Tarzan!" cried the first of the blacks who saw him. "Now indeed shall we all be killed."

Esteban saw the growing excitement among the carriers and askari—he saw the latter seize their rifles and that they were fingering the triggers nervously.

"It is I, Esteban Miranda," he called aloud. "Flora! Flora, tell those fools to lay aside their rifles."

The whites, too, were standing watching him, and at the sound of his voice Flora turned toward the blacks. "It is all right," she said, "that is not Tarzan. Lay aside your rifles."

Esteban entered the camp, smiling. "Here I am," he said.

"We thought that you were dead," said Kraski. "Some of these fellows said that Tarzan said that he had killed you."

"He captured me," said Esteban, "but as you see he did not kill me. I thought that he was going to, but he did not, and finally he turned me loose in the jungle. He may have thought that I could not survive and that he would accomplish his end just as surely without having my blood upon his hands."

" 'E must have knowed you," said Peebles. "You'd die, all right, if you were left alone very long in the jungle—you'd starve to death."

Esteban made no reply to the sally but turned toward Flora. "Are you not glad to see me, Flora?" he asked.

The girl shrugged her shoulders. "What is the difference?" she asked. "Our expedition is a failure. Some of them think you were largely to blame." She nodded her head in the general direction of the other whites.

The Spaniard scowled. None of them cared very much to see him. He did not care about the others, but he had hoped that Flora would show some enthusiasm about his return. Well, if she had known what he had in his mind, she might have been happier to see him, and only too glad to show some kind of affection. But she did not know. She did not know that Esteban Miranda had hidden the golden ingots where he might go another day and get them. It had been his intention to persuade her to desert the others, and then, later, the two would return and recover the treasure, but now he was piqued and offended—none of them would have a shilling of it—he would wait until they left Africa and then he would return and take it all for himself. The only fly in the ointment was the thought that the Waziri knew the location of the treasure, and that, sooner or later, they would return with Tarzan and get it. This weak spot in his calculations must be strengthened, and to strengthen it he must have assistance which would mean sharing his secret with another, but whom?

Outwardly oblivious of the sullen glances of his companions he took his place among them. It was evident to him that they were far from being glad to see him, but just why he did not know, for he had not heard of the plan that Kraski and Owaza had hatched to steal the loot of the ivory raiders, and that their main objection to his presence was the fear that they would be compelled to share the loot with him. It was Kraski who first voiced the thought that was in the minds of all but Esteban.

"Miranda," he said, "it is the consensus of opinion that you and Bluber are largely responsible for the failure of our venture. We are not finding fault. I just mention it as a fact. But since you have been away we have struck upon a plan to take something out of Africa that will partially recompense us for the loss of the gold. We have worked the thing all out carefully and made our plans. We don't need you to carry them out. We have no objection to your coming along with us, if you want to, for company, but we want to have it understood from the beginning that you are not to share in anything that we get out of this."

The Spaniard smiled and waved a gesture of unconcern. "It is perfectly all right," he said. "I shall ask for nothing. I would not wish to take anything from any of you." And he grinned inwardly as he thought of the more than quarter of a million pounds in gold which he would one day take out of Africa for himself, alone.

At this unexpected attitude of acquiescence upon Esteban's part the others were greatly relieved, and immediately the entire atmosphere of constraint was removed.

"You're a good fellow, Esteban," said Peebles. "I've been sayin' right along that you'd want to do the right thing, and I want to say that I'm mighty glad to see you back here safe an' sound. I felt terrible when I 'eard you was croaked, that I did."

"Yes," said Bluber, "John he feel so bad he cry himself to sleep every night, ain't it, John?"

"Don't try to start nothin', Bluber," growled Peebles, glaring at the fat man.

"I vasn't commencing to start nodding," replied Adolph, seeing that the big Englishman was angry; "of course ve vere all sorry dat ve t'ought Esteban was killed und ve is all glad dat he is back."

"And that he don't want any of the swag," added Throck.

"Don't worry," said Esteban. "If I get back to London I'll be happy enough—I've had enough of Africa to last me all the rest of my life."

Before he could get to sleep that night, the Spaniard spent a wakeful hour or two trying to evolve a plan whereby he might secure the gold absolutely to himself, without fear of its being removed by the Waziri later. He knew that he could easily find the spot where he had buried it and remove it to another close by, provided that he could return immediately over the trail along which Usula had led them that day, and he could do this alone, insuring that no one but himself would know the new location of the hiding place of the gold, but he was equally positive that he could never again return later from the coast and find where he had hidden it. This meant that he must share his secret with another—one familiar with the country who could find the spot again at any time and from any direction. But who was there whom he might trust! In his mind he went carefully over the entire personnel of their safari, and continually his mind reverted to a single individual—Owaza. He had no confidence in the wily old scoundrel's integrity, but there was no other who suited his purpose as well, and finally he was forced to the conclusion that he must share his secret with this black, and depend upon avarice rather than honor for his protection. He could repay the fellow well—make him rich beyond his wildest dreams, and this the Spaniard could well afford to do in view of the tremendous fortune at stake. And so he fell asleep dreaming of what gold, to the value of over a quarter of a million pounds sterling, would accomplish in the gay capitals of the world.

The following morning while they were breakfasting Esteban mentioned casually that he had passed a large herd of antelope not far from their camp the previous day, and suggested that he take four or five men and do a little hunting, joining the balance of the party at camp that night. No one raised any objection, possibly for the reason that they assumed that the more he hunted and the further from the safari he went the greater the chances of his being killed, a contingency that none of them would have regretted, since at heart they had neither liking nor trust for him.

"I will take Owaza," he said. "He is the cleverest hunter of them all, and five or six men of his choosing." But later, when he approached Owaza, the black interposed objections to the hunt.

"We have plenty of meat for two days," he said. "Let us go on as fast as we can, away from the land of Waziri and Tarzan. I can find plenty of game anywhere between here and the coast. March for two days, and then I will hunt with you."

"Listen," said Esteban, in a whisper. "It is more than antelope that I would hunt. I cannot tell you here in camp, but when we have left the others I will explain. It will pay you better to come with me today than all the ivory you can hope to get from the raiders." Owaza cocked an attentive ear and scratched his woolly head.

"It is a good day to hunt, Bwana," he said. "I will come with you and bring five boys."

After Owaza had planned the march for the main party and arranged for the camping place for the night, so that he and the Spaniard could find them again, the hunting party set out upon the trail that Usula had followed from the buried treasure the preceding day. They had not gone far before Owaza discovered the fresh spoor of the Waziri.

"Many men passed here late yesterday," he said to Esteban, eyeing the Spaniard quizzically.

"I saw nothing of them," replied the latter. "They must have come this way after I passed."

"They came almost to our camp, and then they turned about and went away again," said Owaza. "Listen, Bwana, I carry a rifle and you shall march ahead of me. If these tracks were made by your people, and you are leading me into ambush, you shall be the first to die."

"Listen, Owaza," said Esteban, "we are far enough from camp now so that I may tell you all. These tracks were made by the Waziri of Tarzan of the Apes, who buried the gold for me a day's march from here. I have sent them home, and I wish you to go back with me and move the gold to another hiding place. After these others have gotten their ivory and returned to England, you and I will come back and get the gold, and then, indeed, shall you be well rewarded."

"Who are you, then?" asked Owaza. "Often I have doubted that you are Tarzan of the Apes. The day that we left the camp outside of Opar one of my men told me that you had been poisoned by your people and left in the camp. He said that he saw it with his own eyes—your body lying hidden behind some bushes—and yet you were with us upon the march that day. I thought that he lied to me, but I saw the consternation in his face when he saw you, and so I have often wondered if there were two Tarzans of the Apes."

"I am not Tarzan of the Apes," said Esteban. "It was Tarzan of the Apes who was poisoned in our camp by the others. But they only gave him something that would put him to sleep for a long time, possibly with the hope that he would be killed by wild animals before he awoke. Whether or not he still lives we do not know. Therefore you have nothing to fear from the Waziri or Tarzan on my account, Owaza, for I want to keep out of their way even more than you."

The black nodded. "Perhaps you speak the truth," he said, but still he walked behind, with his rifle always ready in his hand.

They went warily, for fear of overtaking the Waziri, but shortly after passing the spot where the latter had camped they saw that they had taken another route and that there was no danger of coming in contact with them.

When they had reached a point within about a mile of the spot where the gold had been buried, Esteban told Owaza to have his boys remain there while they went ahead alone to effect the transfer of the ingots.

"The fewer who know of this," he said to the black, "the safer we shall be."

"The Bwana speaks words of wisdom," replied the wily black.

Esteban found the spot near the waterfall without difficulty, and upon questioning Owaza he discovered that the latter knew the location perfectly, and would have no difficulty in coming directly to it again from the coast. They transferred the gold but a short distance, concealing it in a heavy thicket near the edge of the river, knowing that it would be as safe from discovery there as though they had transported it a hundred miles, for the chances were extremely slight that the Waziri or anyone else who should learn of its original hiding place would imagine that anyone would go to the trouble of removing it but a matter of a hundred yards.

When they had finished Owaza looked at the sun.

"We will never reach camp tonight," he said, "and we will have to travel fast to overtake them even tomorrow."

"I did not expect to," replied Esteban, "but could not tell them that. If we never find them again I shall be satisfied." Owaza grinned. In his crafty mind an idea was formed.

"Why," he thought, "risk death in a battle with the Arab ivory raiders on the chance of securing a few tusks, when all this gold awaits only transportation to the coast to be ours?"

13

A Strange, Flat Tower

TARZAN TURNING, DISCOVERED the man standing behind him on the top level of the ivy-covered east tower of the Palace of Diamonds. His knife leaped from its sheath at the touch of his quick fingers. But almost simultaneously his hand dropped to his side, and he stood contemplating the other, with an expression of incredulity upon his face that but reflected a similar emotion registered upon the countenance of the stranger. For what Tarzan saw was no Bolgani, nor a Gomangani, but a white man, bald and old and shriveled, with a long, white beard—a white man, naked but for barbaric ornaments of gold spangles and diamonds.

"God!" exclaimed the strange apparition.

Tarzan eyed the other quizzically. That single English word opened up such tremendous possibilities for conjecture as baffled the mind of the ape-man.

"What are you? Who are you?" continued the old man, but this time in the dialect of the great apes.

"You used an English word a moment ago," said Tarzan. "Do you speak that language?" Tarzan himself spoke in English.

"Ah, dear God!" cried the old man, "that I should have lived to hear that sweet tongue again." And he, too, now spoke in English, halting English, as might one who was long unaccustomed to voicing the language.

"Who are you?" asked Tarzan, "and what are you doing here?"

"It is the same question that I asked you," replied the old man. "Do not be afraid to answer me. You are evidently an Englishman, and you have nothing to fear from me."

"I am here after a woman, captured by the Bolgani," replied Tarzan.

The other nodded. "Yes," he said, "I know. She is here."

"Is she safe?" asked Tarzan.

"She has not been harmed. She will be safe until tomorrow or the next day," replied the old man. "But who are you, and how did you find your way here from the outer world?"

"I am Tarzan of the Apes," replied the ape-man. "I came into this valley looking for a way out of the valley of Opar where the life of my companion was in danger. And you?"

"I am an old man," replied the other, "and I have been here ever since I was a boy. I was a stowaway on the ship that brought Stanley to Africa after the establishment of the station on Stanley Pool, and I came into the interior with him. I went out from camp to hunt, alone, one day. I lost my way and later was captured by unfriendly natives. They took me farther into the interior to their village from which I finally escaped, but so utterly confused and lost that I had no idea what direction to take to find a trail to the coast. I wandered thus for months, until finally, upon an accursed day I found an entrance to this valley. I do not know why they did not put me to death at once, but they did not, and later they discovered that my knowledge could be turned to advantage to them. Since then I have helped them in their quarrying and mining and in their diamond cutting. I have given them iron drills with hardened points and drills tipped with diamonds. Now I am practically one of them, but always in my heart has been the hope that someday I might escape from the valley—a hopeless hope, though, I may assure you."

"There is no way out?" asked Tarzan.

"There is a way, but it is always guarded."

"Where is it?" queried Tarzan.

"It is a continuation of one of the mine tunnels, passing entirely through the mountain to the valley beyond. The mines have been worked by the ancestors of this race for an almost incalculable length of time. The mountains are honeycombed with their shafts and tunnels. Back of the gold-bearing quartz lies an enormous deposit of altered peridotite, which contains diamonds, in the search for which it evidently became necessary to extend one of the shafts to the opposite side of the mountain, possibly for purposes of ventilation. This tunnel and the trail leading down into Opar are the only means of ingress to the valley. From time immemorial they have kept the tunnel guarded, more particularly, I imagine, to prevent the escape of slaves than to thwart the inroads of an enemy, since they believe that there is no fear of the latter emergency. The trail to Opar they do not guard, because they no longer fear the Oparians, and know quite well that none of their Gomangani slaves would dare enter the valley of the sunworshipers. For the same reason, then, that the slaves cannot escape, we, too, must remain prisoners here forever."

"How is the tunnel guarded?" asked Tarzan.

"Two Bolgani and a dozen or more Gomangani warriors are always upon duty there," replied the old man.

"The Gomangani would like to escape?"

"They have tried it many times in the past, I am told," replied the old man, "though never since I have lived here, and always they were caught and tortured. And all their race was punished and worked the harder because of these attempts upon the part of a few."

"They are numerous—the Gomangani?"

"There are probably five thousand of them in the valley," replied the old man.

"And how many Bolgani?" the ape-man asked.

"Between ten and eleven hundred."

"Five to one," murmured Tarzan, "and yet they are afraid to attempt to escape."

"But you must remember," said the old man, "that the Bolgani are the dominant and intelligent race—the others are intellectually little above the beasts of the forest."

"Yet they are men," Tarzan reminded him.

"In figure only," replied the old man. "They cannot band together as men do. They have not as yet reached the community plane of evolution. It is true that families reside in a single village, but that idea, together with their weapons, was given to them by the Bolgani that they might not be entirely exterminated by the lions and panthers. Formerly, I am told, each individual Gomangani, when he became old enough to hunt for himself, constructed a hut apart from others and took up his solitary life, there being at that time no slightest semblance of family life. Then the Bolgani taught them how to build palisaded villages and compelled the men and women to remain in them and rear their children to maturity, after which the children were required to remain in the village, so that now some of the communities can claim as many as forty or fifty people. But the death rate is high among them, and they cannot multiply as rapidly as people living under normal conditions of peace and security. The brutalities of the Bolgani kill many; the carnivora take a considerable toll."

"Five to one, and still they remain in slavery—what cowards they must be," said the ape-man.

"On the contrary, they are far from cowardly," replied the old man. "They will face a lion with the utmost bravery. But for so many ages have they been subservient to the will of the

Bolgani, that it has become a fixed habit in them—as the fear of God is inherent in us, so is the fear of the Bolgani inherent in the minds of the Gomangani from birth."

"It is interesting," said Tarzan. "But tell me now where the woman is of whom I have come in search."

"She is your mate?" asked the old man.

"No," replied Tarzan. "I told the Gomangani that she was, so that they would protect her. She is La, Queen of Opar, High Priestess of the Flaming God."

The old man looked his incredulity. "Impossible!" he cried. "It cannot be that the queen of Opar has risked her life by coming to the home of her hereditary enemies."

"She was forced to it," replied Tarzan, "her life being threatened by a part of her people because she had refused to sacrifice me to their god."

"If the Bolgani knew this there would be great rejoicing," replied the old man.

"Tell me where she is," demanded Tarzan. "She preserved me from her people, and I must save her from whatever fate the Bolgani contemplate for her."

"It is hopeless," said the old man. "I can tell you where she is, but you cannot rescue her."

"I can try," replied the ape-man.

"But you will fail and die."

"If what you tell me is true, that there is absolutely no chance of my escaping from the valley, I might as well die," replied the ape-man. "However, I do not agree with you."

The old man shrugged. "You do not know the Bolgani," he said.

"Tell me where the woman is," said Tarzan.

"Look," replied the old man, motioning Tarzan to follow him into his apartment, and approaching a window which faced toward the west, he pointed toward a strange flat tower which rose above the roof of the main building near the west end of the palace. "She is probably somewhere in the interior of that tower," said the old man to Tarzan, "but as far as you are concerned, she might as well be at the north pole."

Tarzan stood in silence for a moment, his keen eyes taking in every salient detail of the prospect before him. He saw the strange, flat-topped tower, which it seemed to him might be reached from the roof of the main building. He saw, too, branches of the ancient trees that sometimes topped the roof itself, and except for the dim light shining through some of the palace windows he saw no signs of life. He turned suddenly upon the old man.

"I do not know you," he said, "but I believe I may trust you, since after all blood ties are strong, and we are the only men of our race in this valley. You might gain something in favor of betraying me, but I cannot believe that you will do it."

"Do not fear," said the old man, "I hate them. If I could help you I would, but I know that there is no hope of success for whatever plan you may have in mind—the woman will never be rescued; you will never leave the Valley of the Palace of Diamonds—you will never leave the palace itself unless the Bolgani wish it."

The ape-man grinned. "You have been here so long," he said, "that you are beginning to assume the attitude of mind that keeps the Gomangani in perpetual slavery. If you want to escape, come with me. We may not succeed, but at least you will have a better chance if you try than as if you remained forever in this tower."

The old man shook his head. "No," he said, "it is hopeless. If escape had been possible I should have been away from here long ago."

"Good-bye then," said Tarzan, and swinging out of the window he clambered toward the roof below, along the stout stem of the old ivy.

The old man watched him for a moment until he saw him make his way carefully across the roof toward the flat-topped tower where he hoped to find and liberate La. Then the old fellow turned and hurried rapidly down the crude stairway that rose ladderlike to the center of the tower.

Tarzan made his way across the uneven roof of the main building, clambering up the sides of its higher elevations and dropping again to its lower levels as he covered a considerable distance between the east tower and that flat-topped structure of peculiar design in which La was supposed to be incarcerated. His progress was slow, for he moved with the caution of a beast of prey, stopping often in dense shadows to listen.

When at last he reached the tower, he found that it had many openings letting upon the roof—openings which were closed only with hangings of the heavy tapestried stuff which he had seen in the tower. Drawing one of these slightly aside he looked within upon a large chamber, bare of furnishings, from the center of which there protruded through a circular aperture the top of a stairway similar to that he had ascended in the east tower. There was no one in sight within the chamber, and Tarzan crossed immediately to the stairway. Peering cautiously into the opening Tarzan saw that the stairway descended for a great distance, passing many floors. How far it went he could not judge, except it seemed likely that it pierced subterranean chambers beneath the palace. Sounds of life came up to him through the shaft, and odors, too, but the latter largely nullified, insofar as the scent impressions which they offered Tarzan were concerned, by the heavy incense which pervaded the entire palace.

It was this perfume that was to prove the ape-man's undoing, for otherwise his keen nostrils would have detected the scent of a nearby Gomangani. The fellow lay behind one of the hangings at an aperture in the tower wall. He had been lying in such a position that he had seen Tarzan enter the chamber, and he was watching him now as the ape-man stood looking down the shaft of the stairway. The eyes of the black had at first gone wide in terror at sight of this strange apparition, the like of which he had never seen before. Had the creature been of sufficient intelligence to harbor superstition, he would have thought Tarzan a god descended from above. But being of too low an order to possess any imagination whatsoever, he merely knew that he saw a strange creature, and that all strange creatures must be enemies, he was convinced. His duty was to apprise his masters of this presence in the palace, but he did not dare to move until the apparition had reached a sufficient distance from him to insure that the movements of the Gomangani would not be noticed by the intruder—he did not care to call attention to himself, for he had found that the more one effaced oneself in the presence of the Bolgani, the less one was likely to suffer. For a long time the stranger peered down the shaft of the stairway, and for a long time the Gomangani lay quietly watching him. But at last the former descended the stairs and passed out of sight of the watcher, who immediately leaped to his feet and scurried away across the roof of the palace toward a large tower arising at its western end.

As Tarzan descended the ladder the fumes of the incense became more and more annoying. Where otherwise he might have investigated quickly by scent he was now compelled to listen for every sound, and in many cases to investigate the chambers opening upon the central corridor by entering them. Where the doors were locked, he lay flat and listened close to the aperture at their base. On several occasions he risked calling La by name, but in no case did he receive any reply.

He had investigated four landings and was descending to the fifth when he saw standing in one of the doorways upon this level an evidently much excited and possibly terrified black. The fellow was of giant proportions and entirely unarmed. He stood looking at the ape-man with wide eyes as the latter jumped lightly from the stairway and stood facing him upon the same level.

"What do you want?" finally stammered the black. "Are you looking for the white she, your mate, whom the Bolgani took?"

"Yes," replied Tarzan. "What do you know of her?"

"I know where she is hidden," replied the black, "and if you will follow me I will lead you to her."

"Why do you offer to do this for me?" asked Tarzan, immediately suspicious. "Why is it that you do not go at once to your masters and tell them that I am here that they may send men to capture me?"

"I do not know the reason that I was sent to tell you this," replied the black. "The Bolgani sent me. I did not wish to come for I was afraid."

"Where did they tell you to lead me?" asked Tarzan.

"I am to lead you into a chamber, the door of which will be immediately bolted upon us. You will then be a prisoner."

"And you?" inquired Tarzan.

"I, too, shall be a prisoner with you. The Bolgani do not care what becomes of me. Perhaps you will kill me, but they do not care."

"If you lead me into a trap I shall kill you," replied Tarzan. "But if you lead me to the woman perhaps we shall all escape. You would like to escape, would you not?"

"I should like to escape, but I cannot."

"Have you ever tried?"

"No, I have not. Why should I try to do something that cannot be done?"

"If you lead me into the trap I shall surely kill you. If you lead me to the woman, you at least have the chance that I do to live. Which will you do?"

The black scratched his head in thought, the idea slowly filtering through his stupid mind. At last he spoke.

"You are very wise," he said. "I will lead you to the woman."

"Go ahead, then," said Tarzan, "and I will follow you." The black descended to the next level and opening the door entered a long, straight corridor. As the ape-man followed his guide he had leisure to reflect upon the means through which the Bolgani had learned of his presence in the tower, and the only conclusion he could arrive at was that the old man had betrayed him, since insofar as Tarzan was aware he alone knew that the ape-man was in the palace. The corridor along which the black was leading him was very dark, receiving a dim and inadequate illumination from the dimly lighted corridor they had just left, the door into which remained open behind them. Presently the black stopped, before a closed door.

"The woman is in there," said the black, pointing to the door.

"She is alone?" asked Tarzan.

"No," replied the black. "Look," and he opened the door, revealing a heavy hanging, which he gently separated, revealing to Tarzan the interior of the chamber beyond.

Seizing the black by the wrist, that he might not escape, Tarzan stepped forward and put his eyes to the aperture. Before him lay a large chamber, at one end of which was a raised dais, the base of which was of a dark, ornately carved wood. The central figure upon this dais was a huge, black-maned lion—the same that Tarzan had seen escorted through the gardens of the palace. His golden chains were now fastened to rings in the floor, while the four blacks stood in statuesque rigidity, two upon either side of the beast. Upon golden thrones behind the lion sat three magnificently ornamented Bolgani. At the foot of the steps leading to the stair stood La, between two Gomangani guards. Upon either side of a central aisle were carved benches

facing the dais, and occupying the front section of these were
some fifty Bolgani, among whom Tarzan almost immediately
espied the little, old man that he had met in the tower, the sight
of whom instantly crystallized the ape-man's conviction of the
source of his betrayal.

The chamber was lighted by hundreds of cressets, burning a
substance which gave forth both light and the heavy incense
that had assailed Tarzan's nostrils since first he had entered the
domain of the Bolgani. The long, cathedralesque windows
upon one side of the apartment were thrown wide, admitting
the soft air of the jungle summer night. Through them Tarzan
could see the palace grounds and that this chamber was upon
the same level as the terrace upon which the palace stood.
Beyond those windows was an open gateway to the jungle and
freedom, but interposed between him and the windows were
fifty armed gorilla-men. Perhaps, then, strategy would be a
better weapon than force with which to carve his way to
freedom with La. Yet to the forefront of his mind was evidently a belief in the probability that in the end it would be
force rather than strategy upon which he must depend. He
turned to the black at his side.

"Would the Gomangani guarding the lion like to escape
from the Bolgani?" he asked.

"The Gomangani would all escape if they could," replied
the black.

"If it is necessary for me to enter the room, then," said
Tarzan to the black, "will you accompany me and tell the other
Gomangani that if they will fight for me I will take them out of
the valley?"

"I will tell them, but they will not believe," replied the black.

"Tell them that they will die if they do not help me, then,"
said Tarzan.

"I will tell them."

As Tarzan turned his attention again to the chamber before
him he saw that the Bolgani occupying the central golden
throne was speaking.

"Nobles of Numa, King of Beasts, Emperor of All Created
Things," he said in deep, growling tones, "Numa has heard the
words that this she has spoken, and it is the will of Numa that
she die. The Great Emperor is hungry. He, himself, will devour

her here in the presence of his Nobles, and the Imperial Council of Three. It is the will of Numa."

A growl of approval arose from the beastlike audience, while the great lion bared his hideous fangs and roared until the palace trembled, his wicked, yellow-green eyes fixed terribly upon the woman before him, evidencing the fact that these ceremonies were of sufficient frequency to have accustomed the lion to what he might except as the logical termination of them.

"Day after tomorrow," continued the speaker, "the mate of this creature, who is by this time safely imprisoned in the Tower of the Emperors, will be brought before Numa for judgment. Slaves," he cried suddenly in a loud voice, rising to his feet and glaring at the guards holding La, "drag the woman to your emperor."

Instantly the lion became frantic, lashing its tail and straining at its stout chains, roaring and snarling as it reared upon its hind feet and sought to leap upon La, who was now being forcibly conducted up the steps of the dais toward the bejeweled maneater so impatiently awaiting her.

She did not cry out in terror, but she sought to twist herself free from the detaining hands of the powerful Gomangani—all futilely, however.

They had reached the last step, and were about to push La into the claws of the lion, when they were arrested by a loud cry from one side of the chamber—a cry that halted the Gomangani and brought the assembled Bolgani to their feet in astonishment and anger, for the sight that met their eyes was well-qualified to arouse the latter within them. Leaping into the room with raised spear was the almost naked white man of whom they had heard, but whom none of them had as yet seen. And so quick was he that in the very instant of entry—even before they could rise to their feet—he had launched his spear.

14

The Chamber of Horrors

A BLACK-MANED LION moved through the jungle night. With majestic unconcern for all other created things he took his lordly way through the primeval forest. He was not hunting, for he made no efforts toward stealth, nor, on the other hand, did he utter any vocal sound. He moved swiftly, though sometimes stopping with uplifted nose to scent the air and to listen. And thus at last he came to a high wall, along the face of which he sniffed, until the wall was broken by a half-opened gateway, through which he passed into the enclosure.

Before him loomed a great building, and presently as he stood watching it and listening, there broke from the interior the thunderous roar of an angry lion.

He of the black mane cocked his head upon one side and moved stealthily forward.

At the very instant that La was about to be thrust into the clutches of Numa, Tarzan of the Apes leaped into the apartment with a loud cry that brought to momentary pause the Gomangani that were dragging her to her doom, and in that brief instant of respite which the ape-man knew would follow his interruption the swift spear was launched. To the rage and consternation of the Bolgani they saw it bury itself in the heart of their Emperor—the great, black-maned lion.

At Tarzan's side stood the Gomangani whom he had terrified into service, and as Tarzan rushed forward toward La the black accompanied him, crying to his fellows that if they would help this stranger they might be free and escape from the Bolgani forever.

"You have permitted the great Emperor to be slain," he cried to the poor Gomangani who guarded Numa. "For this the Bolgani will kill you. Help to save the strange Tarmangani and his mate and you have at least a chance for life and freedom. And you," he added, addressing the two who had been guarding La, "they will hold you responsible also—your only hope lies with us."

Tarzan had reached La's side and was dragging her up the steps of the dais where he hoped that he might make a momentary stand against the fifty Bolgani who were now rushing forward from their seats toward him.

"Slay the three who sit upon the dais," cried Tarzan to the Gomangani, who were now evidently hesitating as to which side they would cast their lot with. "Slay them if you wish your freedom! Slay them if you wish to live!"

The authoritative tones of his voice, the magnetic appeal of his personality, his natural leadership won them to him for the brief instant that was necessary to turn them upon the hated authority that the three Bolgani upon the dais represented, and as they drove their spears into the shaggy black bodies of their masters they became then and forever the creatures of Tarzan of the Apes, for there could be no future hope for them in the land of the Bolgani.

With one arm around La's waist the ape-man carried her to the summit of the dais, where he seized his spear and drew it from the body of the dead lion. Then, turning about, and facing the advancing Bolgani, he placed one foot upon the carcass of his kill and raised his voice in the terrifying victory cry of the apes of Kerchak.

Before him the Bolgani paused, behind him the Gomangani quailed in terror.

"Stop!" cried Tarzan, raising a palm toward the Bolgani. "Listen! I am Tarzan of the Apes. I sought no quarrel with your people. I but look for a passage through your country to my own. Let me go my way in peace with this woman, taking these Gomangani with me."

For answer a chorus of savage growls arose from the Bolgani as they started forward again toward the dais. From their ranks there suddenly leaped the old man of the east tower, who ran swiftly toward Tarzan.

"Ah, traitor," cried the ape-man, "you would be the first, then, to taste the wrath of Tarzan?" He spoke in English and the old man replied in the same tongue.

"Traitor?" he exclaimed in surprise.

"Yes, traitor," thundered Tarzan. "Did you not hurry here to tell the Bolgani that I was in the palace, that they might send the Gomangani to lure me to a trap?"

"I did nothing of the kind," replied the other. "I came here to place myself near the white woman, with the thought that I might be of service to her or you if I were needed. I come now, Englishman, to stand at your side and die at your side, for die you shall, as sure as there is a God in heaven. Nothing can save you now from the wrath of the Bolgani whose Emperor you have killed."

"Come, then," cried Tarzan, "and prove your loyalty. It were better to die now than to live in slavery forever."

The six Gomangani had ranged themselves, three upon either side of Tarzan and La, while the seventh, who had entered the chamber with Tarzan unarmed, was taking weapons from the body of one of the three Bolgani who had been slain upon the dais.

Before this array of force so new to them, the Bolgani paused at the foot of the steps leading to the dais. But only for a moment they paused, for there were but nine against fifty, and as they surged up the steps, Tarzan and his Gomangani met them with battle-axe, and spear, and bludgeon. For a moment they pressed them back, but the numbers against them were too great, and once again a wave swept up that seemed likely to overwhelm them, when there broke upon the ears of the contestants a frightful roar, which, coming from almost at their sides, brought a sudden, momentary cessation of the battle.

Turning their eyes in the direction of the sound they saw a huge, black-maned lion standing upon the floor of the apartment, just within one of the windows. For an instant he stood like a statue of golden bronze, and then again the building trembled to the reverberations of his mighty roar.

Towering above them all Tarzan of the Apes looked down from the dais upon the great beast below them, and then in quick elation he raised his voice above the growlings of the Bolgani.

"Jad-bal-ja," he cried, and pointing toward the Bolgani, "Kill! Kill!"

Scarcely had the words been uttered ere the huge monster, a veritable devil incarnate, was upon the hairy gorilla-men. And simultaneously there occurred to the mind of the ape-man a daring plan of salvation for himself and the others who were dependent upon him.

"Quick," he cried to the Gomangani, "fall upon the Bolgani. Here at last is the true Numa, King of Beasts, and ruler of all creation. He slays his enemies but he will protect Tarzan of the Apes and the Gomangani, who are his friends."

Seeing their hated masters falling back before the terrific onslaught of the lion, the Gomangani rushed in with battle-axes and clubs, while Tarzan, casting aside his spear, took his place among them with drawn knife, and, keeping close to Jad-bal-ja, directed the lion from one victim to another, lest he fall by mistake upon the Gomangani or the little, old, white man, or even La herself. Twenty of the Bolgani lay dead upon the floor before the balance managed to escape from the chamber, and then Tarzan, turning to Jad-bal-ja, called him to heel.

"Go!" he said, turning toward the Gomangani, "and drag the body of the false Numa from the dais. Remove it from the room, for the true Emperor has come to claim his throne."

The old man and La were eyeing Tarzan and the lion in amazement.

"Who are you," asked the former, "that you can work such miracles with a savage beast of the jungle? Who are you, and what do you intend to do?"

"Wait and see," said Tarzan with a grim smile. "I think that we shall all be safe now, and that the Gomangani may live in comfort for a long time hereafter."

When the blacks had removed the carcass of the lion from the dais and thrown it from one of the windows of the chamber, Tarzan sent Jad-bal-ja to sit in the place upon the dais that had formerly been occupied by the lion, Numa.

"There," he said, turning to the Gomangani, "you see the true Emperor, who does not have to be chained to his throne. Three of you will go to the huts of your people behind the palace and summon them to the throne room, that they, too, may see what has transpired. Hurry, that we may have many warriors here before the Bolgani return in force."

Filled with an excitement which almost shook their dull minds into a semblance of intelligence three of the Gomangani hastened to do Tarzan's bidding, while the others stood gazing at Tarzan with expressions of such awe that might only be engendered by the sight of deity. La came then and stood beside Tarzan, looking up into his face with eyes that reflected a reverence fully as deep as that held by the blacks.

"I have not thanked you, Tarzan of the Apes," she said, "for what you have risked and done for me. I know that you must have come here in search of me, to save me from these creatures, and I know that it was not love that impelled you to this heroic and well-nigh hopeless act. That you have succeeded thus far is little short of miraculous, but, I, in the legends of whose people are recounted the exploits of the Bolgani, know that there can be no hope of eventual escape for us all, and so I beseech that you go at once and make good your escape alone, if possible, for you alone of us have any possible chance of escape."

"I do not agree with you that we have no chance to escape, La," replied the ape-man. "It seems to me that now we not only have every reason to believe that we are practically assured of escape, but that we may insure also to these poor Gomangani freedom from slavery and from the tyranny of the Bolgani. But this is not all. With this I shall not be satisfied. Not only must these people who show no hospitality to strangers be punished, but your own disloyal priests as well. To this latter end I intend to march out of the Valley of the Palace of Diamonds, down upon the city of Opar with a force of Gomangani sufficient to compel Cadj to relinquish the power he has usurped and replace you upon the throne of Opar. Nothing less than this shall satisfy me, and nothing less than this shall I accomplish before I leave."

"You are a brave man," said the old man, "and you have succeeded beyond what I thought could be possible, but La is right, you do not know the ferocity or the resources of the Bolgani, or the power which they wield over the Gomangani. Could you raise from the stupid minds of the blacks the incubus of fear that rests so heavily upon them you might win over a sufficient number to make good your escape from the valley, but that, I fear, is beyond even you. Our only hope, therefore, is to escape from the palace while they are momentarily disorganized, and trust to fleetness and to luck to carry us beyond the limits of the valley before we are apprehended."

"See," cried La, pointing, "even now it is too late—they return."

Tarzan looked in the direction that she indicted and saw through the open doorway at the far end of the chamber a large number of gorilla-men approaching. His eyes moved swiftly to the windows in the other wall. "But wait," he said, "behold another factor in the equation!"

The others looked toward the windows which opened upon the terrace, and they saw beyond them what appeared to be a crowd of several hundred blacks running rapidly toward the windows. The other blacks upon the dais cried out excitedly: "They come! They come! We shall be free, and no longer shall the Bolgani be able to make us work until we drop from exhaustion, or beat us, or torture us, or feed us to Numa."

As the first of the Bolgani reached the doorway leading into the chamber, the Gomangani commenced to pour through the several windows in the opposite wall. They were led by the three who had been sent to fetch them, and to such good effect had these carried their message that the blacks already seemed like a new people, so transfigured were they by the thought of immediate freedom. At sight of them the leader of the Bolgani cried aloud for them to seize the intruders upon the dais, but his answer was a spear hurled by the nearest black, and as he lunged forward, dead, the battle was on.

The Bolgani in the palace greatly outnumbered the blacks, but the latter had the advantage of holding the interior of the throne room in sufficient numbers to prevent the entry of many Bolgani simultaneously. Tarzan, immediately he recognized the temper of the blacks, called Jad-bal-ja to follow him, and, descending from the dais, he took command of the Gomangani. At each opening he placed sufficient men to guard it, and at the center of the room he held the balance in reserve. Then he called the old man into consultation.

"The gate in the east wall is open," he said. "I left it so when

I entered. Would it be possible for twenty or thirty blacks to reach it in safety and, entering the forest, carry word to the villagers of what is transpiring here in the palace, and prevail upon them to send all of their warriors immediately to complete the work of emancipation that we have begun?"

"It is an excellent plan," replied the old man. "The Bolgani are not upon that side of the palace between us and the gate, and if it may ever be accomplished, now is the time. I will pick your men for you. They must be head men, whose words will carry some weight with the villagers outside the palace walls."

"Good!" exclaimed Tarzan. "Select them immediately; tell them what we want and urge upon them the necessity for haste."

One by one the old man chose thirty warriors, whose duty he carefully explained to each. They were delighted with the plan and assured Tarzan that in less than an hour the first of their reinforcements would come.

"As you leave the enclosure," said the ape-man, "destroy the lock if you can, so that the Bolgani may not lock it again and bar out our reinforcements. Carry also the word that the first who come are to remain outside the wall until a sufficient number have arrived to make entry into the palace grounds reasonably safe—at least as many as are within this room now."

The blacks signified their understanding, and a moment later passed out of the room through one of the windows and disappeared into the darkness of the night beyond.

Shortly after the blacks had left the Bolgani made a determined rush upon the Gomangani guarding the main entrance to the throne room, with the result that a score or more of the gorilla-men succeeded in cutting their way into the room. At this first indication of reversal the blacks showed signs of faltering, the fear of the Bolgani that was inherent in them showing in their wavering attitude and seeming reluctance to force a counter attack. As Tarzan leaped forward to assist in checking the rush of the Bolgani into the throne room he called to Jad-bal-ja, and as the great lion leaped from the dais the ape-man, pointing to the nearest Bolgani, cried: "Kill! Kill!"

Straight for the throat of the nearest leaped Jad-bal-ja. The great jaws closed upon the snarling face of the frightened gorilla-man but once, and then, at the command of his master the golden lion dropped the carcass after a single shake and leaped upon another. Three had died thus in quick succession when the balance of the Bolgani turned to flee this chamber of horrors; but the Gomangani, their confidence restored by the ease with which this fierce ally brought death and terror to the tyrants, interposed themselves between the Bolgani and the doorway, shutting off their retreat.

"Hold them! Hold them!" cried Tarzan. "Do not kill them!" And then to the Bolgani: "Surrender and you will not be harmed!"

Jad-bal-ja clung close to the side of his master, glaring and growling at the Bolgani, and casting an occasional beseeching look at the ape-man which said plainer than words, "Send me among them."

Fifteen of the Bolgani who had entered the room survived. For a moment they hesitated, and then one of them threw his weapons upon the floor. Immediately the others followed suit.

Tarzan turned toward Jad-bal-ja. "Back!" he said, pointing toward the dais, and as the lion wheeled and slunk away toward the platform, Tarzan turned again toward the Bolgani.

"Let one of your number go," he said, "and announce to your fellows that I demand their immediate surrender."

The Bolgani whispered among themselves for a few moments and finally one of them announced that he would go and see the others. After he had left the room the old man approached Tarzan.

"They will never surrender," he said. "Look out for treachery."

"It is all right," said Tarzan. "I am expecting that, but I am gaining time, and that is what we need most. If there were a place near where I might confine these others I should feel better, for it would cut down our antagonists by at least that many."

"There is a room there," said the old man, pointing toward one of the doorways in the throne room, "where you can confine them—there are many such rooms in the Tower of the Emperors."

"Good," said Tarzan, and a moment later, following his instructions the Bolgani were safely locked in a room adjoining the throne room. In the corridors without they could hear the main body of the gorilla-men in argument. It was evident that they were discussing the message sent to them by Tarzan. Fifteen minutes passed, and finally thirty, with no word from the Bolgani and no resumption of hostilities, and then there came to the main entrance of the throne room the fellow whom Tarzan had despatched with his demand for surrender.

"Well," asked the ape-man, "what is their answer?"

"They will not surrender," replied the Bolgani, "but they will permit you to leave the valley provided that you will release those whom you have taken prisoner and harm no others."

The ape-man shook his head. "That will not do," he replied. "I hold the power to crush the Bolgani of the Valley of Diamonds. Look," and he pointed toward Jad-bal-ja, "here is the true Numa. The creature you had upon your throne was but a wild beast, but this is Numa, King of Beasts, Emperor of All Created Things. Look at him. Must he be held in leash by golden chains like some prisoner or slave? No! He is indeed an Emperor. But there is one yet greater than he, one from whom he takes commands. And that one is I, Tarzan of the Apes. Anger me and you shall feel not only the wrath of Numa, but the wrath of Tarzan as well. The Gomangani are my people, the Bolgani shall be my slaves. Go and tell your fellows that, and that if they would live at all they had best come soon and sue for mercy. Go!"

When the messenger had again departed Tarzan looked at the old man, who was eyeing him with an expression which might have denoted either awe or reverence, were it not for the vaguest hint of a twinkle in the corners of the eyes. The ape-man breathed a deep sigh of relief. "That will give us at least another half hour," he said.

"We shall need it, and more, too," replied the old man, "though, at that, you have accomplished more than I had thought possible, for at least you have put a doubt in the minds of the Bolgani, who never before have had cause to question their own power."

Presently from the outer corridors the sounds of argument and discussion gave place to that of movement among the Bolgani. A company, comprising some fifty of the gorilla-men, took post directly outside the main entrance of the throne room where they stood in silence, their weapons ready, as though for the purpose of disputing any effort upon the part of the inmates of the room to escape. Beyond them the balance of the gorilla-men could be seen moving away and disappearing through doorways and corridors leading from the main hallway of the palace. The Gomangani, together with La and the old man, watched impatiently for the coming of the black reinforcements, while Tarzan sat upon the edge of the dais half-reclining, with an arm about the neck of Jad-bal-ja.

"They are up to something," said the old man. "We must watch carefully against a surprise. If the blacks would but come now, while the doorway is held by only fifty, we should overcome them easily, and have, I do verily believe, some slight chance of escaping from the palace grounds."

"Your long residence here," said Tarzan, "has filled you with the same senseless fear of the Bolgani that the Gomangani hold. From the attitude of mind which you hold toward them one would think them some manner of supermen—they are only beasts, my friend, and if we remain loyal to our cause we shall overcome them."

"Beasts they may be," replied the old man, "but they are beasts with the brains of men—their cunning and their cruelty are diabolical."

A long silence ensued, broken only by the nervous whisperings of the Gomangani, whose morale, it was evident, was slowly disintegrating under the nervous strain of the enforced wait, and the failure of their fellows of the forest to come quickly to their aid. To this was added the demoralizing effect of speculation upon what the Bolgani were planning or what plan they already were putting into effect. The very silence of the gorilla-men was more terrible than the din of actual assault. La was the first of the whites to break the silence.

"If thirty of the Gomangani could leave the palace so easily, why might not we leave also?" she asked.

"There were two reasons," replied Tarzan. "One was that should we have left simultaneously the Bolgani, greatly outnumbering us as they did, could have harassed us and detained us for a sufficient length of time to have permitted their messengers to reach the villagers ahead of us, with the result that in a short time we should have been surrounded by thousands of hostile warriors. The second reason is that I desire to punish the creatures, so that in future a stranger may be safe in the Valley of the Palace of Diamonds." He paused. "And now I shall give you a third reason why we may not seek to escape at this moment." He pointed toward the windows overlooking the terrace. "Look," he said, "the terrace and the gardens are filled with Bolgani. Whatever their plan I think its success depends upon our attempt to escape from this room through the windows, for, unless I am mistaken, the Bolgani upon the terrace and in the gardens are making an attempt to hide themselves from us."

The old man walked to a part of the room from which he could see the greater part of the terrace and garden upon which the windows of the throne room looked.

"You are right," he said when he returned to the ape-man's side, "the Bolgani are all massed outside these windows with the exception of those who guard the entrance, and possibly some others at the doorways at other portions of the throne room. That, however, we must determine." He walked quickly to the opposite side of the chamber and drew back the hangings before one of the apertures, disclosing beyond a small band of Bolgani. They stood there motionless, not making any effort to seize or harm him. To another exit, and another, he went, and beyond each discovered to the occupants of the chamber the same silent gorilla guardians. He made the circle of the room, passing over the dais behind the three thrones, and then he came back to Tarzan and La.

"It is as I suspected," he said, "we are entirely surrounded. Unless help comes soon we are lost."

"But their force is divided," Tarzan reminded him.

"Even so, it is sufficient to account for us," replied the old man.

"Perhaps you are right," said Tarzan, "but at least we shall have a bully fight."

"What is that!" exclaimed La, and simultaneously, attracted by the same noise, the inmates of the throne room raised their eyes to the ceiling above them, where they saw that traps had been lifted from a dozen openings, revealing the scowling faces of several score of gorilla-men.

"What are they up to now!" exclaimed Tarzan, and as though in answer to the query the Bolgani above began hurling bundles of burning, oil-soaked rags, tied in goat skins, into the throne room, which immediately commenced to fill it with thick, suffocating smoke, accompanied by the stench of burning hide and hair.

15

The Map of Blood

AFTER ESTEBAN AND Owaza had buried the gold they returned to the spot where they had left their five boys, and proceeding with them to the river made camp for the night. Here they discussed their plans, deciding to abandon the balance of the party to reach the coast as best they might, while they returned to another section of the coast where they could recruit sufficient porters to carry out the gold.

"Instead of going way back to the coast for porters," asked Esteban, "why could we not just as well recruit them from the nearest village?"

"Such men would not go with us way to the coast," replied Owaza. "They are not porters. At best they would carry our gold to the next village."

"Why not that, then?" inquired the Spaniard. "And at the next village we could employ porters to carry us on still farther, until we could employ other men to continue on with us."

Owaza shook his head. "It is a good plan, Bwana, but we cannot do it, because we have nothing with which to pay our porters."

Esteban scratched his head. "You are right," he said, "but it would save us that damnable trip to the coast and return." They sat for some moments in silence, thinking. "I have it!" at last exclaimed the Spaniard. "Even if we had the porters now we could not go directly to the coast for fear of meeting Flora Hawkes's party—we must let them get out of Africa before we take the gold to the coast. Two months will be none too long to wait, for they are going to have a devil of a time getting to the coast at all with that bunch of mutinous porters. While we are waiting, therefore, let us take one of the ingots of gold to the nearest point at which we can dispose of it for trade goods. Then we can return and hire porters to carry it from village to village."

"The Bwana speaks words of wisdom," replied Owaza. "It is not as far to the nearest trading post as it is back to the coast, and thus we shall not only save time, but also many long, hard marches."

"In the morning, then, we shall return and unearth one of the ingots, but we must be sure that none of your men accompanies us, for no one must know until it is absolutely necessary where the gold is buried. When we return for it, of course, then others must know, too, but inasmuch as we shall be with it constantly thereafter there will be little danger of its being taken from us."

And so upon the following morning the Spaniard and Owaza returned to the buried treasure, where they unearthed a single ingot.

Before he left the spot the Spaniard drew upon the inner surface of the leopard skin that he wore across his shoulder an accurate map of the location of the treasure, making the drawing with a sharpened stick, dipped in the blood of a small rodent he had killed for the purpose. From Owaza he obtained the native names of the river and of such landmarks as were visible from the spot at which the treasure was buried, together with as explicit directions as possible for reaching the place from the coast. This information, too, he wrote below the map, and when he had finished he felt much relieved from the fear that should aught befall Owaza he might never be able to locate the gold.

When Jane Clayton reached the coast to take passage for London she found awaiting her a wire stating that her father was entirely out of danger, and that there was no necessity for her coming to him. She, therefore, after a few days of rest, turned her face again toward home, and commenced to retrace the steps of the long, hot, weary journey that she had just completed. When, finally, she arrived at the bungalow she learned, to her consternation, that Tarzan of the Apes had not yet returned from his expedition to the city of Opar after the gold from the treasure vaults. She found Korak, evidently much exercised, but unwilling to voice a doubt as to the ability of his father to care for himself. She learned of the escape of the golden lion with regret, for she knew that Tarzan had become attached to the noble beast.

It was the second day after her return that the Waziri who had accompanied Tarzan returned without him. Then, indeed, was her heart filled with fear for her lord and master. She questioned the men carefully, and when she learned from them that Tarzan had suffered another accident that had again affected his memory, she immediately announced that she would set out on the following day in search of him, commanding the Waziri who had just returned to accompany her.

Korak attempted to dissuade her, but failing in that insisted upon accompanying her.

"We must not all be away at once," she said. "You remain here, my son. If I fail I shall return and let you go."

"I cannot let you go alone, Mother," replied Korak.

"I am not alone when the Waziri are with me," she laughed. "And you know perfectly well, boy, that I am as safe anywhere in the heart of Africa with them as I am here at the ranch."

"Yes, yes, I suppose so," he replied, "but I wish I might go, or that Meriem were here."

"Yes, I, too, wish that Meriem were here," replied Lady Greystoke. "However, do not worry. You know that my jungle-craft, while not equal to that of Tarzan or Korak, is by no means a poor asset, and that, surrounded by the loyalty and bravery of the Waziri, I shall be safe."

"I suppose you are right," replied Korak, "but I do not like to see you go without me."

And so, notwithstanding his objections, Jane Clayton set out the next morning with fifty Waziri warriors in search of her savage mate.

When Esteban and Owaza had not returned to camp as they had promised, the other members of the party were at first inclined to anger, which was later replaced by concern, not so much for the safety of the Spaniard but for fear that Owaza might have met with an accident and would not return to take them in safety to the coast, for of all the blacks he alone seemed competent to handle the surly and mutinous carriers. The negroes scouted the idea that Owaza had become lost and were more inclined to the opinion that he and Esteban had deliberately deserted them. Luvini, who acted as head man in Owaza's absence, had a theory of his own.

"Owaza and the Bwana have gone after the ivory raiders alone. By trickery they may accomplish as much as we could have accomplished by force, and there will only be two among whom to divide the ivory."

"But how may two men overcome a band of raiders?" inquired Flora, skeptically.

"You do not know Owaza," answered Luvini. "If he can gain the ears of their slaves he will win them over, and when the Arabs see that he who accompanies Owaza and who fights at the head of the mutinous slaves is Tarzan of the Apes, they will flee in terror."

"I believe he is right," muttered Kraski, "it sounds just like the Spaniard," and then suddenly he turned upon Luvini. "Can you lead us to the raiders' camp?" he demanded.

"Yes," replied the negro.

"Good," exclaimed Kraski, "and now, Flora, what do you think of this plan? Let us send a swift runner to the raiders, warning them against Owaza and the Spaniard, and telling them that the latter is not Tarzan of the Apes, but an impostor. We can ask them to capture and hold the two until we come, and after we arrive we can make such further plans as the circumstances permit. Very possibly we can carry out our original design after we have once entered their camp as friends."

"Yes, that sounds good," replied Flora, "and it is certainly crooked enough—just like you, yourself."

The Russian blushed. " 'Birds of a feather'—" he quoted.

The girl shrugged her shoulders indifferently, but Bluber, who, with Peebles and Throck, had been silent listeners to the conversation, blustered.

"Vot do you mean birds vit fedders?" he demanded. "Who vas a crook? I tell you, Master Carl Kraski, I am an honest man, dot is von t'ing dot no man don't say about Adolph Bluber, he is a crook."

"O shut up," snapped Kraski, "if there's anything in it you'll be for it—if there's no risk. These fellows stole the ivory themselves, and killed a lot of people, probably, to do it. In addition, they have taken slaves, which we will free."

"O vell," said Bluber, "if it is fair and eqvitable, vy, all right, but just remember, Mister Kraski, dot *I* am an honest man."

"Blime!" exclaimed Throck, "we're all honest; I've never seen such a downy bunch of parsons in all me life."

"Sure we're honest," roared John Peebles, "and anyone 'at says we ain't gets 'is bally 'ead knocked off, and 'ere we are, 'n that's that."

The girl smiled wearily. "You can always tell honest men," she said. "They go around telling the world how honest they are. But never mind that; the thing now is to decide whether we want to follow Kraski's suggestion or not. It's something we've got all pretty well to agree upon before we undertake it. There are five of us. Let's leave it to a vote. Do we, or don't we?"

"Will the men accompany us?" asked Kraski, turning to Luvini.

"If they are promised a share of the ivory they will," replied the black.

"How many are in favor of Carl's plan?" asked Flora.

They were unanimously for it, and so it was decided that they would undertake the venture, and a half hour later a runner was despatched on the trail to the raiders' camp with a message for the raider chief. Shortly after, the party broke camp and took up its march in the same direction.

A week later, when they reached the camp of the raiders they found that their messenger had arrived safely and that they were expected. Esteban and Owaza had not put in an appearance nor had anything been seen or heard of them in the vicinity. The result was that the Arabs were inclined to be suspicious and surly, fearing that the message brought to them had been but a ruse to permit this considerable body of whites and armed blacks to enter their stockade in safety.

Jane Clayton and her Waziri moving rapidly, picked up the spoor of Flora Hawkes's safari at the camp where the Waziri had last seen Esteban, whom they still thought to have been

Tarzan of the Apes. Following the plainly marked trail, and moving much more rapidly than the Hawkes safari, Jane and the Waziri made camp within a mile of the ivory raiders only about a week after the Hawkes party had arrived and where they still remained, waiting either for the coming of Owaza and Esteban, or for a propitious moment in which they could launch their traitorous assault upon the Arabs. In the meantime, Luvini and some of the other blacks had succeeded in secretly spreading the propaganda of revolt among the slaves of the Arabs. Though he reported his progress daily to Flora Hawkes, he did not report the steady growth and development of a little private plan of his own, which contemplated, in addition to the revolt of the slaves, and the slaying of the Arabs, the murder of all the whites in the camp, with the exception of Flora Hawkes, whom Luvini wished to preserve either for himself or for sale to some black sultan of the north. It was Luvini's shrewd plan first to slay the Arabs, with the assistance of the whites, and then to fall upon the whites and slay them, after their body servants had stolen their weapons from them.

That Luvini would have been able to carry out his plan with ease there is little doubt, had it not been for the loyalty and affection of a young black boy attached to Flora Hawkes for her personal service.

The young white woman, notwithstanding the length to which she would go in the satisfaction of her greed and avarice, was a kind and indulgent mistress. The kindnesses she had shown this ignorant little black boy were presently to return her dividends far beyond her investment.

Luvini had been to her upon a certain afternoon to advise her that all was ready, and that the revolt of the slaves and the murder of the Arabs should take place that evening, immediately after dark. The cupidity of the whites had long been aroused by the store of ivory possessed by the raiders, with the result that all were more than eager for the final step in the conspiracy that would put them in possession of considerable wealth.

It was just before the evening meal that the little negro boy crept into Flora Hawkes's tent. He was very wide-eyed, and terribly frightened.

"What is the matter?" she demanded.

"S-sh!" he cautioned. "Do not let them hear you speak to me, but put your ear close to me while I tell you in a low voice what Luvini is planning."

The girl bent her head close to the lips of the little black. "You have been kind to me," he whispered, "and now that Luvini would harm you I have come to tell you."

"What do you mean?" exclaimed Flora, in a low voice.

"I mean that Luvini, after the Arabs are killed, has given orders that the black boys kill all the white men and take you prisoner. He intends either to keep you for himself or to sell you in the north for a great sum of money."

"But how do you know all this?" demanded the girl.

"All the blacks in camp know it," replied the boy. "I was to have stolen your rifle and your pistol, as each of the boys will steal the weapons of his white master."

The girl sprang to her feet. "I'll teach that traitor a lesson," she cried, seizing her pistol and striding toward the flap of the tent.

The boy seized her about the knees and held her. "No! no!" he cried. "Do not do it. Do not say anything. It will only mean that they will kill the white men sooner and take you prisoner just the same. Every black boy in the camp is against you. Luvini has promised that the ivory shall be divided equally among them all. They are ready now, and if you should threaten Luvini, or if in any other way they should learn that you were aware of the plot, they would fall upon you immediately."

"What do you expect me to do then?" she asked.

"There is but one hope, and that is in flight. You and the white men must escape into the jungle. Not even I may accompany you."

The girl stood looking at the little boy in silence for a moment, and then finally she said, "Very well, I will do as you say. You have saved my life. Perhaps I may never be able to repay you, and perhaps, again, I may. Go, now, before suspicion alights upon you."

The black withdrew from the tent, crawling beneath the back wall to avoid being seen by any of his fellows who were in the center of the camp from which the front of the tent was in plain view. Immediately after he was gone Flora walked casually into the open and went to Kraski's tent, which the Russian occupied in common with Bluber. She found the two men and in low whispers apprised them of what the black had told her. Kraski then called Peebles and Throck, it being decided that they should give no outward sign of holding any suspicion that aught was wrong. The Englishmen were for jumping in upon the blacks and annihilating them, but Flora Hawkes dissuaded them from any such rash act by pointing out how greatly they were outnumbered by the natives, and how hopeless it would be to attempt to overpower them.

Bluber, with his usual cunning and shrewdness which inclined always to double dealing where there was the slightest possibility for it, suggested that they secretly advise the Arabs of what they had learned, and joining forces with them take up as strong a position in the camp as possible and commence to fire into the blacks without waiting for their attack.

Again Flora Hawkes vetoed the suggestion. "It will not do," she said, "for the Arabs are at heart as much our enemies as the blacks. If we were successful in subduing the latter it would be but a question of minutes before the Arabs knew every detail of the plot that we had laid against them, after which our lives would not be worth *that*," and she snapped her fingers.

"I guess Flora is right, as usual," growled Peebles, "but what in 'ell are we goin' to do wanderin' around in this 'ere jungle without nobody to hunt for us, or cook for us, or carry things for us, or find our way for us, that's wot I'd like to know, and 'ere we are, 'n that's that."

"I guess there ain't nothin' else to do," said Throck; "but blime if I likes to run away."

There came then to the ears of the whites, rumbling from the far distance in the jungle, the roar of a lion.

"*Ach, weh!*" cried Bluber. "Ve go out all alone in dot jungle *Mein Gott!* I just as soon stay here und get killed like a vite man."

"They won't kill you like a white man," said Kraski. "They'll torture you if you stay."

Bluber wrung his hands, and the sweat of fear rolled down his oily face. "*Ach!* vy did I done it? vy did I done it?" he wailed. "Vy didn't I stay home in London vere I belong?"

"Shut up!" snapped Flora. "Don't you know that if you do anything to arouse the suspicion of these fellows they will be on us at once? There is only one thing for us to do and that is to wait until they precipitate the attack upon the Arabs. We will still have our weapons, for they do not plan to steal them from us until after the Arabs are killed. In the confusion of the fight, we must make our escape into the jungle, and after that—God knows—and God help us."

"Yes," blubbered Bluber, who was in a blue funk, "*Gott* help us!"

A moment later Luvini came to them. "All is ready, Bwanas," he said. "As soon as the evening meal has been eaten, be in readiness. You will hear a shot, that will be the signal. Then open fire upon the Arabs."

"Good," said Kraski, "we have just been talking about it and we have decided that we will take our stand near the gate to prevent their escape."

"It is well," said Luvini, "but you must remain here." He was addressing Flora. "It would not be safe for you to be where there is to be fighting. Remain here in your tent, and we will confine the fighting to the other side of the village and possibly to the gate, if any of them makes a break for escape."

"All right," said Flora, "I will remain here where it is safe."

Satisfied that things could not have worked into his hands to better advantage the black left them, and presently the entire camp was occupied with the evening meal. There was an atmosphere of restraint, and high, nervous tension throughout the entire camp that must have been noticeable, even to the Arabs, though they, alone of the entire company, were ignorant as to its cause. Bluber was so terrified that he could not eat, but sat white and trembling with his eyes roving wildly about the camp—first to the blacks, then to the Arabs, and then to the gate, the distance to which he must have measured a hundred times as he sat there waiting for the shot that was to be the signal for the massacre that was to send him out into the jungle to be, he surely thought, the immediate prey of the first hunting lion that passed.

Peebles and Throck ate their meal stolidly, much to Bluber's disgust. Kraski, being of a highly nervous temperament, ate but little, but he showed no signs of fear. Nor did Flora Hawkes, though at heart she realized the hopelessness of their situation.

Darkness had fallen. Some of the blacks and Arabs were still eating, when suddenly the silence was shattered by the sharp staccato report of a rifle. An Arab sank silently to the earth. Kraski rose and grasped Flora by the arm. "Come!" he cried.

Followed by Peebles and Throck, and preceded by Bluber, to whose feet fright had lent wings, they hurried toward the gate of the palisade.

By now the air was filled with the hoarse cries of fighting men and the report of rifles. The Arabs, who had numbered but a dozen, were putting up a game fight, and being far better marksmen than the blacks, the issue of the battle was still in doubt when Kraski opened the gate and the five whites fled into the darkness of the jungle.

The outcome of the fight within the camp could not have been other than it was, for so greatly did the blacks outnumber the Arabs, that eventually, notwithstanding their poor marksmanship, they succeeded in shooting down the last of the nomads of the north. Then it was that Luvini turned his attention to the other whites only to discover that they had fled the village. The black realized two things instantly. One was that someone had betrayed him, and the other, that the whites could not have gone far in the short time since they had left the camp.

Calling his warriors about him he explained to them what had happened, and impressing upon them that the whites, if permitted to escape, would eventually return with reinforcements to punish the blacks, he aroused his followers, who now numbered over two hundred warriors, to the necessity of setting out immediately upon the trail of the fugitives and overtaking them before they could carry word even to a neighboring village, the nearest of which was not more than a day's march distant.

16

The Diamond Hoard

As THE PRIMITIVE smoke bombs filled the throne room of the Tower of the Emperors with their suffocating fumes, the Gomangani clustered about Tarzan begging him to save them, for they, too, had seen the massed Bolgani before every entrance and the great body of them that awaited in the gardens and upon the terrace without.

"Wait a minute," said Tarzan, "until the smoke is thick enough to hide our movements from the Bolgani, and then we will rush the windows overlooking the terrace, for they are nearer the east gate than any other exit, and thus some of us will have a better chance for escape."

"I have a better plan," said the old man. "When the smoke conceals us, follow me. There is one exit that is unguarded, probably because they do not dream that we would use it. When I passed over the dais behind the throne I took occasion to note that there were no Bolgani guarding it."

"Where does it lead?" asked Tarzan.

"Into the basement of the Tower of Diamonds—the tower in which I discovered you. That portion of the palace is nearest to the east gate, and if we can reach it before they suspect our purpose there will be little doubt that we can reach the forest at least."

"Splendid!" ejaculated the ape-man. "It will not be long now before the smoke hides us from the Bolgani."

In fact it was so thick by this time that the occupants of the throne room were finding difficulty in breathing. Many of them were coughing and choking and the eyes of all were watering from the effects of the acrid smoke. And yet they were not entirely hidden from the observation of the watchers all about them.

"I don't know how much more of this we can stand," said Tarzan. "I have about all I care for, now."

"It *is* thickening up a bit," said the old man. "Just a moment more and I think we can make it unseen."

"I can stand it no longer," cried La. "I am suffocating and I am half-blinded."

"Very well," said the old man, "I doubt if they can see us now. It is pretty thick. Come, follow me." And he led the way up the steps of the dais and through an aperture behind the thrones—a small opening hidden by hangings. The old man went first, and then La, followed by Tarzan and Jad-bal-ja, who had about reached the limit of his endurance and patience, so that it had been with difficulty that Tarzan had restrained him, and who now was voicing his anger in deep growls which might have apprised the Bolgani of their avenue of escape. Behind Tarzan and the lion crowded the coughing Gomangani; but because Jad-bal-ja was just in front of them they did not crowd as closely upon the party ahead of them as they probably would have done otherwise.

The aperture opened into a dark corridor which led down a flight of rough steps to a lower level, and then straight through utter darkness for the rather considerable distance which separated the Tower of Diamonds from the Tower of the Emperors. So great was their relief at escaping the dense smoke of the throne room that none of the party minded the darkness of the corridor, but followed patiently the lead of the old man who had explained that the first stairs down which they had passed were the only obstacles to be encountered in the tunnel.

At the corridor's end the old man halted before a heavy door, which after considerable difficulty he managed to open.

"Wait a moment," he said, "until I find a cresset and make a light."

They heard him moving about beyond the doorway for a moment and then a dim light flared, and presently the wick in a cresset flickered. In the dim rays Tarzan saw before them a large rectangular chamber, the great size of which was only partially suggested in the wavering light of the cresset.

"Get them all in," said the old man, "and close the door." When that had been done he called to Tarzan. "Come!" he said. "Before we leave this chamber I want to show you such a sight as no other human eyes have ever rested upon."

He led him to the far side of the chamber where, in the light of the cresset, Tarzan saw tier after tier of shelves, upon which were stacked small sacks made of skins. The old man set the cresset upon one of the shelves and taking a sack opened it and spilled a portion of the contents into the palm of his hand. "Diamonds," he said. "Each of these packages weighs five pounds and each contains diamonds. They have been accumulating them for countless ages, for they mine far more than they can use themselves. In their legends is the belief that someday the Atlantians will return and they can sell the diamonds to them. And so they continue to mine them and store them as though there was a constant and ready market for them. Here, take one of the bags with you," he said. He handed one to Tarzan and another to La.

"I do not believe that we shall ever leave the valley alive, but we might." He took a third bag for himself.

From the diamond vault the old man led them up a primitive ladder to the floor above, and quickly to the main entrance of the Tower. Only two heavy doors, bolted upon the inside, now lay between them and the terrace, a short distance beyond which the east gate swung open. The old man was about to open the doors when Tarzan stopped him.

"Wait a moment," he said, "until the rest of the Gomangani come. It takes them some time to ascend the ladder. When they are all here behind us, swing the doors open, and you and La, with this ten or a dozen Gomangani that are immediately around us, make a break for the gate. The rest of us will bring up the rear and hold the Bolgani off in case they attack us. Get ready," he added a moment later, "I think they are all up."

Carefully Tarzan explained to the Gomangani the plan he had in mind, and then, turning to the old man, he commanded, "Now!" The bolt slipped, the doors swung open, and simultaneously the entire party started at a run toward the east gate. The Bolgani, who were still massed about the throne room, were not aware that their victims had eluded them until Tarzan, bringing up the rear with Jad-bal-ja was passing through the east gate. Then the Bolgani discovered him, and immediately set up a hue and cry that brought several hundred of them on a mad run in pursuit.

"Here they come," cried Tarzan to the others, "make a run of it—straight down the valley toward Opar, La."

"And you?" demanded the young woman.

"I shall remain a moment with the Gomangani, and attempt to punish these fellows."

La stopped in her tracks. "I shall not go a step without you, Tarzan of the Apes," she said. "Too great already are the risks you have taken for me. No, I shall not go without you."

The ape-man shrugged. "As you will," he said. "Here they come."

With great difficulty he rallied a portion of the Gomangani who, once through the gate, seemed imbued but with a single purpose, and that to put as much distance between the Palace of Diamonds and themselves as possible. Perhaps fifty warriors rallied to his call, and with these he stood in the gateway toward which several hundred Bolgani were now charging.

The old man came and touched Tarzan on the arm. "You had better fly," he said. "The Gomangani will break and run at the first assault."

"We will gain nothing by flying," said Tarzan, "for we should only lose what we have gained with the Gomangani, and then we should have the whole valley about us like hornets."

He had scarcely finished speaking when one of the Gomangani cried: "Look! Look! They come." He pointed along the trail into the forest.

"And just in time, too," remarked Tarzan, as he saw the first of a swarm of Gomangani pouring out of the forest toward the east gate. "Come!" he cried to the advancing blacks, "the Bolgani are upon us. Come, and avenge your wrongs!" Then he turned, and calling to the blacks around him, leaped forward to meet the onrushing gorilla-men. Behind them wave after wave of Gomangani rolled through the east gate of the Palace of Diamonds, carrying everything before them to break at last like surf upon the wavering wall of Bolgani that was being relentlessly hurled back against the palace walls.

The shouting and the fighting and the blood worked Jad-bal-ja into such a frenzy of excitement that Tarzan with difficulty restrained him from springing upon friend and foe alike, with the result that it required so much of the ape-man's time to hold in leash his ferocious ally that he was able to take but little part in the battle, yet he saw that it was going his way, and that, but for the occurrence of some untoward event, the complete defeat of the Bolgani was assured.

Nor were his deductions erroneous. So frantic were the Gomangani with the blood-lust of revenge and so enthused by the first fruits of victory, that they went fully as mad as Jad-bal-ja himself. They neither gave nor asked quarter, and the fighting ended only when they could find no more Bolgani to slay.

The fighting over, Tarzan, with La and the old man, returned to the throne room, from which the fumes of the smoke bombs had now disappeared. To them they summoned the head man of each village, and when they had assembled before the dais, above which stood the three whites, with the great, black-maned lion Jad-bal-ja, Tarzan addressed them.

"Gomangani of the Valley of the Palace of Diamonds," he said, "you have this night won your freedom from the tyrannical masters that have oppressed you since far beyond the time the oldest of you may remember. For so many countless ages have you been oppressed that there has never developed among you a leader capable of ruling you wisely and justly. Therefore you must select a ruler from another race than your own."

"You! You!" cried voice after voice as the head men clamored to make Tarzan of the Apes their king.

"No," cried the ape-man, holding up his hand for silence, "but there is one here who has lived long among you, and who knows your habits and your customs, your hopes and your needs better than any other. If he will stay with you, and rule you he will, I am sure, make you a good king," and Tarzan pointed to the old man.

The old man looked at Tarzan in bewilderment. "But I want to go away from here," he said; "I want to get back into the world of civilization, from which I have been buried all these years."

"You do not know what you are talking about," replied the ape-man. "You have been gone very long. You will find no friends left back there from whence you came. You will find deceit, and hypocrisy, and greed, and avarice, and cruelty. You will find that no one will be interested in you and that you will be interested in no one there. I, Tarzan of the Apes, have left my jungle and gone to the cities built by men, but always I have been disgusted and been glad to return to my jungle—to the noble beasts that are honest in their loves and in their hates—to the freedom and genuineness of nature.

"If you return you will be disappointed, and you will realize that you have thrown away an opportunity of accomplishing a work well worth your while. These poor creatures need you. I cannot remain to guide them out of darkness, but you may, and you may so mold them that they will be an industrious, virtuous, and kindly people, not untrained, however, in the arts of warfare, for when we have that which is good, there will always be those who are envious and who, if they are more powerful than we, will attempt to come and take what we have by force. Therefore, you must train your people to protect their country and their rights, and to protect them they must have the ability and the knowledge to fight successfully, and the weapons wherewith to wage their wars."

"You speak the truth, Tarzan of the Apes," replied the old man. "There is nothing for me in that other world, so, if the Gomangani wish me to be their chief I will remain here."

The head men, when he questioned them, assured Tarzan that if they could not have him for chief they would be very glad to have the old man, whom they all knew, either by sight or reputation, as one who had never perpetrated any cruelties upon the Gomangani.

The few surviving Bolgani who had taken refuge in various parts of the palace were sought out and brought to the throne room. Here they were given the option of remaining in the valley as slaves, or leaving the country entirely. The Gomangani would have fallen upon them and slain them, but that their new king would not permit.

"But where shall we go if we leave the Valley of the Palace of Diamonds?" asked one of the Bolgani. "Beyond the city of Opar we know not what exists, and in Opar may we find only enemies."

Tarzan sat eyeing them quizzically, and in silence. For a

long time he did not speak, while several of the Gomangani head men, and others of the Bolgani, made suggestions for the future of the gorilla-men. Finally the ape-man arose and nodded toward the Bolgani.

"There are a hundred of you," he said. "You are powerful creatures and should be ferocious fighters. Beside me sits La, the High Priestess and Queen of Opar. A wicked priest, usurping her power, has driven her from her throne, but tomorrow we march upon Opar with the bravest Gomangani of the Valley of the Palace of Diamonds, and there we punish Cadj, the High Priest, who has proven a traitor to his queen; and La, once more, ascends the throne of Opar. But where the seeds of treason have once been broadcast the plant may spring up at any time and where least expected. It will be long, therefore, before La of Opar may have full confidence in the loyalty of her people—a fact which offers you an opportunity and a country. Accompany us, therefore, to Opar, and fight with us to replace La upon her throne, and then, when the fighting is over, remain there as La's bodyguard to protect her, not only from enemies without, but from enemies within."

The Bolgani discussed the matter for several minutes, and then one of them came to Tarzan. "We will do as you suggest," he said.

"And you will be loyal to La?" asked the ape-man.

"A Bolgani is never a traitor," replied the gorilla-man.

"Good!" exclaimed Tarzan, "and you, La, are you satisfied with this arrangement?"

"I accept them in my service," replied she.

Early the next morning Tarzan and La set out with three thousand Gomangani and a hundred Bolgani to punish the traitorous Cadj. There was little or no attempt at strategy or deception. They simply marched down through the Valley of the Palace of Diamonds, descended the rocky ravine into the Valley of Opar, and made straight for the rear of the palace of La.

A little gray monkey, sitting among the vines and creepers upon the top of the temple walls, saw them coming. He cocked his head, first upon one side and then upon the other, and became so interested and excited that for a moment he forgot to scratch his belly—an occupation he had been assiduously pursuing for some time. The closer the column approached the more excited became Manu, the monkey, and when he realized vaguely the great numbers of the Gomangani he was fairly beside himself, but the last straw that sent him scampering madly back to the palace of Opar was the sight of the Bolgani—the ogres of his little world.

Cadj was in the courtyard of the inner temple, where at sunrise he had performed a sacrifice to the Flaming God. With Cadj were a number of the lesser priests, and Oah and her priestesses. That there was dissension among them was evident by the scowling faces fully as much as by the words which Oah directed to Cadj.

"Once again have you gone too far, Cadj," she cried bitterly. "Only may the High Priestess of the Flaming God perform the act of sacrifice. Yet again and again do you persist in defiling the sacred knife with your unworthy hand."

"Silence, woman," growled the High Priest. "I am Cadj, King of Opar, High Priest of the Flaming God. You are what you are only because of the favor of Cadj. Try not my patience too far or you shall indeed know the feel of the sacred knife." There could be no mistaking the sinister menace in his words. Several of those about him could ill conceal the shocked surprise they felt at his sacrilegious attitude toward their High Priestess. However little they thought of Oah, the fact remained that she had been elevated to the highest place among them, and those that believed that La was dead, as Cadj had taken great pains to lead them all to believe, gave in full to Oah the reverence which her high office entitled her to.

"Have a care, Cadj," warned one of the older priests. "There is a limit beyond which not even you may pass."

"You dare threaten me?" cried Cadj, the maniacal fury of fanaticism gleaming in his eyes. "You dare threaten *me*, Cadj, the High Priest of the Flaming God?" And as he spoke he leaped toward the offending man, the sacrificial knife raised menacingly above his head, and just at that moment a little gray monkey came chattering and screaming through an embrasure in the wall overlooking the court of the temple.

"The Bolgani! The Bolgani!" he shrieked. "They come! They come!"

Cadj stopped and wheeled toward Manu, the hand that held the knife dropping at his side. "You saw them, Manu?" he asked. "You are speaking the truth? If this is another of your tricks you will not live to play another joke upon Cadj."

"I speak the truth," chattered the little monkey. "I saw them with my own eyes."

"How many of them are there?" asked Cadj. "And how near to Opar have they come?"

"There are as many as the leaves upon the trees," replied Manu, "and they are already close to the temple wall—the Bolgani and the Gomangani, they come as the grasses that grow in the ravines where it is cool and damp."

Cadj turned and raised his face toward the sun, and throwing back his head gave voice to a long-drawn scream that ended in a piercing shriek. Three times he voiced the hideous cry, and then with a command to the others in the court to follow him he started at a brisk trot toward the palace proper. As Cadj directed his steps toward the ancient avenue, upon which the palace of Opar faced, there issued from every corridor and doorway groups of the knurled and hairy men of Opar, armed with their heavy bludgeons and their knives. Screaming and chattering in the trees above them were a score or more of little gray monkeys.

"Not here," they cried, "not here," and pointed toward the south side of the city.

Like an undisciplined mob the horde of priests and warriors reentered the palace at Cadj's heels, and retraced their steps toward the opposite side of the edifice. Here they scrambled to the summit of the lofty wall which guards the palace, just as Tarzan's forces came to a halt outside.

"Rocks! Rocks!" screamed Cadj, and in answer to his commands the women in the courtyard below commenced to gather the loose fragments of stone that had crumbled from the wall and from the palace, and to toss them up to the warriors above.

"Go away!" screamed Cadj to the army outside his gates. "Go away! I am Cadj, High Priest of the Flaming God, and this is his temple. Defile not the temple of the Flaming God or you shall know his wrath."

"La, your High Priestess and your queen, is here," he cried to the Oparians upon the wall. "Cadj is a traitor and an impostor. Open your gates and receive your queen. Give up the traitors to justice, and no harm will befall you; but refuse La entry to her city and we shall take by force and with bloodshed that which belongs to La rightfully."

As he ceased speaking La stepped to his side that all her people might see her, and immediately there were scattering cries for La and a voice or two raised against Cadj. Evidently realizing that it would not take much to turn the scale against him, Cadj shrieked to his men to attack, and simultaneously launched a stone at Tarzan. Only the wondrous agility that he possessed saved the ape-man, and the missile passed by, and striking a Gomangani over the heart, felled him. Instantly a shower of missiles fell upon them, and then Tarzan called to his followers to charge. Roaring and growling, the Bolgani and Gomangani leaped forward to the attack. Catlike they ran up the rough wall in the face of the menacing bludgeons above. Tarzan, who had chosen Cadj as his objective, was among the first to reach the summit. A hairy, crooked warrior struck at him with a bludgeon, and hanging to the summit of the wall with one hand, Tarzan caught the weapon in the other and wrested it from his assailant. At the same time he saw Cadj turn and disappear into the courtyard beyond. Then Tarzan drew himself to the top where he was immediately engaged by two other warriors of Opar. With the weapon he had wrested from their fellow he knocked them to right and left, so great an advantage his great height and strength gave him over them, and then, remembering only that Cadj, who was the ringleader of the revolt against La, must not be permitted to escape Tarzan leaped to the pavement below just as the High Priest disappeared through an archway at the opposite end of the courtyard.

Some priests and priestesses sought to impede his progress. Seizing one of the former by the ankles he swung the body in circles and about him, clearing his own pathway as he ran for the opposite end of the courtyard, and there he halted and wheeled and putting all the strength of his great muscles into the effort, he swung the body of the priest once more and hurled it back into the faces of his pursuers.

Without waiting to note the effect of his act he turned again and continued in pursuit of Cadj. The fellow kept always just ahead of him, because Cadj knew his way through the labyrinthian mazes of the palace and temple and courtyards better than Tarzan. That the trail was leading toward the inner courts of the temple Tarzan was convinced. There Cadj would find easy ingress to the pit beneath the palace and a hiding place from which it would be difficult to dislodge him, so numerous and winding were the dark subterranean tunnels. And so Tarzan put forth every effort to reach the sacrificial court in time to prevent Cadj from gaining the comparative safety of the underground passages; but as he finally leaped through the doorway into the court, a noose, cunningly laid, closed about one of his ankles and he was hurled heavily to the ground. Almost instantly a number of the crooked little men of Opar leaped upon him, where he lay, half-stunned by the fall, and before he had fully regained his faculties they had trussed him securely.

Only about half conscious, he felt them raise him from the ground and carry him, and presently he was deposited upon a cold stone surface. Then it was that full consciousness returned to him, and he realized that he lay outstretched once more upon the sacrificial altar of the inner court of the Temple of the Flaming God and above him stood Cadj, the High Priest, his cruel face contorted in a grimace of hate and the anticipation of revenge long deferred.

"At last!" gloated the creature of hate. "This time, Tarzan of the Apes, you shall know the fury not of the Flaming God, but of Cadj, the man; nor shall there be any wait nor interference."

He swung the sacrificial knife high above his head. Beyond the point of the knife Tarzan of the Apes saw the summit of the courtyard wall, and just surmounting it the head and shoulders of a mighty, black-maned lion.

"Jad-bal-ja!" he cried. "Kill! Kill!"

Cadj hesitated, his knife poised on high. He saw the direction of the ape-man's eyes and followed them, and in that instant the golden lion leaped to the pavement, and with two mighty bounds was upon the High Priest of Opar. The knife clattered to the floor and the great jaws closed upon the horrid face.

The lesser priests who had seized Tarzan, and who had remained to witness his death at the hands of Cadj, had fled screaming from the court the instant that the golden lion had leaped upon their master, and now Tarzan and Jad-bal-ja and the corpse of Cadj were the sole occupants of the sacrificial courtyard of the temple.

"Come, Jad-bal-ja," commanded Tarzan; "let no one harm Tarzan of the Apes."

An hour later the victorious forces of La were overrunning the ancient palace and temples of Opar. The priests and warriors who had not been killed had quickly surrendered and acknowledged La as their queen and High Priestess, and now at La's command the city was being searched for Tarzan and Cadj. It was thus that La herself, leading a searching party, entered the sacrificial courtyard.

The sight that met her eyes brought her to a sudden halt, for there, bound upon the altar, lay Tarzan of the Apes, and standing above him, his snarling face and gleaming eyes glaring directly at her was Jad-bal-ja, the golden lion.

"Tarzan!" shrieked La, taking a step toward the altar. "Cadj has had his way at last. God of my fathers have pity on me—Tarzan is dead."

"No," cried the ape-man, "far from dead. Come and release me. I am only bound, but had it not been for Jad-bal-ja I had been dead beneath your sacrificial knife."

"Thank God," cried La, and started to approach the altar, but paused before the menacing attitude of the growling lion.

"Down!" cried Tarzan, "let her approach." Jad-bal-ja lay down beside his master and stretched his whiskered chin across the ape-man's breast.

La came then, and picking up the sacrificial knife, cut the bonds that held the Lord of the Jungle captive, and then she saw beyond the altar the corpse of Cadj.

"Your worst enemy is dead," said Tarzan, "and for his death you may thank Jad-bal-ja, as I thank him for my life. You should rule now in peace and happiness and in friendship with the people of the Valley of the Palace of Diamonds."

That night Tarzan and the Bolgani and the head men of the Gomangani, and the priests and priestesses of Opar, sat in the great banquet hall of the Palace of Opar, as the guests of La, the queen, and ate from the golden platters of the ancient Atlantians—platters that had been fashioned on a continent that exists today only in the legends of antiquity.

And the following morning Tarzan and Jad-bal-ja set forth upon their return journey to the land of the Waziri and home.

17

The Torture of Fire

FLORA HAWKES AND her four confederates, pursued by Luvini and his two hundred warriors, stumbled through the darkness of the jungle night. They had no objective, for, guided entirely as they had been by the blacks, they knew not where they were and were completely lost. The sole idea dominating the mind of each was to put as much distance between themselves and the camp of the ivory raiders as possible, for no matter what the outcome of the battle there might have been, their fate would be the same should the victorious party capture them. They had stumbled on for perhaps half an hour when, during a momentary rest, they heard plainly behind them the sound of pursuit, and again they plunged on in their aimless flight of terror.

Presently, to their surprise, they discerned the glow of a light ahead. What could it be? Had they made a complete circle, and was this again the camp they had been fleeing? They pushed on to reconnoiter, until at last they saw before them the outlines of a camp surrounded by a thorn boma, in the center of which was burning a small campfire. About the fire were congregated half a hundred black warriors, and as the fugitives crept closer they saw among the blacks a figure standing out clearly in the light of the campfire—a white woman—and behind them rose louder and louder the sound of pursuit.

From the gestures and gesticulations of the blacks around the campfire it was evident that they were discussing the sounds of the battle they had recently heard in the direction of the raiders' camp, for they often pointed in that direction, and now the woman raised her hand for silence and they all listened, and it was evident that they, too, heard the coming of the warriors who were pursuing Flora Hawkes and her confederates.

"There is a white woman there," said Flora to the others. "We do not know who she is, but she is our only hope, for those who are pursuing us will overtake us quickly. Perhaps this woman will protect us. Come, I am going to find out." Without waiting for an answer she walked boldly toward the boma.

They had come but a short distance when the keen eyes of the Waziri discovered them, and instantly the boma wall was ringed with bristling spears.

"Stop!" cried one of the warriors. "We are the Waziri of Tarzan. Who are you?"

"I am an Englishwoman," called Flora in reply. "I and my companions are lost in the jungle. We have been betrayed by our safari—our head man is pursuing us now with warriors. There are but five of us and we ask your protection."

"Let them come," said Jane to the Waziri.

As Flora Hawkes and the four men entered the boma beneath the scrutiny of Jane Clayton and the Waziri, another pair of eyes watched from the foliage of the great tree that overhung the camp upon the opposite side—gray eyes to which a strange light came as they recognized the girl and her companions.

As the newcomers approached Lady Greystoke the latter gave an exclamation of surprise. "Flora!" she exclaimed, in astonishment. "Flora Hawkes, what in the world are you doing here?"

The girl, startled too, came to a full stop. "Lady Greystoke!" she ejaculated.

"I do not understand," continued Lady Greystoke. "I did not know that you were in Africa."

For a moment the glib Flora was overcome by consternation, but presently her native wit came to her assistance. "I am here with Mr. Bluber and his friends," she said, "who came to make scientific researches, and brought me along because I had been to Africa with you and Lord Greystoke, and knew something of the manners and customs of the country, and now our boys have turned against us and unless you can help us we are lost."

"Are they west coast boys?" asked Jane.

"Yes," replied Flora.

"I think my Waziri can handle them. How many of them are there?"

"About two hundred," said Kraski.

Lady Greystoke shook her head. "The odds are pretty heavy," she commented, and then she called to Usula, who was in charge. "There are two hundred west coast boys coming after these people," she said; "we shall have to fight to defend them."

"We are Waziri," replied Usula, simply, and a moment later the van of Luvini's forces broke into view at the outer rim of the campfire's reach.

At sight of the glistening warriors ready to receive them the west coast boys halted. Luvini, taking in the inferior numbers of the enemy at a glance, stepped forward a few paces ahead of his men and commenced to shout taunts and insults, demanding the return of the whites to him. He accompanied his words with fantastic and grotesque steps, at the same time waving his rifle and shaking his fist. Presently his followers took up the refrain until the whole band of two hundred was shrieking and yelling and threatening, the while they leaped up and down as they worked themselves into a frenzy of excitement that would impart to them the courage necessary for the initiating of a charge.

The Waziri, behind the boma wall, schooled and disciplined by Tarzan of the Apes, had long since discarded the fantastic overture to battle so dear to the hearts of other warlike tribes and, instead, stood stolid and grim awaiting the coming of the foe.

"They have a number of rifles," commented Lady Greystoke; "that looks rather bad for us."

"There are not over half-a-dozen who can hit anything with their rifles," said Kraski.

"You men are all armed. Take your places among my Waziri. Warn your men to go away and leave us alone. Do not fire until they attack, but at the first overt act, commence firing, and keep it up—there is nothing that so discourages a west coast black as the rifle fire of white men. Flora and I will remain at the back of the camp, near that large tree." She spoke authoritatively, as one who is accustomed to command and knows whereof she speaks. The men obeyed her, even Bluber, though he trembled pitiably as he moved forward to take his place in the front ranks among the Waziri.

Their movements, in the light of the campfire, were all plainly discernible to Luvini, and also to that other who watched from the foliage of the tree beneath which Jane Clayton and Flora Hawkes took refuge. Luvini had not come to fight. He had come to capture Flora Hawkes. He turned to his men. "There are only fifty of them," he said. "We can kill them easily, but we did not come to make war. We came to get the white girl back again. Stay here and make a great show against those sons of jackals. Keep them always looking at you. Advance a little and then fall back again, and while you are thus keeping their attention attracted in this direction I will take fifty men and go to the rear of their camp and get the white girl, and when I have her I will send word to you and immediately you can return to the village, where, behind the palisade, we shall be safe against attack."

Now this plan well suited the west coast blacks, who had no stomach for the battle looming so imminent, and so they danced and yelled and menaced more vociferously than before, for they felt they were doing it all with perfect impunity, since presently they should retire, after a bloodless victory, to the safety of their palisade.

As Luvini, making a detour, crept through the concealment of the dense jungles to the rear of the camp while the din of the west coast blacks arose to almost deafening proportions, there dropped suddenly to the ground before the two white women from the tree above them, the figure of a white giant, naked except for loincloth and leopard skin—his godlike contour picked out by the flickering light of the beast fire.

"John!" exclaimed Lady Greystoke. "Thank God it is you."

"S-s-sh!" cautioned the white giant, placing a forefinger to his lips, and then suddenly he wheeled upon Flora Hawkes. "It is you I want," he cried, and seizing the girl he threw her lightly across his shoulders, and before Lady Greystoke could interfere—before she half-realized what had occurred—he had lightly leaped the protecting boma in the rear of the camp and disappeared into the jungle beyond.

For a moment Jane Clayton stood reeling as one stunned by an unexpected blow, and then, with a stifled moan, she sank sobbing to the ground, her face buried in her arms.

It was thus that Luvini and his warriors found her as they crept stealthily over the boma and into the camp in the rear of the defenders upon the opposite side of the beast fire. They had come for a white woman and they had found one, and roughly dragging her to her feet, smothering her cries with rough and filthy palms, they bore her out into the jungle toward the palisaded village of the ivory raiders.

Ten minutes later the white men and the Waziri saw the west coast blacks retire slowly into the jungle, still yelling and threatening, as though bent on the total annihilation of their enemies—the battle was over without a shot fired or a spear hurled.

"Blime," said Throck, "what was all the bloomin' fuss about anyhow? I thought they was goin' to eat us up, an' the blighters never done nothin' but yell, an' 'ere we are, 'n that's that."

Bluber swelled out his chest. "It takes more than a bunch of natives to bluff Adolph Bluber," he said pompously.

Kraski looked after the departing blacks, and then, scratching his head, turned back toward the campfire. "I can't understand it," he said, and then, suddenly, "Where are Flora and Lady Greystoke?"

It was then that they discovered that the two women were missing.

The Waziri were frantic. They called the name of their mistress aloud, but there was no reply. "Come!" cried Usula, "we, the Waziri, shall fight, after all," and running to the boma he leaped it, and, followed by his fifty blacks, set out in pursuit of the west coast boys.

It was but a moment or two before they overtook them, and that which ensued resembled more a rout than a battle. Fleeing in terror toward their palisade with the Waziri at their heels the west coast blacks threw away their rifles that they might run the faster, but Luvini and his party had had sufficient start so that they were able to reach the village and gain the safety of the palisade before pursued and pursuers reached it. Once inside the gate the defenders made a stand, for they realized that if the Waziri entered they should all be massacred, and so they fought as a cornered rat will fight, with the result that they managed to hold off the attackers until they could close and bar the gate. Built as it had been as a defense against far greater numbers the village was easy to defend, for there were less than fifty Waziri now, and nearly two hundred fighting men within the village to defend it against them.

Realizing the futility of blind attack Usula withdrew his forces a short distance from the palisade, and there they squatted, their fierce, scowling faces glaring at the gateway while Usula pondered schemes for outwitting the enemy, which he realized he could not overcome by force alone.

"It is only Lady Greystoke that we want," he said; "vengeance can wait until another day."

"But we not even know that she is within the village," reminded one of his men.

"Where else could she be, then?" asked Usula. "It is true that you may be right—she may not be within the village, but that I intend to find out. I have a plan. See, the wind is from the opposite side of the village. Ten of you will accompany me, the others will advance again before the gate and make much noise, and pretend that you are about to attack. After awhile the gate will open and they will come out. That I promise you. I will try to be here before that happens, but if I am not, divide into two parties and stand upon either side of the gateway and let the west coast blacks escape; we do not care for them. Watch only for Lady Greystoke, and when you see her take her away from those who guard her. Do you understand?" His companions nodded. "Then come," he said, and selecting ten men disappeared into the jungle.

Luvini had carried Jane Clayton to a hut not far from the gateway to the village. Here he had bound her securely and tied her to a stake, still believing that she was Flora Hawkes, and then he had left her to hurry back toward the gate that he might take command of his forces in defense of the village.

So rapidly had the events of the past hour transpired that Jane Clayton was still half dazed from the series of shocks that she had been called upon to endure. Dwarfing to nothingness the menace of her present position was the remembrance that her Tarzan had deserted her in her hour of need, and carried off into the jungle another woman. Not even the remembrance of what Usula had told her concerning the accident that Tarzan had sustained, and which had supposedly again affected his memory, could reconcile her to the brutality of his desertion, and now she lay, facedown, in the filth of the Arab hut, sobbing as she had not for many years.

As she lay there torn by grief, Usula and his ten crept stealthily and silently around the outside of the palisade to the rear of the village. Here they found great quantities of dead brush left from the clearing which the Arabs had made when constructing their village. This they brought and piled along the palisade, close against it, until nearly three-quarters of the palisade upon that side of the village was banked high with it. Finding that it was difficult to prosecute their work in silence, Usula despatched one of his men to the main body upon the opposite side of the village, with instructions that they were to keep up a continuous din of shouting to drown the sound of the operations of their fellows. The plan worked to perfection, yet even though it permitted Usula and his companions to labor with redoubled efforts, it was more than an hour before the brush pile was disposed to his satisfaction.

Luvini, from an aperture in the palisade, watched the main body of the Waziri who were now revealed by the rising of the moon, and finally he came to the conclusion that they did not intend to attack that night, and therefore he might relax his watchfulness and utilize the time in another and more agreeable manner. Instructing the bulk of his warriors to remain near the gate and ever upon the alert, with orders that he be summoned the moment that the Waziri showed any change in attitude, Luvini repaired to the hut in which he had left Lady Greystoke.

The black was a huge fellow, with low, receding forehead and prognathous jaw. As he entered the hut with a lighted torch which he stuck in the floor, his bloodshot eyes gazed greedily at the still form of the woman lying prone before him. He licked his thick lips and, coming closer, reached out and touched her. Jane Clayton looked up, and recoiling in revulsion shrunk away. At sight of the woman's face the black looked his surprise.

"Who are you?" he demanded in the pidgin English of the coast.

"I am Lady Greystoke, wife of Tarzan of the Apes," replied Jane Clayton. "If you are wise you will release me at once."

Surprise and terror showed in the eyes of Luvini, and another emotion as well, but which would dominate the muddy brain it was difficult, then, to tell. For a long time he sat gazing at her, and slowly the greedy, gloating expression upon his face dominated and expunged the fear that had at first been written there, and in the change Jane Clayton read her doom.

With fumbling fingers Luvini untied the knots of the bonds that held Jane Clayton's wrists and ankles. She felt his hot breath upon her and saw his bloodshot eyes and the red tongue that momentarily licked the thick lips, The instant that she felt the last thong with which she was tied fall away she leaped to her feet and sprang for the entrance to the hut, but a great hand reached forth and seized her, and as Luvini dragged her back toward him, she wheeled like a mad tigress and struck repeatedly at his grinning, ugly face. By brute force, ruthless and indomitable, he beat down her weak resistance and slowly and surely dragged her closer to him. Oblivious to aught else, deaf to the cries of the Waziri before the gate and to the sudden new commotion that arose in the village, the two struggled on, the woman, from the first, foredoomed to defeat.

Against the rear palisade Usula had already put burning torches to his brush pile at half-a-dozen different places. The flames, fanned by a gentle jungle breeze, had leaped almost immediately into a roaring conflagration, before which the dry wood of the palisade crumbled in a shower of ruddy sparks which the wind carried to the thatched roofs of the huts beyond, until in an incredibly short period of time the village was a roaring inferno of flames. And even as Usula had predicted the gate swung open and the west coast blacks swarmed forth in terror toward the jungle. Upon either side of the gateway the Waziri stood, looking for their mistress, but though they waited and watched in silence until no more came from the gateway of the village, and until the interior of the palisade was a seething hell of fire, they saw nothing of her.

Long after they were convinced that no human being could remain alive in the village they still waited and hoped; but at last Usula gave up the useless vigil.

"She was never there," he said, "and now we must pursue

the blacks and capture some of them, from whom we may learn the whereabouts of Lady Greystoke."

It was daylight before they came upon a small band of stragglers, who were in camp a few miles toward the west. These they quickly surrounded, winning their immediate surrender by promises of immunity in the event that they would answer truthfully the questions that Usula should propound.

"Where is Luvini?" demanded Usula, who had learned the name of the leader of the west coast boys from the Europeans the evening before.

"We do not know; we have not see him since we left the village," replied one of the blacks. "We were some of the slaves of the Arabs, and when we escaped the palisade last night we ran away from the others, for we thought that we should be safer alone than with Luvini, who is even crueler than the Arabs."

"Did you see the white women that he brought to the camp last night?" demanded Usula.

"He brought but one white woman," replied the other.

"What did he do with her? Where is she now?" asked Usula.

"I do not know. When he brought her he bound her hand and foot and put her in the hut which he occupied near the village gate. We have not seen her since."

Usula turned and looked at his companions. A great fear was in his eyes, a fear that was reflected in the countenances of the others.

"Come!" he said, "we shall return to the village. And you will go with us," he added, addressing the west coast blacks, "and if you have lied to us—" he made a significant movement with his forefinger across his throat.

"We have not lied to you," replied the others.

Quickly they retraced their steps toward the ruins of the Arab village, nothing of which was left save a few piles of smouldering embers.

"Where was the hut in which the white woman was confined?" demanded Usula, as they entered the smoking ruins.

"Here," said one of the blacks, and walked quickly a few paces beyond what had been the village gateway. Suddenly he halted and pointed at something which lay upon the ground.

"There," he said, "is the white woman you seek."

Usula and the others pressed forward. Rage and grief

contended for mastery of them as they beheld, lying before them, the charred remnants of a human body.

"It is she," said Usula, turning away to hide his grief as the tears rolled down his ebon cheeks. The other Waziri were equally affected, for they all had loved the mate of the big Bwana.

"Perhaps it is not she," suggested one of them; "perhaps it is another."

"We can tell quickly," cried a third. "If her rings are among the ashes it is indeed she," and he knelt and searched for the rings which Lady Greystoke habitually wore.

Usula shook his head despairingly. "It is she," he said, "there is the very stake to which she was fastened"—he pointed to the blackened stub of a stake close beside the body—"and as for the rings, even if they are not there it will mean nothing, for Luvini would have taken them away from her as soon as he captured her. There was time for everyone else to leave the village except she, who was bound and could not leave—no, it cannot be another."

The Waziri scooped a shallow grave and reverently deposited the ashes there, marking the spot with a little cairn of stones.

18

The Spoor of Revenge

As Tarzan of the Apes, adapting his speed to that of Jad-bal-ja, made his comparatively slow way toward home, he reviewed with varying emotions the experiences of the past week. While he had been unsuccessful in raiding the treasure vaults of Opar, the sack of diamonds which he carried compensated several-fold for this miscarriage of his plans. His only concern now was for the safety of his Waziri, and, perhaps, a troublesome desire to seek out the whites who had drugged him and mete out to them the punishment they deserved. In view, however, of his greater desire to return home he decided to make no effort at apprehending them for the time being at least.

Hunting together, feeding together, and sleeping together, the man and the great lion trod the savage jungle trails toward home. Yesterday they had shared the meat of Bara, the deer, today they feasted upon the carcass of Horta, the boar, and between them there was little chance that either would go hungry.

They had come within a day's march of the bungalow when Tarzan discovered the spoor of a considerable body of warriors. As some men devour the latest stock-market quotations as though their very existence depended upon an accurate knowledge of them, so Tarzan of the Apes devoured every scrap of information that the jungle held for him, for, in truth, an accurate knowledge of all that this information could impart to him had been during his lifetime a *sine qua non* to his existence. So now he carefully examined the spoor that lay before him, several days old though it was and partially obliterated by the passage of beasts since it had been made, but yet legible enough to the keen eyes and nostrils of the ape-man. His partial indifference suddenly gave way to keen interest, for among the footprints of the great warriors he saw now and again the smaller one of a white woman—a loved footprint that he knew as well as you know your mother's face.

"The Waziri returned and told her that I was missing," he soliloquized, "and now she has set out with them to search for me." He turned to the lion. "Well, Jad-bal-ja, once again we turn away from home—but no, where she is is home."

The direction that the trail led rather mystified Tarzan of the Apes, as it was not along the direct route toward Opar, but in a rather more southerly direction. On the sixth day his keen ears caught the sound of approaching men, and presently there was wafted to his nostrils the spoor of blacks. Sending Jad-bal-ja into a thicket to hide, Tarzan took to the trees and moved rapidly in the direction of the approaching negroes. As the distance between them lessened the scent became stronger, until, even before he saw them, Tarzan knew that they were Waziri, but the one effluvium that would have filled his soul with happiness was lacking.

It was a surprised Usula who, at the head of the sad and dejected Waziri, came at the turning of the trail suddenly face to face with his master.

"Tarzan of the Apes!" cried Usula. "Is it indeed you?"

"It is none other," replied the ape-man, "but where is Lady Greystoke?"

"Ah, master, how can we tell you!" cried Usula.

"You do not mean—" cried Tarzan. "It cannot be. Nothing could happen to her while she was guarded by my Waziri!"

The warriors hung their heads in shame and sorrow. "We offer our lives for hers," said Usula, simply. He threw down his spear and shield and, stretching his arms wide apart, bared his great breast to Tarzan. "Strike, Bwana," he said.

The ape-man turned away with bowed head. Presently he looked at Usula again. "Tell me how it happened," he said, "and forget your foolish speech as I have forgotten the suggestion which prompted it."

Briefly Usula narrated the events which had led up to the death of Jane, and when he was done Tarzan of the Apes spoke but three words, voicing a question which was typical of him.

"Where is Luvini?" he asked.

"Ah, that we do not know," replied Usula.

"But I shall know," said Tarzan of the Apes. "Go upon your way, my children, back to your huts, and your women and your children, and when next you see Tarzan of the Apes you will know that Luvini is dead."

They begged permission to accompany him, but he would not listen to them.

"You are needed at home at this time of year," he said. "Already have you been gone too long from the herds and fields. Return, then, and carry word to Korak, but tell him that it is my wish that he, too, remains at home—if I fail, then may he come and take up my unfinished work if he wishes to do so." As he ceased speaking he turned back in the direction from which he had come, and whistled once a single, low, long-drawn note, and a moment later Jad-bal-ja, the golden lion, bounded into view along the jungle trail.

"The golden lion!" cried Usula. "When he escaped from Keewazi it was to search for his beloved Bwana."

Tarzan nodded. "He followed many marches to a strange country until he found me," he said, and then he bid the Waziri good-bye and bent his steps once more away from home in search of Luvini and revenge.

John Peebles, wedged in the crotch of a large tree, greeted the coming dawn with weary eyes. Near him was Dick Throck, similarly braced in another crotch, while Kraski, more intelligent and therefore possessing more inventive genius, had rigged a small platform of branches across two parallel boughs, upon which he lay in comparative comfort. Ten feet above him Bluber swung, half exhausted and wholly terrified, to a smaller branch, supported in something that approximated safety by a fork of the branch to which he clung.

"Gord," groaned Peebles, "hi'll let the bloody lions 'ave me before hi'll spend another such a night as this, an' 'ere we are, 'n that's that!"

"And blime, too," said Throck, "hi sleeps on the ground hafter this, lions or no lions."

"If the combined intelligence of the three of you was equal to that of a walrus," remarked Kraski, "we might have slept in comparative safety and comfort last night on the ground."

"Hey there, Bluber, *Mister* Kraski is spikin' to yer," called Peebles in fine sarcasm, accenting the Mister.

"*Ach weh!* I don't care vat nobody says," moaned Bluber.

" 'E wants us to build a 'ouse for 'im hevery night," continued Peebles, "while 'e stands abaht and tells us bloomin' well 'ow to do it, and 'im, bein' a fine gentleman, don't do no work."

"Why should I do any work with my hands when you two big beasts haven't got anything else to work with?" asked Kraski. "You would all have starved by this time if I hadn't found food for you. And you'll be lion meat in the end, or die of exhaustion if you don't listen to me—not that it would be much loss."

The others paid no attention to his last sally. As a matter of fact they had all been quarreling so much for such a long time that they really paid little attention to one another. With the exception of Peebles and Throck they all hated one another cordially, and only clung together because they were afraid to separate. Slowly Peebles lowered his bulk to the ground. Throck followed him, and then came Kraski, and then, finally, Bluber, who stood for a moment in silence, looking down at his disreputable clothing.

"Mein Gott!" he exclaimed at last. "Look at me! Dis suit, vat it cost me twenty guineas, look at it. Ruined. Ruined. It vouldn't bring vun penny in der pound."

"The hell with your clothes!" exclaimed Kraski. "Here we are, lost, half starved, constantly menaced by wild animals, and maybe, for all we know, by cannibals, with Flora missing in the jungle, and you can stand there and talk about your 'tventy guinea' suit. You make me tired, Bluber. But come on, we might as well be moving."

"Which way?" asked Throck.

"Why, to the west, of course," replied Kraski. "The coast is there, and there is nothing else for us to do but try to reach it."

"We can't reach it by goin' east," roared Peebles, "an' 'ere we are, 'n that's that."

"Who said we could?" demanded Kraski.

"Well, we was travelin' east all day yesterday," said Peebles. "I knew all the time that there was somethin' wrong, and I just got it figured out."

Throck looked at his partner in stupid surprise. "What do you mean?" he growled. "What makes you think we was travelin' east?"

"It's easy enough," replied Peebles, "and I can prove it to you. Because this party here knows so much more than the rest of us we've been travelin' straight toward the interior ever since the natives deserted us." He nodded toward the Russian, who stood with his hands on his hips, eyeing the other quizzically.

"If you think I'm taking you in the wrong direction, Peebles," said Kraski, "you just turn around and go the other way; but I'm going to keep on the way we've been going, which is the right way."

"It ain't the right way," retorted Peebles, "and I'll show yer. Listen here. When you travel west the sun is at your left side, isn't it—that is, all durin' the middle of the day. Well, ever since we've been travelin' without the natives the sun has been on our right. I thought all the time there was somethin' wrong, but I could never figure it out until just now. It's plain as the face on your nose. We've been travelin' due east right along."

"Blime," cried Throck, "that we have, due east, and this blighter thinks as 'ow 'e knows it all."

"*Ach!*" groaned Bluber, "und ve got to valk it all back again yet, once more?"

Kraski laughed and turned away to resume the march in the direction he had chosen. "You fellows go on your own way if you want to," he said, "and while you're traveling, just ponder the fact that you're south of the equator and that therefore the sun is always in the north, which, however, doesn't change its old-fashioned habit of setting in the west."

Bluber was the first to grasp the truth of Kraski's statement. "Come on, boys," he said, "Carl vas right," and he turned and followed the Russian.

Peebles stood scratching his head, entirely baffled by the puzzling problem, which Throck, also, was pondering deeply. Presently the latter turned after Bluber and Kraski. "Come on, John," he said to Peebles, "hi don't hunderstand it, but hi guess they're right. They are headin' right toward where the sun set last night, and that sure must be west."

His theory tottering, Peebles followed Throck, though he remained unconvinced.

The four men, hungry and footsore, had dragged their weary way along the jungle trail toward the west for several hours in vain search for game. Unschooled in jungle craft they blundered on. There might have been on every hand fierce carnivore or savage warriors, but so dull are the perceptive faculties of civilized man, the most blatant foe might have stalked them unperceived.

And so it was that shortly after noon, as they were crossing a small clearing, the zip of an arrow that barely missed Bluber's head, brought them to a sudden, terrified halt. With a shrill scream of terror Adolph crumpled to the ground. Kraski threw his rifle to his shoulder and fired.

"There!" he cried, "behind those bushes," and then another arrow, from another direction, pierced his forearm. Peebles and Throck, beefy and cumbersome, got into action with less celerity than the Russian, but, like him, they showed no indication of fear.

"Down," cried Kraski, suiting the action to the word. "Lie down and let them have it."

Scarcely had the three men dropped among the long grass when a score of pigmy hunters came into the open, and a volley of arrows whizzed above the prone men, while from a nearby tree two steel-gray eyes looked down upon the ambush.

Bluber lay upon his belly with his face buried in his arms, his useless rifle lying at his side, but Kraski, Peebles, and Throck, fighting for their lives, pumped lead into the band of yelling pigmies.

Kraski and Peebles each dropped a native with his rifle and then the foe withdrew into the concealing safety of the surrounding jungle. For a moment there was a cessation of hostilities. Utter silence reigned, and then a voice broke the quiet from the verdure of a nearby forest giant.

"Do not fire until I tell you to," it said, in English, "and I will save you."

Bluber raised his head. "Come qvick! Come qvick!" he cried, "ve vill not shoot. Safe me, safe me, und I giff you five pounds."

From the tree from which the voice had issued there came a single, low, long-drawn, whistled note, and then silence for a time.

The pigmies, momentarily surprised by the mysterious voice emanating from the foliage of a tree, ceased their activities, but presently, hearing nothing to arouse their fear, they emerged from the cover of the bushes and launched another volley of arrows toward the four men lying among the grasses in the clearing. Simultaneously the figure of a giant white leaped from the lower branches of a patriarch of the jungle, as a great black-maned lion sprang from the thicket below.

"*Ach!*" shrieked Bluber, and again buried his face in his arms.

For an instant the pigmies stood terrified, and then their leader cried: "It is Tarzan!" and turned and fled into the jungle.

"Yes, it is Tarzan—Tarzan of the Apes," cried Lord Greystoke. "It is Tarzan and the golden lion," but he spoke in the dialect of the pigmies, and the whites understood no word of what he said. Then he turned to them. "The Gomangani have gone," he said; "get up."

The four men crawled to their feet. "Who are you, and what are you doing here?" demanded Tarzan of the Apes. "But I do not need to ask who you are. You are the men who drugged me, and left me helpless in your camp, a prey to the first passing lion or savage native."

Bluber stumbled forward, rubbing his palms together and cringing and smiling. "*Ach, nein!* Mr. Tarzan, ve did not know you. Neffer vould ve did vat ve done, had ve known it vas Tarzan of der Apes. Safe me! Ten pounds—tventy pounds— anyt'ing. Name your own price. Safe me, und it is yours."

Tarzan ignored Bluber and turned toward the others. "I am looking for one of your men," he said, "a black named Luvini. He killed my wife. Where is he?"

"We know nothing of that," said Kraski. "Luvini betrayed us and deserted us. Your wife and another white woman were in our camp at the time. None of us knows what became of them. They were behind us when we took our post to defend the camp from our men and the slaves of the Arabs. Your Waziri were there. After the enemy had withdrawn we found that the two women had disappeared. We do not know what became of them. We are looking for them now."

"My Waziri told me as much," said Tarzan, "but have you seen aught of Luvini since?"

"No, we have not," replied Kraski.

"What are you doing here?" demanded Tarzan.

"We came with Mr. Bluber on a scientific expedition," replied the Russian. "We have had a great deal of trouble. Our head men, askari, and porters have mutinied and deserted. We are absolutely alone and helpless."

"*Ja, Ja!*" cried Bluber. "Safe us! Safe us! But keep dat lion avay. He makes me nerfous."

"He will not hurt you—unless I tell him to," said Tarzan.

"Den please don't tell him to," cried Bluber.

"Where do you want to go?" asked Tarzan.

"We are trying to get back to the coast," replied Kraski, "and from there to London."

"Come with me," said Tarzan, "possibly I can help you. You

do not deserve it, but I cannot see white men perish here in the jungle."

They followed him toward the west, and that night they made camp beside a small jungle stream.

It was difficult for the four Londoners to accustom themselves to the presence of the great lion, and Bluber was in a state of palpable terror.

As they squatted around the fire after the evening meal, which Tarzan had provided, Kraski suggested that they set to and build some sort of a shelter against the wild beasts.

"It will not be necessary," said Tarzan. "Jad-bal-ja will guard you. He will sleep here beside Tarzan of the Apes, and what one of us does not hear the other will."

Bluber sighed. *"Mein Gott!"* he cried. "I should giff ten pounds for vun night's sleep."

"You may have it tonight for less than that," replied Tarzan, "for nothing shall befall you while Jad-bal-ja and I are here."

"Vell, den I t'ink I say good night," said Bluber, and moving a few paces away from the fire he curled up and was soon asleep. Throck and Peebles followed suit, and shortly after Kraski, too.

As the Russian lay, half dozing, his eyes partially open, he saw the ape-man rise from the squatting position he had maintained before the fire, and turn toward a nearby tree. As he did so something fell from beneath his loincloth—a little sack made of hides—a little sack, bulging with its contents.

Kraski, thoroughly awakened now, watched it as the ape-man moved off a short distance, accompanied by Jad-bal-ja, and lay down to sleep.

The great lion curled beside the prostrate man, and presently the Russian was assured that both slept. Immediately he commenced crawling, stealthily and slowly toward the little package lying beside the fire. With each forward move that he made he paused and looked at the recumbent figures of the two ferocious beasts before him, but both slept on peacefully. At last the Russian could reach out and grasp the sack, and drawing it toward him he stuffed it quickly inside his shirt. Then he turned and crawled slowly and carefully back to his place beyond the fire. There, lying with his head upon one arm as though in profound slumber, he felt carefully of the sack with the fingers of his left hand.

"They feel like pebbles," he muttered to himself, "and doubtless that is what they are, for the barbaric ornamentation of this savage barbarian who is a peer of England. It does not seem possible that this wild beast has sat in the House of Lords."

Noiselessly Kraski undid the knot which held the mouth of the sack closed, and a moment later he let a portion of the contents trickle forth into his open palm.

"My God!" he cried, "diamonds!"

Greedily he poured them all out and gloated over them— great scintillating stones of the first water—five pounds of pure, white diamonds, representing so fabulous a fortune that the very contemplation of it staggered the Russian.

"My God!" he repeated, "the wealth of Croesus in my own hand."

Quickly he gathered up the stones and replaced them in the sack, always with one eye upon Tarzan and Jad-bal-ja; but neither stirred, and presently he had returned them all to the pouch and slipped the package inside his shirt.

"Tomorrow," he muttered, "tomorrow—would to God that I had the nerve to attempt it tonight."

In the middle of the following morning Tarzan, with the four Londoners, approached a good-sized, stockaded village, containing many huts. He was received not only graciously, but with the deference due an emperor.

The whites were awed by the attitude of the black chief and his warriors as Tarzan was conducted into their presence.

After the usual ceremony had been gone through, Tarzan turned and waved his hand toward the four Europeans. "These are my friends," he said to the black chief, "and they wish to reach the coast in safety. Send with them, then, sufficient warriors to feed and guard them during the journey. It is I, Tarzan of the Apes, who requests this favor."

"Tarzan of the Apes, the great chief, Lord of the Jungle, has but to command," replied the black.

"Good!" exclaimed Tarzan, "feed them well and treat them well. I have other business to attend to and may not remain."

"Their bellies shall be filled, and they shall reach the coast unscathed," replied the chief.

Without a word of farewell, without even a sign that he realized their existence, Tarzan of the Apes passed from the sight of the four Europeans, while at his heels paced Jad-bal-ja, the golden lion.

19

A Barbed Shaft Kills

KRASKI SPENT A sleepless night. He could not help but realize that sooner or later Tarzan would discover the loss of his pouch of diamonds, and that he would return and demand an accounting of the four Londoners he had befriended. And so it was that as the first streak of dawn lighted the eastern horizon, the Russian arose from his pallet of dried grasses within the hut that had been assigned him and Bluber by the chief, and crept stealthily out into the village street.

"God!" he muttered to himself. "There is only one chance in a thousand that I can reach the coast alone, but this," and he pressed his hand over the bag of diamonds that lay within his shirt—"but this, this is worth every effort, even to the sacrifice of life—the fortune of a thousand kings—my God, what could I not do with it in London, and Paris, and New York!"

Stealthily he slunk from the village, and presently the verdure of the jungle beyond closed about Carl Kraski, the Russian, as he disappeared forever from the lives of his companions.

Bluber was the first to discover the absence of Kraski, for, although there was no love between the two, they had been thrown together owing to the friendship of Peebles and Throck.

"Have you seen Carl dis morning?" he asked Peebles as the

three men gathered around the pot containing the unsavory stew that had been brought to them for their breakfast.

"No," said Peebles. "He must be asleep yet."

"He is not in der hut," replied Bluber. He vas not dere ven I woke up."

"He can take care of himself," growled Throck, resuming his breakfast. "You'll likely find him with some of the ladies," and he grinned in appreciation of his little joke on Kraski's well-known weakness.

They had finished their breakfast and were attempting to communicate with some of the warriors, in an effort to learn when the chief proposed that they should set forth for the coast, and still Kraski had not made an appearance. By this time Bluber was considerably concerned, not at all for Kraski's safety, but for his own, since, if something could happen to Kraski in this friendly village in the still watches of the night, a similar fate might overtake him, and when he made this suggestion to the others it gave them food for thought, too, so that there were three rather apprehensive men who sought an audience with the chief.

By means of signs and pidgin English, and distorted native dialect, a word or two of which each of the three understood, they managed to convey to the chief the information that Kraski had disappeared, and they wanted to know what had become of him.

The chief was, of course, as much puzzled as they, and immediately instituted a thorough search of the village, with the result that it was soon found that Kraski was not within the palisade, and shortly afterward footprints were discovered leading through the village gateway into the jungle.

"Mein Gott!" exclaimed Bluber, "he vent out dere, und he vent alone, in der middle of der night. He must have been crazy."

"Gord!" cried Throck, "what did he want to do that for?"

"You ain't missed nothin', have you?" asked Pebbles of the other two. " 'E might 'ave stolen somethin'."

"Ach, weh! Vot have ve got to steal?" cried Bluber. "Our guns, our ammunition—dey are here beside us. He did not take them. Beside dose ve have nothing of value except my tventy guinea suit."

"But what did 'e do it for?" demanded Peebles.

" 'E must 'ave been walkin' in 'is bloomin' sleep," said Throck. And that was as near to an explanation of Kraski's mysterious disappearance as the three could reach. An hour later they set out toward the coast under the protection of a company of the chief's warriors.

Kraski, his rifle slung over his shoulder, moved doggedly along the jungle trail, a heavy automatic pistol grasped in his right hand. His ears were constantly strained for the first intimation of pursuit as well as for whatever other dangers might lurk before or upon either side. Alone in the mysterious jungle he was experiencing a nightmare of terror, and with each mile that he traveled the value of the diamonds became less and less by comparison with the frightful ordeal that he realized he must pass through before he could hope to reach the coast.

One Histah, the snake, swinging from a low-hung branch across the trail, barred his way, and the man dared not fire at him for fear of attracting the attention of possible pursuers to his position. He was forced, therefore, to make a detour through the tangled mass of underbrush which grew closely upon either side of the narrow trail. When he reached it again, beyond the snake, his clothing was more torn and tattered than before, and his flesh was scratched and cut and bleeding from the innumerable thorns past which he had been compelled to force his way. He was soaked with perspiration and panting from exhaustion, and his clothing was filled with ants whose vicious attacks upon his flesh rendered him half mad with pain.

Once again in the clear he tore his clothing from him and sought frantically to rid himself of the torturing pests.

So thick were the myriad ants upon his clothing that he dared not attempt to reclaim it. Only the sack of diamonds, his ammunition and his weapons did he snatch from the ravening horde whose numbers were rapidly increasing, apparently by millions, as they sought again to lay hold upon him and devour him.

Shaking the bulk of the ants from the articles he had retrieved, Kraski dashed madly along the trail as naked as the day he was born, and when, a half hour later, stumbling and at last falling exhausted, he lay panting upon the damp jungle earth, he realized the utter futility of his mad attempt to reach the coast alone, even more fully than he ever could have under any other circumstances, since there is nothing that so paralyzes the courage and self-confidence of a civilized man as to be deprived of his clothing.

However scant the protection that might have been afforded by the torn and tattered garments he had discarded, he could not have felt more helpless had he lost his weapons and ammunitions instead, for to such an extent are we the creatures of habit and environment. It was, therefore, a terrified Kraski, already foredoomed to failure, who crawled fearfully along the jungle trail.

That night, hungry and cold, he slept in the crotch of a tree while the hunting carnivore roared, and coughed, and growled through the blackness of the jungle about him. Shivering with terror he started momentarily to fearful wakefulness, and when, from exhaustion, he would doze again it was not to rest but to dream of horrors that a sudden roar would merge into reality. Thus the long hours of a frightful night dragged out their tedious length, until it seemed that dawn would never come. But come it did, and once again he took up his stumbling way toward the west.

Reduced by fear and fatigue and pain to a state bordering upon half consciousness, he blundered on, with each passing hour becoming perceptibly weaker, for he had been without food or water since he had deserted his companions more than thirty hours before.

Noon was approaching. Kraski was moving but slowly now with frequent rests, and it was during one of these that there came to his numbed sensibilities an insistent suggestion of the voices of human beings not far distant. Quickly he shook himself and attempted to concentrate his waning faculties. He listened intently, and presently with a renewal of strength he arose to his feet.

There was no doubt about it. He heard voices but a short distance away and they sounded not like the tones of natives, but rather those of Europeans. Yet he was still careful, and so he crawled cautiously forward, until at a turning of the trail he saw before him a clearing dotted with trees which bordered the banks of a muddy stream. Near the edge of the river was a small hut thatched with grasses and surrounded by a rude palisade protected by an outer boma of thorn bushes.

It was from the direction of the hut that the voices were coming, and now he clearly discerned a woman's voice raised in protest and in anger, and replying to it the deep voice of a man.

Slowly the eyes of Carl Kraski went wide in incredulity, not unmixed with terror, for the tones of the voice of the man he heard were the tones of the dead Esteban Miranda, and the voice of the woman was that of the missing Flora Hawkes, whom he had long since given up as dead also. But Carl Kraski was no great believer in the supernatural. Disembodied spirits need no huts or palisades, or bomas of thorns. The owners of those voices were as live—as material—as he.

He started forward toward the hut, his hatred of Esteban and his jealousy almost forgotten in the relief he felt in the realization that he was to again have the companionship of creatures of his own kind. He had moved, however, but a few steps from the edge of the jungle when the woman's voice came again to his ear, and with it the sudden realization of his nakedness. He paused in thought, looking about him, and presently he was busily engaged gathering the long, broad-leaved jungle grasses, from which he fabricated a rude but serviceable skirt, which he fastened about his waist with a twisted rope of the same material. Then with a feeling of renewed confidence he moved forward toward the hut. Fearing that they might not recognize him at first, and, taking him for an enemy, attack him, Kraski, before he reached the entrance to the palisade, called Esteban by name. Immediately the Spaniard came from the hut, followed by the girl. Had Kraski not heard his voice and recognized him by it, he would have thought him Tarzan of the Apes, so close was the remarkable resemblance.

For a moment the two stood looking at the strange apparition before them.

"Don't you know me?" asked Kraski. "I am Carl—Carl Kraski. You know me, Flora."

"Carl!" exclaimed the girl, and started to leap forward, but Esteban grasped her by the wrist and held her back.

"What are you doing here, Kraski?" asked the Spaniard in a surly tone.

"I am trying to make my way to the coast," replied the Russian. "I am nearly dead from starvation and exposure."

"The way to the coast is there," said the Spaniard, and

pointed down the trail toward the west. "Keep moving, Kraski, it is not healthy for you here."

"You mean to say that you will send me on without food or water?" demanded the Russian.

"There is water," said Esteban, pointing at the river, "and the jungle is full of food for one with sufficient courage and intelligence to gather it."

"You cannot send him away," cried the girl. "I did not think it possible that even you could be so cruel," and then, turning to the Russian, "O Carl," she cried, "do not go. Save me! Save me from this beast!"

"Then stand aside," cried Kraski, and as the girl wrenched herself free from the grasp of Miranda the Russian leveled his automatic and fired point-blank at the Spaniard. The bullet missed its target; the empty shell jammed in the breach and as Kraski pulled the trigger again with no result he glanced at his weapon and, discovering its uselessness, hurled it from him with an oath. As he strove frantically to bring his rifle into action Esteban threw back his spear hand with the short, heavy spear that he had learned by now so well to use, and before the other could press the trigger of his rifle the barbed shaft tore through his chest and heart. Without a sound Carl Kraski sank dead at the foot of his enemy and his rival, while the woman both had loved, each in his own selfish or brutal way, sank sobbing to the ground in the last and deepest depths of despair.

Seeing that the other was dead, Esteban stepped forward and wrenched his spear from Kraski's body and also relieved his dead enemy of his ammunition and weapons. As he did so his eyes fell upon a little bag made of skins which Kraski had fastened to his waist by the grass rope he had recently fashioned to uphold his primitive skirt.

The Spaniard felt of the bag and tried to figure out the nature of its contents, coming to the conclusion that it was ammunition, but he did not examine it closely until he had carried the dead man's weapons into his hut, where he had also taken the girl, who crouched in a corner, sobbing.

"Poor Carl! Poor Carl!" she moaned, and then to the man facing her: "You beast!"

"Yes," he cried, with a laugh, "I am a beast. I am Tarzan of the Apes, and that dirty Russian dared to call me Esteban. I am

Tarzan! I am Tarzan of the Apes!" he repeated in a loud scream. "Who dares call me otherwise dies. I will show them. I will show them," he mumbled.

The girl looked at him with wide and flaming eyes and shuddered.

"Mad," she muttered. "Mad! My God—alone in the jungle with a maniac!" And, in truth, in one respect was Esteban Miranda mad—mad with the madness of the artist who lives the part he plays. And for so long, now, had Esteban Miranda played the part, and so really proficient had he become in his interpretation of the noble character, that he believed himself Tarzan, and in outward appearance he might have deceived the ape-man's best friend. But within that godlike form was the heart of a cur and the soul of a craven.

"He would have stolen Tarzan's mate," muttered Esteban. "Tarzan, Lord of the Jungle! Did you see how I slew him, with a single shaft? You could love a weakling, could you, when you could have the love of the great Tarzan!"

"I loathe you," said the girl. "You are indeed a beast. You are lower than the beasts."

"You are mine, though," said the Spaniard, "and you shall never be another's—first I would kill you—but let us see what the Russian had in his little bag of hides, it feels like ammunition enough to kill a regiment," and he untied the thongs that held the mouth of the bag closed and let some of the contents spill out upon the floor of the hut. As the sparkling stones rolled scintillant before their astonished eyes, the girl gasped in incredulity.

"Holy Mary!" exclaimed the Spaniard, "they are diamonds."

"Hundreds of them," murmured the girl. "Where could he have gotten them?"

"I do not know and I do not care," said Esteban. "They are mine. They are all mine—I am rich, Flora. I am rich, and if you are a good girl you shall share my wealth with me."

Flora Hawkes's eyes narrowed. Awakened within her breast was the always-present greed that dominated her being, and beside it, and equally as powerful now to dominate her, her hatred for the Spaniard. Could he have known it, possession of those gleaming baubles had crystallized at last in the mind of the woman a determination she had long fostered to slay the

Spaniard while he slept. Heretofore she had been afraid of being left alone in the jungle, but now the desire to possess this great wealth overcame her terror.

Tarzan, ranging the jungle, picked up the trail of the various bands of west coast boys and the fleeing slaves of the dead Arabs, and overhauling each in turn he prosecuted his search for Luvini, awing the blacks into truthfulness and leaving them in a state of terror when he departed. Each and every one, they told him the same story. There was none who had seen Luvini since the night of the battle and the fire, and each was positive that he must have escaped with some other band.

So thoroughly occupied had the ape-man's mind been during the past few days with his sorrow and his search that lesser considerations had gone neglected, with the result that he had not noted that the bag containing the diamonds was missing. In fact, he had practically forgotten the diamonds when, by the merest vagary of chance his mind happened to revert to them, and then it was that he suddenly realized that they were missing, but when he had lost them, or the circumstances surrounding the loss, he could not recall.

"Those rascally Europeans," he muttered to Jad-bal-ja, "they must have taken them," and suddenly with the thought the scarlet scar flamed brilliantly upon his forehead, as just anger welled within him against the perfidy and ingratitude of the men he had succored. "Come," he said to Jad-bal-ja, "as we searched for Luvini we shall search for these others also." And so it was that Peebles and Throck and Bluber had traveled but a short distance toward the coast when, during a noon-day halt, they were surprised to see the figure of the ape-man moving majestically toward them while, at his side, paced the great, black-maned lion.

Tarzan made no acknowledgment of their exuberant greeting, but came forward in silence to stand at last with folded arms before them. There was a grim, accusing expression upon his countenance that brought the chill of fear to Bluber's cowardly heart, and blanched the faces of the two hardened English pugs.

"What is it?" they chorused. "What is wrong? What has happened?"

"I have come for the bag of stones you took from me," said Tarzan simply.

Each of the three eyed his companion suspiciously.

"I do not understand vot you mean, Mr. Tarzan," purred Bluber, rubbing his palms together. "I am sure dere is some mistake, unless—" he cast a furtive and suspicious glance in the direction of Peebles and Throck.

"I don't know nothin' about no bag of stones," said Peebles, "but I will say as 'ow you can't trust the likes of you."

"I don't trust any of you," said Tarzan. "I will give you five seconds to hand over the bag of stones, and if you don't produce it in that time I shall have you thoroughly searched."

"Sure," cried Bluber, "search me, search me, by all means. Vy, Mr. Tarzan, I vouldn't take notting from you for notting."

"There's something wrong here," growled Throck. "I ain't got nothin' of yours and I'm sure these two haven't neither."

"Where is the other?" asked Tarzan.

"Oh, Kraski? He disappeared the same night you brought us to that village. We hain't seen him since—that's it; I got it now—we wondered why he left, and now I see it as plain as the face on me nose. It was him that stole that bag of stones. That's what he done. We've been tryin' to figure out ever since he left what he stole, and now I see it plain enough."

"Sure," exclaimed Peebles. "That's it, and 'ere we are, 'n that's that."

"Ve might have knowed it, ve might have knowed it," agreed Bluber.

"But nevertheless I'm going to have you all searched," said Tarzan, and when the head man came and Tarzan had explained what he desired, the three whites were quickly stripped and searched. Even their few belongings were thoroughly gone through, but no bag of stones was revealed.

Without a word Tarzan turned back toward the jungle, and in another moment the blacks and the three Europeans saw the leafy sea of foliage swallow the ape-man and the golden lion.

"Gord help Kraski!" exclaimed Peebles.

"Wot do yer suppose he wants with a bag o' stones?" inquired Throck. " 'E must be a bit balmy, I'll say."

"Balmy nudding," exclaimed Bluber. "Dere is but vun kind

of stones in Africa vot Kraski would steal and run off into der jungle alone mit—diamonds."

Peebles and Throck opened their eyes in surprise. "The damned Russian!" exclaimed the former. "He double-crossed us, that's what 'e did."

"He likely as not saved our lives, says hi," said Throck. "If this ape feller had found Kraski and the diamonds with us we'd of all suffered alike—you couldn't 'a' made 'im believe we didn't 'ave a 'and in it. And Kraski wouldn't 'a' done nothin' to help us out."

"I 'opes 'e catches the beggar!" exclaimed Peebles, fervently.

They were startled into silence a moment later by the sight of Tarzan returning to the camp, but he paid no attention to the whites, going instead directly to the head man, with whom he conferred for several minutes. Then, once more, he turned and left.

Acting on information gained from the head man, Tarzan struck off through the jungle in the general direction of the village where he had left the four whites in charge of the chief, and from which Kraski had later escaped alone. He moved rapidly, leaving Jad-bal-ja to follow behind, covering the distance to the village in a comparatively short time, since he moved almost in an air line through the trees, where there was no matted undergrowth to impede his progress.

Outside the village gate he took up Kraski's spoor, now almost obliterated, it is true, but still legible to the keen perceptive faculties of the ape-man. This he followed swiftly, since Kraski had clung tenaciously to the open trail that wound in a general westward direction.

The sun had dropped almost to the western treetops, when Tarzan came suddenly upon a clearing beside a sluggish stream, near the banks of which stood a small, rude hut, surrounded by a palisade and a thorn boma.

The ape-man paused and listened, sniffing the air with his sensitive nostrils, and then on noiseless feet he crossed the clearing toward the hut. In the grass outside the palisade lay the dead body of a white man, and a single glance told the ape-man that it was the fugitive whom he sought. Instantly he realized the futility of searching the corpse for the bag of diamonds, since it was a foregone conclusion that they were now in the possession of whoever had slain the Russian. A perfunctory examination revealed the fact that he was right insofar as the absence of the diamonds was concerned.

Both inside the hut and outside the palisade were indications of the recent presence of a man and woman, the spoor of the former tallying with that of the creature who had killed Gobu, the great ape, and hunted Bara, the deer, upon the preserves of the ape-man. But the woman—who was she? It was evident that she had been walking upon sore, tired feet, and that in lieu of shoes she wore bandages of cloth.

Tarzan followed the spoor of the man and the woman where it led from the hut into the jungle. As it progressed it became apparent that the woman had been lagging behind, and that she had commenced to limp more and more painfully. Her progress was very slow, and Tarzan could see that the man had not waited for her, but that he had been, in some places, a considerable distance ahead of her.

And so it was that Esteban had forged far ahead of Flora Hawkes, whose bruised and bleeding feet would scarce support her.

"Wait for me, Esteban," she had pleaded. "Do not desert me. Do not leave me alone here in this terrible jungle."

"Then keep up with me," growled the Spaniard. "Do you think that with this fortune in my possession I am going to wait here forever in the middle of the jungle for someone to come and take it away from me? No, I am going on to the coast as fast as I can. If you can keep up, well and good. If you cannot, that is your own lookout."

"But you could not desert me. Even you, Esteban, could not be such a beast after all that you have forced me to do for you."

The Spaniard laughed. "You are nothing more to me," he said, "than an old glove. With this," and he held the sack of diamonds before him, "I can purchase the finest gloves in the capitals of the world—new gloves," and he laughed grimly at his little joke.

"Esteban, Esteban," she cried, "come back, come back. I can go no farther. Do not leave me. Please come back and save me." But he only laughed at her, and as a turn of the trail shut him from her sight, she sank helpless and exhausted to the ground.

20

The Dead Return

THAT NIGHT ESTEBAN made his lonely camp beside a jungle trail that wound through the dry wash of an old riverbed, along which a tiny rivulet still trickled, according the Spaniard the water which he craved.

The obsession which possessed him that he was in truth Tarzan of the Apes, imparted to him a false courage, so that he could camp alone upon the ground without recourse to artificial protection of any kind, and fortune had favored him in this respect in that it had sent no prowling beasts of prey to find him upon those occasions that he had dared too much. During the period that Flora Hawkes had been with him he had built shelters for her, but now that he had deserted her and was again alone, he could not, in the role that he had assumed, consider so effeminate an act as the building of even a thorn boma for protection during the darkness of the night.

He did, however, build a fire, for he had made a kill and had not yet reached a point of primitive savagery which permitted him even to imagine that he enjoyed raw meat.

Having devoured what meat he wanted and filled himself at the little rivulet, Esteban came back and squatted before his fire, where he drew the pouch of diamonds from his loincloth and, opening it, spilled a handful of the precious gems into his palm. The flickering firelight playing upon them sent scintillant gleams shooting into the dark of the surrounding jungle night as the Spaniard let a tiny stream of the sparkling stones trickle from one hand to the other, and in the pretty play of light the

Spaniard saw visions of the future—power, luxury, beautiful women—all that great wealth might purchase for a man. With half-closed eyes he dreamed of the ideal that he should search the world over to obtain—the dream-woman for whom he had always searched—the dream-woman he had never found, the fit companion for such as Esteban Miranda imagined himself to be. Presently through the dark lashes that veiled his narrowed lids the Spaniard seemed to see before him in the flickering light of his campfire a vague materialization of the figure of his dream—a woman's figure, clothed in flowing diaphanous white which appeared to hover just above him at the outer rim of his firelight at the summit of the ancient riverbank.

It was strange how the vision persisted. Esteban closed his eyes tightly, and then opened them ever so little, and there, as it had been before he closed them, the vision remained. And then he opened his eyes wide, and still the figure of the woman in white floated above him.

Esteban Miranda went suddenly pale. "Mother of God!" he cried. "It is Flora. She is dead and has come back to haunt me."

With staring eyes he slowly rose to his feet to confront the apparition, when in soft and gentle tones it spoke.

"Heart of my heart," it cried, "it is really you!"

Instantly Esteban realized that this was no disembodied spirit, nor was it Flora—but who was it? Who was this vision of beauty, alone in the savage African wilderness?

Very slowly now it was descending the embankment and coming toward him. Esteban returned the diamonds to the pouch and replaced it inside his loincloth.

With outstretched arms the girl came toward him. "My love, my love," she cried, "do not tell me that you do not know me." She was close enough now for the Spaniard to see her rapidly rising and falling breasts and her lips trembling with love and passion. A sudden wave of hot desire swept over him, so with outstretched arms he sprang forward to meet her and crush her to his breast.

Tarzan, following the spoor of the man and the woman, moved in a leisurely manner along the jungle trail, for he realized that no haste was essential to overtake these two. Nor was he at all surprised when he came suddenly upon the huddled figure of a woman, lying in the center of the pathway.

He knelt beside her and laid a hand upon her shoulder, eliciting a startled scream.

"God!" she cried, "this is the end!"

"You are in no danger," said the ape-man. "I will not harm you."

She turned her eyes and looked up at him. At first she thought he was Esteban. "You have come back to save me, Esteban?" she asked.

"Esteban!" he exclaimed. "I am not Esteban. That is not my name." And then she recognized him.

"Lord Greystoke!" she cried. "It is really you?"

"Yes," he said, "and who are you?"

"I am Flora Hawkes. I was Lady Greystoke's maid."

"I remember you," he said. "What are you doing here?"

"I am afraid to tell you," she said. "I am afraid of your anger."

"Tell me," he commanded. "You should know, Flora, that I do not harm women."

"We came to get gold from the vaults of Opar," she said. "But that you know."

"I know nothing of it," he replied. "Do you mean that you were with those Europeans who drugged me and left me in their camp?"

"Yes," she said, "we got the gold, but you came with your Waziri and took it from us."

"I came with no Waziri and took nothing from you," said Tarzan. "I do not understand you."

She raised her eyebrows in surprise, for she knew that Tarzan of the Apes did not lie.

"We became separated," she said, "after our men turned against us. Esteban stole me from the others, and then, after a while Kraski found us. He was the Russian. He came with a bagful of diamonds and then Esteban killed him and took the diamonds."

It was now Tarzan's turn to experience surprise.

"And Esteban is the man who is with you?" he asked.

"Yes," she said, "but he has deserted me. I could not walk farther on my sore feet. He has gone and left me here to die and he has taken the diamonds with him."

"We shall find him," said the ape-man. "Come."

"But I cannot walk," said the girl.

"That is a small matter," he said, and stooping lifted her to his shoulder.

Easily the ape-man bore the exhausted girl along the trail. "It is not far to water," he said, "and water is what you need. It will help revive you and give you strength, and perhaps I shall be able to find food for you soon."

"Why are you so good to me?" asked the girl.

"You are a woman. I could not leave you alone in the jungle to die, no matter what you may have done," replied the ape-man. And Flora Hawkes could only sob a broken plea for forgiveness for the wrong she had done him.

It grew quite dark, but still they moved along the silent trail until presently Tarzan caught in the distance the reflection of firelight.

"I think we shall soon find your friend," he whispered. "Make no noise."

A moment later his keen ears caught the sound of voices. He halted and lowered the girl to her feet.

"If you cannot follow," he said, "wait here. I do not wish him to escape. I will return for you. If you can follow on slowly, do so." And then he left her and made his way cautiously forward toward the light and the voices. He heard Flora Hawkes moving directly behind him. It was evident that she could not bear the thought of being left alone again in the dark jungle. Almost simultaneously Tarzan heard a low whine a few paces to his right. "Jad-bal-ja," he whispered in a low voice, "heel," and the great black-maned lion crept close to him, and Flora Hawkes, stifling a scream, rushed to his side and grasped his arms.

"Silence," he whispered; "Jad-bal-ja will not harm you."

An instant later the three came to the edge of the ancient riverbank, and through the tall grasses growing there looked down upon the little camp beneath.

Tarzan, to his consternation, saw a counterpart of himself standing before a little fire, while slowly approaching the man, with outstretched arms, was a woman, draped in flowing white. He heard her words; soft words of love and endearment, and at the sound of the voice and the scent spoor that a vagrant wind carried suddenly to his nostrils, a strange complex of emotion overwhelmed him—happiness, despair, rage, love, and hate.

He saw the man at the fire step forward with open arms to take the woman to his breast, and then Tarzan separated the grasses and stepped to the very edge of the embankment, his voice shattering the jungle with a single word.

"Jane!" he cried, and instantly the man and woman turned and looked up at him, where his figure was dimly revealed in the light of the campfire. At sight of him the man wheeled and raced for the opposite side of the river, and then Tarzan leaped to the bottom of the wash below and ran toward the woman.

"Jane," he cried, "it is you, it is you!"

The woman showed her bewilderment. She looked first at the retreating figure of the man she had been about to embrace and then turned her eyes toward Tarzan. She drew her fingers across her brow and looked back toward Esteban, but Esteban was no longer in sight. Then she took a faltering step toward the ape-man.

"My God," she cried, "what does it mean? Who are you, and if you are Tarzan who was he?"

"I am Tarzan, Jane," said the ape-man.

She looked back and saw Flora Hawkes approaching. "Yes," she said, "you are Tarzan. I saw you when you ran off into the jungle with Flora Hawkes. I cannot understand, John. I could not believe that you, even had you suffered an accident to your head, could have done such a thing."

"I, run off into the jungle with Flora Hawkes?" he asked, in unfeigned surprise.

"I saw you," said Jane.

The ape-man turned toward Flora. "I do not understand it," he said.

"It was Esteban who ran off into the jungle with me, Lady Greystoke," said the girl. "It was Esteban who was about to deceive you again. This is indeed Lord Greystoke. The other was an impostor, who only just deserted me and left me to die in the jungle. Had not Lord Greystoke come when he did I should be dead by now."

Lady Greystoke took a faltering step toward her husband. "Ah, John," she said, "I knew it could not have been you. My heart told me, but my eyes deceived me. Quick," she cried, "that impostor must be captured. Hurry, John, before he escapes."

"Let him go," said the ape-man. "As much as I want him, as much as I want that which he has stolen from me, I will not leave you alone again in the jungle, Jane, even to catch him."

"But Jad-bal-ja," she cried. "What of him?"

"Ah," cried the ape-man, "I had forgotten," and turning to the lion he pointed toward the direction in which the Spaniard had escaped. "Fetch him, Jad-bal-ja," he cried; and, with a bound, the tawny beast was off upon the spoor of his quarry.

"He will kill him?" asked Flora Hawkes, shuddering. And yet at heart she was glad of the just fate that was overtaking the Spaniard.

"No, he will not kill him," said Tarzan of the Apes. "He may maul him a bit, but he will bring him back alive if it is possible." And then, as though the fate of the fugitive were already forgotten, he turned toward his mate.

"Jane," he said, "Usula told me that you were dead. He said that they found your burned body in the Arab village and that they buried it there. How is it, then, that you are here alive and unharmed? I have been searching the jungles for Luvini to avenge your death. Perhaps it is well that I did not find him."

"You would never have found him," replied Jane Clayton, "but I cannot understand why Usula should have told you that he had found my body and buried it."

"Some prisoners that he took," replied Tarzan, "told him that Luvini had taken you bound hand and foot into one of the Arab huts near the village gateway, and that there he had further secured you to a stake driven into the floor of the hut. After the village had been destroyed by fire Usula and the other Waziri returned to search for you with some of the prisoners they had taken who pointed out the location of the hut, where the charred remains of a human body were found beside a burned stake to which it had apparently been tied."

"Ah!" exclaimed the girl, "I see. Luvini did bind me hand and foot and tie me to the stake, but later he came back into the hut and removed the bonds. He attempted to attack me—how long we fought I do not know, but so engrossed were we in our struggle that neither one of us was aware of the burning of the village about us. As I persistently fought him off I caught a glimpse of a knife in his belt, and then I let him seize me and as his arms encircled me I grasped the knife and, drawing it from its sheath, plunged it into his back, below his left shoulder—that was the end. Luvini sank lifeless to the floor of the hut. Almost simultaneously the rear and roof of the structure burst into flames.

"I was almost naked, for he had torn nearly all my clothing from me in our struggles. Hanging upon the wall of the hut was this white burnoose, the property, doubtless, of one of the murdered Arabs. I seized it, and throwing it about me ran into the village street. The huts were now all aflame, and the last of the natives was disappearing through the gateway. To my right was a section of palisade that had not yet been attacked by the flames. To escape into the jungle by the gateway would have meant running into the arms of my enemies, and so, somehow, I managed to scale the palisade and drop into the jungle unseen by any.

"I have had considerable difficulty eluding the various bands of blacks who escaped the village. A part of the time I have been hunting for the Waziri and the balance I have had to remain in hiding. I was resting in the crotch of a tree, about half a mile from here, when I saw the light of this man's fire, and when I came to investigate I was almost stunned by joy to discover that I had, as I imagined, stumbled upon my Tarzan."

"It was Luvini's body, then, and not yours that they buried," said Tarzan.

"Yes," said Jane, "and it was this man who just escaped whom I saw run off into the jungle with Flora, and not you, as I believed."

Flora Hawkes looked up suddenly. "And it must have been Esteban who came with the Waziri and stole the gold from us. He fooled our men and he must have fooled the Waziri, too."

"He might have fooled anyone if he could deceive me," said Jane Clayton. "I should have discovered the deception in a few minutes I have no doubt, but in the flickering light of the campfire, and influenced as I was by the great joy of seeing Lord Greystoke again, I believed quickly that which I wanted to believe."

The ape-man ran his fingers through his thick shock of hair in a characteristic gesture of meditation. "I cannot understand how he fooled Usula in broad daylight," he said with a shake of his head.

"I can," said Jane. "He told him that he had suffered an injury to his head which had caused him to lose his memory partially—an explanation which accounted for many lapses in the man's interpretation of your personality."

"He was a clever devil," commented the ape-man.

"He was a devil, all right," said Flora.

It was more than an hour later that the grasses at the river-bank suddenly parted and Jad-bal-ja emerged silently into their presence. Grasped in his jaws was a torn and bloody leopard skin which he brought and laid at the feet of his master.

The ape-man picked the thing up and examined it, and then he scowled. "I believe Jad-bal-ja killed him after all," he said.

"He probably resisted," said Jane Clayton, "in which event Jad-bal-ja could do nothing else in self-defense but slay him."

"Do you suppose he ate him?" cried Flora Hawkes, drawing fearfully away from the beast.

"No," said Tarzan, "he has not had time. In the morning we will follow the spoor and find his body. I should like to have the diamonds again." And then he told Jane the strange story connected with his acquisition of the great wealth represented by the little bag of stones.

The following morning they set out in search of Esteban's corpse. The trail led through dense brush and thorns to the edge of the river farther downstream, and there it disappeared, and though the ape-man searched both sides of the river for a couple of miles above and below the point at which he had lost the spoor, he found no further sign of the Spaniard. There was blood along the tracks that Esteban had made and blood upon the grasses at the river's brim.

At last the ape-man returned to the two women. "That is the end of the man who would be Tarzan," he said.

"Do you think he is dead?" asked Jane.

"Yes, I am sure of it," said the ape-man. "From the blood I imagine that Jad-bal-ja mauled him, but that he managed to break away and get into the river. The fact that I can find no indication of his having reached the bank within a reasonable distance of this spot leads me to believe that he has been devoured by crocodiles."

Again Flora Hawkes shuddered. "He was a wicked man,"

she said, "but I would not wish even the wickedest such a fate as that."

The ape-man shrugged. "He brought it upon himself, and, doubtless, the world is better off without him."

"It was my fault," said Flora. "It was my wickedness that brought him and the others here. I told them of what I had heard of the gold in the treasure vaults of Opar—it was my idea to come here and steal it and to find a man who could impersonate Lord Greystoke. Because of my wickedness many men have died, and you, Lord Greystoke, and your lady, have almost met your death—I do not dare to ask for forgiveness."

Jane Clayton put her arm about the girl's shoulder. "Avarice has been the cause of many crimes since the world began," she said, "and when crime is invoked in its aid it assumes its most repulsive aspect and brings most often its own punishment, as you, Flora, may well testify. For my part I forgive you. I imagine that you have learned your lesson."

"You have paid a heavy price for your folly," said the ape-man. "You have been punished enough. We will take you to your friends who are on their way to the coast under escort of a friendly tribe. They cannot be far distant, for, from the condition of the men when I saw them, long marches are beyond their physical powers."

The girl dropped to her knees at his feet. "How can I thank you for your kindness?" she said. "But I would rather remain here in Africa with you and Lady Greystoke, and work for you and show by my loyalty that I can redeem the wrong I did you."

Tarzan glanced at his wife questioningly, and Jane Clayton signified her assent to the girl's request.

"Very well, then," said the ape-man, "you may remain with us, Flora."

"You will never regret it," said the girl. "I will work my fingers off for you."

The three, and Jad-bal-ja, had been three days upon the march toward home when Tarzan, who was in the lead, paused, and, raising his head, sniffed the jungle air. Then he turned to them with a smile. "My Waziri are disobedient," he said. "I sent them home and yet here they are, coming toward us, directly away from home."

A few minutes later they met the van of the Waziri, and

great was the rejoicing of the blacks when they found both their master and mistress alive and unscathed.

"And now that we have found you," said Tarzan, after the greetings were over, and innumerable questions had been asked and answered, "tell me what you did with the gold that you took from the camp of the Europeans."

"We hid it, O Bwana, where you told us to hide it," replied Usula.

"I was not with you, Usula," said the ape-man. "It was another, who deceived Lady Greystoke even as he deceived you—a bad man—who impersonated Tarzan of the Apes so cleverly that it is no wonder that you were imposed upon."

"Then it was not you who told us that your head had been injured and that you could not remember the language of the Waziri?" demanded Usula.

"It was not I," said Tarzan, "for my head has not been injured, and I remember well the language of my children."

"Ah," cried Usula, "then it was not our Big Bwana who ran from Buto, the rhinoceros?"

Tarzan laughed. "Did the other run from Buto?"

"That he did," cried Usula; "he ran in great terror."

"I do not know that I blame him," said Tarzan, "for Buto is no pleasant playfellow."

"But our Big Bwana would not run from him," said Usula, proudly.

"Even if another than I hid the gold it was you who dug the hole. Lead me to the spot then, Usula."

The Waziri constructed rude yet comfortable litters for the two white women, though Jane Clayton laughed at the idea that it was necessary that she be carried and insisted upon walking beside her bearers more often than she rode. Flora Hawkes, however, weak and exhausted as she was, could not have proceeded far without being carried, and was glad of the presence of the brawny Waziri who bore her along the jungle trail so easily.

It was a happy company that marched in buoyant spirits toward the spot where the Waziri had cached the gold for Esteban. The blacks were overflowing with good nature because they had found their master and their mistress, while the relief and joy of Tarzan and Jane were too deep for expression.

When at last they came to the place beside the river where they had buried the gold the Waziri, singing and laughing, commenced to dig for the treasure, but presently their singing ceased and their laughter was replaced by expressions of puzzled concern.

For a while Tarzan watched them in silence and then a slow smile overspread his countenance. "You must have buried it deep, Usula," he said.

The black scratched his head. "No, not so deep as this, Bwana," he cried. "I cannot understand it. We should have found the gold before this."

"Are you sure you are looking in the right place?" asked Tarzan.

"This is the exact spot, Bwana," the black assured him, "but the gold is not here. Someone has removed it since we buried it."

"The Spaniard again," commented Tarzan. "He was a slick customer."

"But he could not have taken it alone," said Usula. "There were many ingots of it."

"No," said Tarzan, "he could not, and yet it is not here."

The Waziri and Tarzan searched carefully about the spot where the gold had been buried, but so clever had been the woodcraft of Owaza that he had obliterated even from the keen senses of the ape-man every vestige of the spoor that he and the Spaniard had made in carrying the gold from the old hiding place to the new.

"It is gone," said the ape-man, "but I shall see that it does not get out of Africa," and he despatched runners in various directions to notify the chiefs of the friendly tribes surrounding his domain to watch carefully every safari crossing their territory, and to let none pass who carried gold.

"That will stop them," he said after the runners had departed.

That night as they made their camp upon the trail toward home, the three whites were seated about a small fire with Jadbal-ja lying just behind the ape-man, who was examining the leopard skin that the golden lion had retrieved in his pursuit of the Spaniard, when Tarzan turned to his wife.

"You were right, Jane," he said. "The treasure vaults of Opar are not for me. This time I have lost not only the gold but a fabulous fortune in diamonds as well, beside risking that greatest of all treasures—yourself."

"Let the gold and the diamonds go, John," she said; "we have one another, and Korak."

"And a bloody leopard skin," he supplemented, "with a mysterious map painted upon it in blood."

Jad-bal-ja sniffed the hide and licked his chops in— anticipation or retrospection—which?

21

An Escape and a Capture

AT SIGHT OF the true Tarzan, Esteban Miranda turned and fled blindly into the jungle. His heart was cold with terror as he rushed on in blind fear. He had no objective in mind. He did not know in what direction he was going. His only thought— the thought which dominated him—was based solely upon a desire to put as much distance as possible between himself and the ape-man, and so he blundered on, forcing his way through dense thickets of thorns that tore and lacerated his flesh until at every step he left a trail of blood behind him.

At the river's edge the thorns reached out and seized again, as they had several times before, the precious leopard skin to which he clung with almost the same tenacity as he clung to life itself. But this time the thorns would not leave go their hold, and as he struggled to tear it away from them his eyes turned back in the direction from which he had come. He heard the sound of a great body moving rapidly through the thicket toward him, and an instant later saw the baleful glare of two gleaming, yellow-green spots of flame. With a stifled cry of terror the Spaniard relinquished his hold upon the leopard skin and, wheeling, dived into the river.

As the black waters closed above his head Jad-bal-ja came to the edge of the bank and looked down upon the widening circles which marked the spot of his quarry's disappearance, for Esteban, who was a strong swimmer, struck boldly for the opposite side of the stream, keeping himself well submerged.

For a moment the golden lion scanned the surface of the river, and then he turned and sniffed at the hide the Spaniard had been forced to leave behind, and grasping it in his jaws tore it from the thorns that held it and carried it back to lay it at the feet of his master.

Forced at last to come to the surface for air the Spaniard arose amid a mass of tangled foliage and branches. For a moment he thought that he was lost, so tightly held was he by the entangling boughs, but presently he forced his way upward, and as his head appeared above the surface of the water amidst the foliage he discovered that he had arisen directly beneath a fallen tree that was floating down the center of the stream. After considerable effort he managed to draw himself up to the boughs and find a place astride the great bole, and thus he floated downstream in comparative safety.

He breathed a deep sigh of relief as he realized with what comparative ease he had escaped the just vengeance of the ape-man. It is true that he bemoaned the loss of the hide which carried the map to the location of the hidden gold, but he still retained in his possession a far greater treasure, and as he thought of it his hands gloatingly fondled the bag of diamonds fastened to his loincloth. Yet, even though he possessed this great fortune in diamonds, his avaricious mind constantly returned to the golden ingots by the waterfall.

"Owaza will get it," he muttered to himself. "I never trusted the black dog, and when he deserted me I knew well enough what his plans were."

All night long Esteban Miranda floated downstream upon the fallen tree, seeing no sign of life, until shortly after daybreak he passed a native village upon the shore.

It was the village of Obebe, the cannibal, and at sight of the strange figure of the white giant floating down the stream upon the bole of a tree, the young woman who espied him raised a great hue and cry until the population of the village lined the shore watching him pass.

"It is a strange god," cried one.

"It is the river devil," said the witch doctor. "He is a friend of mine. Now, indeed, shall we catch many fish if for each ten that you catch you give one to me."

"It is not the river devil," rumbled the deep voice of Obebe, the cannibal. "You are getting old," he said to the witch doctor, "and of late your medicine has been poor medicine, and now you tell me that Obebe's greatest enemy is the river devil. That is Tarzan of the Apes. Obebe knows him well." And in truth every cannibal chief in the vicinity knew Tarzan of the Apes well and feared and hated him, for relentless had been the apeman's war against them.

"It is Tarzan of the Apes," repeated Obebe, "and he is in trouble. Perhaps it is our chance to capture him."

He called his warriors about him, and presently half a hundred brawny young bucks started at a jog trot down the trail that paralleled the river. For miles they followed the slowly moving tree which carried Esteban Miranda until at last at a bend in the river the tree was caught in the outer circle of a slow-moving eddy, which carried it beneath the overhanging limbs of the trees growing close to the river's edge.

Cramped and chilled and hungry as he was, Esteban was glad of the opportunity to desert his craft and gain the shore. And so, laboriously, he drew himself up among the branches of the tree that momentarily offered him a haven of retreat from the river, and crawling to its stem lowered himself to the ground beneath, unconscious of the fact that in the grasses around him squatted half a hundred cannibal warriors.

Leaning against the bole of the tree the Spaniard rested for a moment. He felt for the diamonds and found that they were safe.

"I am a lucky devil, after all," he said aloud, and almost simultaneously the fifty blacks arose about him and leaped upon him. So sudden was the attack, so overwhelming the force, that the Spaniard had no opportunity to defend himself against them, with the result that he was down and securely bound almost before he could realize what was happening to him.

"Ah, Tarzan of the Apes, I have you at last," gloated Obebe, the cannibal, but Esteban did not understand a word the man said, and so he could make no reply. He talked to Obebe in English, but that language the latter did not understand.

Of only one thing was Esteban certain; that he was a prisoner and that he was being taken back toward the interior. When they reached Obebe's village there was great rejoicing on the part of the women and the children and the warriors who had remained behind. But the witch doctor shook his head and made wry faces and dire prophecies.

"You have seized the river devil," he said. "We shall catch no more fish, and presently a great sickness will fall upon Obebe's people and they will all die like flies." But Obebe only laughed at the witch doctor for, being an old man and a great king, he had accumulated much wisdom and, with the acquisition of wisdom man is more inclined to be skeptical in matters of religion.

"You may laugh now, Obebe," said the witch doctor, "but later you will not laugh. Wait and see."

"When, with my own hands, I kill Tarzan of the Apes, then indeed shall I laugh," replied the chief, "and when I and my warriors have eaten his heart and his flesh, then, indeed, shall we no longer fear any of your devils."

"Wait," cried the witch doctor angrily, "and you shall see."

They took the Spaniard, securely bound, and threw him into a filthy hut, through the doorway of which he could see the women of the village preparing cooking fires and pots for the feast of the coming night. A cold sweat stood out upon the brow of Esteban Miranda as he watched these gruesome preparations, the significance of which he could not misinterpret, when coupled with the gestures and the glances that were directed toward the hut where he lay, by the inhabitants of the village.

The afternoon was almost spent and the Spaniard felt that he could count the hours of life remaining to him upon possibly two fingers of one hand, when there came from the direction of the river a series of piercing screams which shattered the quiet of the jungle, and brought the inhabitants of the village to startled attention, and an instant later sent them in a mad rush in the direction of the fear-laden shrieks. But they were too late and reached the river only just in time to see a woman dragged beneath the surface by a huge crocodile.

"Ah, Obebe, what did I tell you?" demanded the witch doctor, exultantly. "Already has the devil god commenced his revenge upon your people."

The ignorant villagers, steeped in superstition, looked fearfully from their witch doctor to their chief. Obebe scowled. "He is Tarzan of the Apes," he insisted.

"He is the river devil who has taken the shape of Tarzan of the Apes," insisted the witch doctor.

"We shall see," replied Obebe. "If he is the river devil he can escape our bonds. If he is Tarzan of the Apes he cannot. If he is the river devil he will not die a natural death, like men die, but will live on forever. If he is Tarzan of the Apes some day he will die. We will keep him, then, and see, and that will prove whether or not he is Tarzan of the Apes or the river devil."

"How?" asked the witch doctor.

"It is very simple," replied Obebe. "If some morning we find that he has escaped we will know that he is the river devil, and because we have not harmed him but have fed him well while he has been here in our village, he will befriend us and no harm will come of it. But if he does not escape we will know that he is Tarzan of the Apes, provided he dies a natural death. And so, if he does not escape, we shall keep him until he dies and then we shall know that he was, indeed, Tarzan of the Apes."

"But suppose he does not die?" asked the witch doctor, scratching his woolly head.

"Then," exclaimed Obebe triumphantly, "we will know that you are right, and that he was, indeed, the river devil."

Obebe went and ordered women to take food to the Spaniard while the witch doctor stood, where Obebe had left him, in the middle of the street, still scratching his head in thought.

And thus was Esteban Miranda, possessor of the most fabulous fortune in diamonds that the world had ever known, condemned to life imprisonment in the village of Obebe, the cannibal.

While he had been lying in the hut his traitorous confederate, Owaza, from the opposite bank of the river from the spot where he and Esteban had hidden the golden ingots, saw Tarzan and his Waziri come and search for the gold and go away again, and the following morning Owaza came with fifty men whom he had recruited from a neighboring village and dug up the gold and started with it toward the coast.

That night Owaza made camp just outside a tiny village of a minor chief, who was weak in warriors. The old fellow invited Owaza into his compound, and there he fed him and gave him native beer, while the chief's people circulated among Owaza's boys plying them with innumerable questions until at last the truth leaked out and the chief knew that Owaza's porters were carrying a great store of yellow gold.

When the chief learned this for certain he was much perturbed, but finally a smile crossed his face as he talked with the half-drunken Owaza.

"You have much gold with you," said the old chief, "and it is very heavy. It will be hard to get your boys to carry it all the way back to the coast."

"Yes," said Owaza, "but I shall pay them well."

"If they did not have to carry it so far from home you would not have to pay them so much, would you?" asked the chief.

"No," said Owaza, "but I cannot dispose of it this side of the coast."

"I know where you can dispose of it within two days' march," replied the old chief.

"Where?" demanded Owaza. "And who here in the interior will buy it?"

"There is a white man who will give you a little piece of paper for it and you can take that paper to the coast and get the full value of your gold."

"Who is this white man?" demanded Owaza, "and where is he?"

"He is a friend of mine," said the chief, "and if you wish I will take you to him on the morrow, and you can bring with you all your gold and get the little piece of paper."

"Good," said Owaza, "and then I shall not have to pay the carriers but a very small amount."

The carriers were glad, indeed, to learn the next day that they were not to go all the way to the coast, for even the lure of payment was not sufficient to overcome their dislike to so long a journey, and their fear of being at so great a distance from home. They were very happy, therefore, as they set forth on a two days' march toward the northeast. And Owaza was happy and so was the old chief, who accompanied them himself, though why he was happy about it Owaza could not guess.

They had marched for almost two days when the chief sent one of his own men forward with a message.

"It is to my friend," he said, "to tell him to come and meet us and lead us to his village." And a few hours later, as the little caravan emerged from the jungle onto a broad, grassy plain, they saw not far from them, and approaching rapidly, a large band of warriors. Owaza halted.

"Whose are those?" he demanded.

"Those are the warriors of my friend," replied the chief, "and he is with them. See?" and he pointed toward a figure at the head of the blacks, who were approaching at a trot, their spears and white plumes gleaming in the sunshine.

"They come for war and not for peace," said Owaza fearfully.

"That depends upon you, Owaza," replied the chief.

"I do not understand you," said Owaza.

"But you will in a few minutes after my friend has come."

As the advancing warriors approached more closely Owaza saw a giant white at their head—a white whom he mistook for Esteban—the confederate he had so traitorously deserted. He turned upon the chief. "You have betrayed me," he cried.

"Wait," said the old chief; "nothing that belongs to you shall be taken from you."

"The gold is not his," cried Owaza. "He stole it," and he pointed at Tarzan who had approached and halted before him, but who ignored him entirely and turned to the chief.

"Your runner came," he said to the old man, "and brought your message, and Tarzan and his Waziri have come to see what they could do for their old friend."

The chief smiled. "Your runner came to me, O Tarzan, four days since, and two days later came this man with his carriers, bearing golden ingots toward the coast. I told him that I had a friend who would buy them, giving him a little piece of paper for them, but that, of course, only in case the gold belonged to Owaza."

The ape-man smiled. "You have done well, my friend," he said. "The gold does not belong to Owaza."

"It does not belong to you, either," cried Owaza. "You are

not Tarzan of the Apes. I know you. You came with the four white men and the white woman to steal the gold from Tarzan's country, and then you stole it from your own friends."

The chief and the Waziri laughed. The ape-man smiled one of his slow smiles.

"The other was an impostor, Owaza," he said, "but *I* am Tarzan of the Apes, and I thank you for bringing my gold to me. Come," he said, "it is but a few more miles to my home," and the ape-man compelled Owaza to direct his carriers to bear the golden ingots to the Greystoke bungalow. There Tarzan fed the carriers and paid them, and the next morning sent them back to their own country. He sent Owaza with them, but not without a gift of value, accompanied with an admonition that the black never again return to Tarzan's country.

When they had departed, and Tarzan, Jane, and Korak were standing upon the veranda of the bungalow with Jad-bal-ja lying at their feet, the ape-man threw an arm about his mate's shoulders.

"I shall have to retract what I said about the gold of Opar not being for me, for you see before you a new fortune that has come all the way from the treasure vaults of Opar without any effort on my part."

"Now, if someone would only bring your diamonds back," laughed Jane.

"No chance of that," said Tarzan. "They are unquestionably at the bottom of the Ugogo River," and far away, upon the banks of the Ugogo, in the village of Obebe, the cannibal, Esteban Miranda lay in the filth of the hut that had been assigned to him, gloating over the fortune that he could never utilize as he entered upon a life of captivity that the stubbornness and superstition of Obebe had doomed him to undergo.

TARZAN
AND THE
ANT MEN

1

IN THE FILTH of a dark hut, in the village of Obebe the cannibal, upon the banks of the Ugogo, Esteban Miranda squatted upon his haunches and gnawed upon the remnants of a half-cooked fish. About his neck was an iron slave collar from which a few feet of rusty chain ran to a stout post set deep in the ground near the low entranceway that let upon the village street not far from the hut of Obebe himself.

For a year Esteban Miranda had been chained thus, like a dog, and like a dog he sometimes crawled through the low doorway of his kennel and basked in the sun outside. Two diversions had he; and only two. One was the persistent idea that he was Tarzan of the Apes, whom he had impersonated for so long and with such growing success that, like the good actor he was, he had come not only to act the part, but to live it—to *be* it. He *was*, as far as he was concerned, Tarzan of the Apes—there was no other—and he was Tarzan of the Apes to Obebe, too; but the village witch doctor still insisted that he was the river devil and as such, one to propitiate rather than to anger.

It had been this difference of opinion between the chief and the witch doctor that had kept Esteban Miranda from the fleshpots of the village, for Obebe had wanted to eat him, thinking him his old enemy the ape-man; but the witch doctor had aroused the superstitious fears of the villagers by half convincing them that their prisoner was the river devil masquerading as Tarzan, and, as such, dire disaster would descend upon the village were he harmed. The result of this difference between Obebe and the witch doctor had been to preserve the life of the Spaniard until the truth of one claim or the other was proved—if Esteban died a natural death he was Tarzan, the mortal, and Obebe the chief was vindicated; if he lived on forever, or mysteriously disappeared, the claim of the witch doctor would be accepted as gospel.

After he had learned their language and thus come to a realization of the accident of fate that had guided his destiny by so narrow a margin from the cooking pots of the cannibals he was less eager to proclaim himself Tarzan of the Apes. Instead he let drop mysterious suggestions that he was, indeed, none other than the river devil. The witch doctor was delighted, and everyone was fooled except Obebe, who was old and wise and did not believe in river devils, and the witch doctor who was old and wise and did not believe in them either, but realized that they were excellent things for his parishioners to believe in.

Esteban Miranda's other diversion, aside from secretly believing himself Tarzan, consisted in gloating over the bag of diamonds that Kraski the Russian had stolen from the ape-man, and that had fallen into the Spaniard's hands after he had murdered Kraski—the same bag of diamonds that the man had handed to Tarzan in the vaults beneath The Tower of Diamonds, in the Valley of The Palace of Diamonds, when he had rescued the Gomangani of the valley from the tyrannical oppression of the Bolgani.

For hours at a time Esteban Miranda sat in the dim light of his dirty kennel counting and fondling the brilliant stones. A thousand times had he weighed each one in an appraising palm, computing its value and translating it into such pleasures of the flesh as great wealth might buy for him in the capitals of the world. Mired in his own filth, feeding upon rotted scraps tossed to him by unclean hands, he yet possessed the wealth of a Croesus, and it was as Croesus he lived in his imaginings, his dismal hut changed into the pomp and circumstance of a palace by the scintillant gleams of the precious stones. At the sound of each approaching footstep he would hastily hide his fabulous fortune in the wretched loincloth that was his only garment, and once again become a prisoner in a cannibal hut.

And now, after a year of solitary confinement, came a third diversion, in the form of Uhha, the daughter of Khamis the witch doctor. Uhha was fourteen, comely and curious. For a year now she had watched the mysterious prisoner from a distance until, at last, familiarity had overcome her fears and one day she approached him as he lay in the sun outside his hut. Esteban, who had been watching her half-timorous advance, smiled encouragingly. He had not a friend among the villagers. If he could make but one his lot would be much the easier and freedom a step nearer. At last Uhha came to a halt a few steps from him. She was a child, ignorant and a savage; but she was a woman-child and Esteban Miranda knew women.

"I have been in the village of the chief Obebe for a year," he said haltingly, in the laboriously acquired language of his captors, "but never before did I guess that its walls held one so beautiful as you. What is your name?"

Uhha was pleased. She smiled broadly. "I am Uhha," she told him. "My father is Khamis the witch doctor."

It was Esteban who was pleased now. Fate, after rebuffing him for long, was at last kind. She had sent him one who, with cultivation, might prove a flower of hope indeed.

"Why have you never come to see me before?" asked Esteban.

"I was afraid," replied Uhha simply.

"Why?"

"I was afraid—" she hesitated.

"Afraid that I was the river devil and would harm you?" demanded the Spaniard, smiling.

"Yes," she said.

"Listen!" whispered Esteban; "but tell no one. I am the river devil, but I shall not harm you."

"If you are the river devil why then do you remain chained to a stake?" inquired Uhha. "Why do you not change yourself to something else and return to the river?"

"You wonder about that, do you?" asked Miranda, sparring for time that he might concoct a plausible answer.

"It is not only Uhha who wonders," said the girl. "Many others have asked the same question of late. Obebe asked it first and there was none to explain. Obebe says that you are Tarzan, the enemy of Obebe and his people; but my father Khamis says that you are the river devil, and that if you wanted to get away you would change yourself into a snake and crawl through the iron collar that is about your neck. And the people wonder why you do not, and many of them are commencing to believe that you are not the river devil at all."

"Come closer, beautiful Uhha," whispered Miranda, "that no other ears than yours may hear what I am about to tell you."

The girl came a little closer and leaned toward him where he squatted upon the ground.

"I am indeed the river devil," said Esteban, "and I come and go as I wish. At night, when the village sleeps, I am wandering through the waters of the Ugogo, but always I come back again. I am waiting, Uhha, to try the people of the village of Obebe that I may know which are my friends and which my enemies. Already have I learned that Obebe is no friend of mine, and I am not sure of Khamis. Had Khamis been a good friend he would have brought me fine food and beer to drink. I could go when I pleased, but I wait to see if there be one in the village of Obebe who will set me free. Thus may I learn which is my best friend. Should there be such a one, Uhha, fortune would smile upon him always, his every wish would be granted and he would live to a great age, for he would have nothing to fear from the river devil, who would help him in all his undertakings. But listen, Uhha, tell no one what I have told you! I shall wait a little longer and then if there be no such friend in the village of Obebe I shall return to my father and mother, the Ugogo, and destroy the people of Obebe. Not one shall remain alive."

The girl drew away, terrified. It was evident that she was much impressed.

"Do not be afraid," he reassured her. "I shall not harm you."

"But if you destroy all the people?" she demanded.

"Then, of course," he said, "I cannot help you; but let us hope that someone comes and sets me free so that I shall know that I have at least one good friend here. Now run along, Uhha, and remember that you must tell no one what I have told you."

She moved off a short distance and then returned.

"When will you destroy the village?" she asked.

"In a few days," he said.

Uhha, trembling with terror, ran quickly away in the direction of the hut of her father, Khamis, the witch doctor. Esteban Miranda smiled a satisfied smile and crawled back into his hole to play with his diamonds.

Khamis the witch doctor was not in his hut when Uhha his daughter, faint from fright, crawled into the dim interior. Nor were his wives. With their children, the latter were in the fields beyond the palisade, where Uhha should have been. And so it was that the girl had time for thought before she saw any of them again, with the result that she recalled distinctly, what she had almost forgotten in the first frenzy of fear, that the river devil had impressed upon her that she must reveal to no one the thing that he had told her.

And she had been upon the point of telling her father all! What dire calamity then would have befallen her? She trembled at the very suggestion of a fate so awful that she could not even imagine it. How close a call she had had! But what was she to do?

She lay huddled upon a mat of woven grasses, racking her poor, savage little brain for a solution of the immense problem that confronted her—the first problem that had ever entered her young life other than the constantly recurring one of how most easily to evade her share of the drudgery of the fields. Presently she sat suddenly erect, galvanized into statuesque rigidity by a thought engendered by the recollection of one of the river devil's remarks. Why had it not occurred to her before? Very plainly he had said, and he had repeated it, that if he were released he would know that he had at least one friend in the village of Obebe, and that whoever released him would live to a great age and have everything he wished for; but after a few minutes of thought Uhha drooped again. How was she, a little girl, to compass the liberation of the river devil alone?

"How, *baba*," she asked her father, when he had returned to the hut, later in the day, "does the river devil destroy those who harm him?"

"As the fish in the river, so are the ways of the river devil—without number," replied Khamis. "He might send the fish from the river and the game from the jungle and cause our crops to die. Then we should starve. He might bring the fire out of the sky at night and strike dead all the people of Obebe."

"And you think he may do these things to us, *baba*?"

"He will not harm Khamis, who saved him from the death that Obebe would have inflicted," replied the witch doctor.

Uhha recalled that the river devil had complained that

Khamis had not brought him good food nor beer, but she said nothing about that, although she realized that her father was far from being so high in the good graces of the river devil as he seemed to think he was. Instead, she took another tack.

"How can he escape," she asked, "while the collar is about his neck—who will remove it for him?"

"No one can remove it but Obebe, who carries in his pouch the bit of brass that makes the collar open," replied Khamis; "but the river devil needs no help, for when the time comes that he wishes to be free he has but to become a snake and crawl forth from the iron band about his neck. Where are you going, Uhha?"

"I am going to visit the daughter of Obebe," she called back over her shoulder.

The chief's daughter was grinding maize, as Uhha should have been doing. She looked up and smiled as the daughter of the witch doctor approached.

"Make no noise, Uhha," she cautioned, "for Obebe, my father, sleeps within." She nodded toward the hut. The visitor sat down and the two girls chatted in low tones. They spoke of their ornaments, their coiffures, of the young men of the village, and often, when they spoke of these, they giggled. Their conversation was not unlike that which might pass between two young girls of any race or clime. As they talked, Uhha's eyes often wandered toward the entrance to Obebe's hut and many times her brows were contracted in much deeper thought than their idle passages warranted.

"Where," she demanded suddenly, "is the armlet of copper wire that your father's brother gave you at the beginning of the last moon?"

Obebe's daughter shrugged. "He took it back from me," she replied, "and give it to the sister of his youngest wife."

Uhha appeared crestfallen. Could it be that she had coveted the copper bracelet? Her eyes closely scrutinized the person of her friend. Her brows almost met, so deeply was she thinking. Suddenly her face brightened.

"The necklace of many beads that your father took from the body of the warrior captured for the last feast!" she exclaimed. "You have not lost it?"

"No," replied her friend. "It is in the house of my father. When I grind maize it gets in my way and so I laid it aside."

"May I see it?" asked Uhha. "I will fetch it."

"No, you will awaken Obebe and he will be very angry," said the chief's daughter.

"I will not awaken him," replied Uhha, and started to crawl toward the hut's entrance.

Her friend tried to dissuade her. "I will fetch it as soon as *baba* has awakened," she told Uhha, but Uhha paid no attention to her and presently was crawling cautiously into the interior of the hut. Once within she waited silently until her eyes became accustomed to the dim light. Against the opposite wall of the hut Obebe lay sprawled upon a sleeping mat. He snored lustily. Uhha crept toward him. Her stealth was the stealth of Sheeta the leopard. Her heart was beating like the tom-tom when the dance is at its height. She feared that its noise and her rapid breathing would awaken the old chief, of whom she was as terrified as of the river devil; but Obebe snored on.

Uhha came close to him. Her eyes were accustomed now to the half-light of the hut's interior. At Obebe's side and half beneath his body she saw the chief's pouch. Cautiously she reached forth a trembling hand and laid hold upon it. She tried to draw it from beneath Obebe's weight. The sleeper stirred uneasily and Uhha drew back, terrified. Obebe changed his position and Uhha thought that he had awakened. Had she not been frozen with horror she would have rushed into headlong flight, but fortunately for her she could not move, and presently she heard Obebe resume his interrupted snoring; but her nerve was gone and she thought now only of escaping from the hut without being detected. She cast a last frightened glance at the chief to reassure herself that he still slept. Her eyes fell upon the pouch. Obebe had turned away from it and it now lay within her reach, free from the weight of his body.

She reached for it only to withdraw her hand suddenly. She turned away. Her heart was in her mouth. She swayed dizzily and then she thought of the river devil and of the possibilities for horrid death that lay within his power. Once more she reached for the pouch and this time she picked it up. Hurriedly opening it she examined the contents. The brass key was there. She recognized it because it was the only thing the purpose of which she was not familiar with. The collar, chain, and key had been taken from an Arab slave raider that Obebe had killed and eaten and as some of the old men of Obebe's village had worn similar bonds in the past, there was no difficulty in adapting it to its intended purpose when occasion demanded.

Uhha hastily closed the pouch and replaced it at Obebe's side. Then, clutching the key in a clammy palm, she crawled hurriedly toward the doorway.

That night, after the cooking fires had died to embers and been covered with earth and the people of Obebe had withdrawn into their huts, Esteban Miranda heard a stealthy movement at the entrance to his kennel. He listened intently. Someone was creeping into the interior—someone or something.

"Who is it?" demanded the Spaniard in a voice that he tried hard to keep from trembling.

"Hush!" responded the intruder in soft tones. "It is I, Uhha, the daughter of Khamis the witch doctor. I have come to set you free that you may know that you have a good friend in the village of Obebe and will, therefore, not destroy us."

Miranda smiled. His suggestion had borne fruit more quickly than he had dared to hope, and evidently the girl had obeyed his injunction to keep silent. In that matter he had reasoned wrongly, but of what moment that, since his sole aim in life—freedom—was to be accomplished. He had cautioned the girl to silence believing this the surest way to disseminate the word he had wished spread through the village, where, he was positive, it would have come to the ears of someone of the superstitious savages with the means to free him now that the incentive was furnished.

"And how are you going to free me?" demanded Miranda.

"See!" exclaimed Uhha. "I have brought the key to the collar about your neck."

"Good," cried the Spaniard. "Where is it?"

Uhha crawled closer to the man and handed him the key. Then she would have fled.

"Wait!" demanded the prisoner. "When I am free you must lead me forth into the jungle. Whoever sets me free must do this if he would win the favor of the river god."

Uhha was afraid, but she did not dare refuse. Miranda fumbled with the ancient lock for several minutes before it at last gave to the worn key the girl had brought. Then he snapped the padlock again and carrying the key with him crawled toward the entrance.

"Get me weapons," he whispered to the girl and Uhha departed through the shadows of the village street. Miranda knew that she was terrified but was confident that this very terror would prove the means of bringing her back to him with the weapons. Nor was he wrong, for scarce five minutes had elapsed before Uhha had returned with a quiver of arrows, a bow, and a stout knife.

"Now lead me to the gate," commanded Esteban.

Keeping out of the main street and as much in rear of the huts as possible Uhha led the fugitive toward the village gates. It surprised her a little that he, a river devil, should not know how to unlock and open them, for she had thought that river devils were all-wise; but she did as he bid and showed him how the great bar could be withdrawn, and helped him push the gates open enough to permit him to pass through. Beyond was the clearing that led to the river, on either hand rose the giants of the jungle. It was very dark out there and Esteban Miranda suddenly discovered that his newfound liberty had its drawbacks. To go forth alone at night into the dark, mysterious jungle filled him with a nameless dread.

Uhha drew back from the gates. She had done her part and saved the village from destruction. Now she wished to close the gates again and hasten back to the hut of her father, there to lie trembling in nervous excitement and terror against the morning that would reveal to the village the escape of the river devil.

Esteban reached forth and took her by the arm. "Come," he said, "and receive your reward."

Uhha shrank away from him. "Let me go!" she cried. "I am afraid."

But Esteban was afraid, too, and he had decided that the company of this little Negro girl would be better than no company at all in the depths of the lonely jungle. Possibly when daylight came he would let her go back to her people, but tonight he shuddered at the thought of entering the jungle without human companionship.

Uhha tried to tear herself free from his grasp. She struggled like a little lion cub, and at last would have raised her voice in a wild scream for help had not Miranda suddenly clapped his palm across her mouth, lifted her bodily from the ground and running swiftly across the clearing disappeared into the jungle.

Behind them the warriors of Obebe the cannibal slept in peaceful ignorance of the sudden tragedy that had entered the life of little Uhha and before them, far out in the jungle, a lion roared thunderously.

2

THREE PERSONS STEPPED from the veranda of Lord Greystoke's African bungalow and walked slowly toward the gate along a rose-embowered path that swung in a graceful curve through the well-ordered, though unpretentious, grounds surrounding the ape-man's rambling, one-story home. There were two men and a woman, all in khaki, the older man carrying a flier's helmet and a pair of goggles in one hand. He was smiling quietly as he listened to the younger man.

"You wouldn't be doing this now if mother were here," said the latter, "she would never permit it."

"I'm afraid you are right, my son," replied Tarzan; "but only this one flight alone and then I'll promise not to go up again until she returns. You have said yourself that I am an apt pupil and if you are any sort of an instructor you should have perfect confidence in me after having said that I was perfectly competent to pilot a ship alone. Eh, Meriem, isn't that true?" he demanded of the young woman.

She shook her head. "Like My Dear, I am always afraid for you, *mon pere,*" she replied. "You take such risks that one would think you considered yourself immortal. You should be more careful."

The younger man threw his arm about his wife's shoulders. "Meriem is right," he said; "you *should* be more careful, Father."

Tarzan shrugged. "If you and mother had your way my nerves and muscles would have atrophied long since. They were given me to use and I intend using them—with discretion. Doubtless I shall be old and useless soon enough, and long enough, as it is."

A child burst suddenly from the bungalow, pursued by a perspiring governess, and raced to Meriem's side.

"Muvver," he cried, "Dackie doe? Dackie doe?"

"Let him come along," urged Tarzan.

"Dare!" exclaimed the boy, turning triumphantly upon the governess; "Dackie do doe yalk!"

Out on the level plain, that stretched away from the bungalow to the distant jungle the verdant masses and deep shadows of which were vaguely discernible to the northwest, lay a biplane, in the shade of which lolled two Waziri warriors who had been trained by Korak, the son of Tarzan, in the duties of mechanicians, and, later, to pilot the ship themselves; a fact that had not been without weight in determining Tarzan of the Apes to perfect himself in the art of flying, since, as chief of the Waziri, it was not mete that the lesser warriors of his tribe should excel him in any particular. Adjusting his helmet and goggles Tarzan climbed into the cockpit.

"Better take me along," advised Korak.

Tarzan shook his head, smiling good-naturedly.

"Then one of the boys, here," urged his son. "You might develop some trouble that would force you to make a landing and if you have no mechanician along to make repairs what are you going to do?"

"Walk," replied the ape-man. "Turn her over, Andua!" he directed one of the blacks.

A moment later the ship was bumping over the veldt, from which, directly, it rose in smooth and graceful flight, circled, climbing to a greater altitude, and then sped away in an air line, while on the ground below the six strained their eyes until the wavering speck that it had dwindled to disappeared entirely from their view.

"Where do you suppose he is going?" asked Meriem.

Korak shook his head. "He isn't supposed to be going anywhere in particular," he replied, "just making his first practice flight alone. But, knowing him as I do, I wouldn't be surprised to learn that he had taken it into his head to fly to London and see mother."

"But he could never do it!" cried Meriem.

"No ordinary man could, with no more experience than he has had; but then, you will have to admit, father is no ordinary man."

For an hour and a half Tarzan flew without altering his course and without realizing the flight of time or the great distance he had covered, so delighted was he with the ease with which he controlled the ship, and so thrilled by this new power that gave him the freedom and mobility of the birds, the only denizens of his beloved jungle that he ever had had cause to envy.

Presently, ahead, he discerned a great basin, or what might better be described as a series of basins, surrounded by wooded hills, and immediately he recognized to the left of it the winding Ugogo; but the country of the basins was new to him and he was puzzled. He recognized, simultaneously, another fact; that he was over a hundred miles from home, and he determined to put back at once; but the mystery of the basins lured him on—he could not bring himself to return home without a closer view of them. Why was it that he had never come upon this country in his many wanderings? Why had he never even heard of it from the natives living within easy access to it? He dropped to a lower level the better to inspect the basins, which now appeared to him as a series of shallow craters of long extinct volcanoes. He saw forests, lakes and rivers, the very existence of which he had never dreamed, and then quite suddenly he discovered a solution of the seeming mystery that there should exist in a country with which he was familiar so large an area of which he had been in total ignorance, in common with the natives of the country surrounding it. He recognized it now—the so-called Great Thorn Forest. For years he had been familiar with that impenetrable thicket that was supposed to cover a vast area of territory into which only the smallest of animals might venture, and now he saw it was but a relatively narrow fringe encircling a pleasant, habitable country, but a fringe so cruelly barbed as to have forever protected the secret that it held from the eyes of man.

Tarzan determined to circle the long hidden land of mystery before setting the nose of his ship toward home, and, to obtain a closer view, he accordingly dropped nearer the earth. Beneath him was a great forest and beyond that an open veldt that ended at the foot of precipitous, rocky hills. He saw that absorbed as he had been in the strange, new country he had permitted the plane to drop too low. Coincident with the realization and before he could move the control within his hand, the ship touched the leafy crown of some old monarch of the jungle, veered, swung completely around and crashed downward through the foliage amidst the snapping and rending of broken branches and the splintering of its own woodwork. Just for a second this noise and then silence.

Along a forest trail slouched a mighty creature, manlike in its physical attributes, yet vaguely inhuman; a great brute that walked erect upon two feet and carried a club in one horny, calloused hand. Its long hair fell, unkempt, about its shoulders, and there was hair upon its chest and a little upon its arms and legs, though no more than is found upon many males of civilized races. A strip of hide about its waist supported the ends of a narrow G-string as well as numerous rawhide strands to the lower ends of which were fastened round stones from one to two inches in diameter. Close to each stone were attached several small feathers, for the most part of brilliant hues. The strands supporting the stones being fastened to the belt at intervals of one to two inches and the strands themselves being about eighteen inches long the whole formed a skeleton skirt, fringed with round stones and feathers, that fell almost to the creature's knees. Its large feet were bare and its white skin tanned to a light brown by exposure to the elements. The illusion of great size was suggested more by the massiveness of the shoulders and the development of the muscles of the back and arms than by height, though the creature measured close to six feet. Its face was massive, with a broad nose, and a wide, full-lipped mouth; the eyes, of normal size, were set beneath heavy, beetling brows, topped by a wide, low forehead. As it walked it flapped its large, flat ears and occasionally moved rapidly portions of its skin on various parts of its head and body to dislodge flies, as you have seen a horse do with the muscles along its sides and flanks.

It moved silently, its dark eyes constantly on the alert, while the flapping ears were often momentarily stilled as the woman listened for sounds of quarry or foe.

She stopped now, her ears bent forward, her nostrils, expanded, sniffing the air. Some scent or sound that our dead sensitory organs could not have perceived had attracted her attention. Warily she crept forward along the trail until, at a turning, she saw before her a figure lying face downward in the path. It was Tarzan of the Apes. Unconscious he lay while above him the splintered wreckage of his plane was wedged among the branches of the great tree that had caused its downfall.

The woman gripped her club more firmly and approached. Her expression reflected the puzzlement the discovery of this strange creature had engendered in her elementary mind, but she evinced no fear. She walked directly to the side of the prostrate man, her club raised to strike; but something stayed her hand. She knelt beside him and fell to examining his clothing. She turned him over on his back and placed one of her ears above his heart. Then she fumbled with the front of his shirt for a moment and suddenly taking it in her two mighty hands tore it apart. Again she listened, her ear this time against his naked flesh. She arose and looked about, sniffing and listening, then she stooped and lifting the body of the ape-man she swung it lightly across one of her broad shoulders and continued along the trail in the direction she had been going. The trail, winding through the forest, broke presently from the leafy shade into an open, parklike strip of rolling land that stretched at the foot of rocky hills, and, crossing this, disappeared within the entrance of a narrow gorge, eroded by the elements from the native sandstone fancifully as the capricious architecture of a dream, among whose grotesque domes and miniature rocks the woman bore her burden.

A half mile from the entrance to the gorge the trail entered a roughly circular amphitheater, the precipitous walls of which were pierced by numerous cave-mouths before several of which squatted creatures similar to that which bore Tarzan into this strange, savage environment.

As she entered the amphitheater all eyes were upon her, for their large, sensitive ears had warned them of her approach long before she had arrived within scope of their vision. Immediately they beheld her and her burden several of them arose and came to meet her. All females, these, similar in physique and scant garb to the captor of the ape-man, though differing in proportions and physiognomy as do the individuals of all races differ from their fellows. They spoke no words nor uttered any sounds, nor did she whom they approached, as she moved straight along her way which was evidently directed toward one of the cave-mouths, but she gripped her bludgeon firmly and swung it to and fro, while her eyes, beneath their scowling brows, kept sullen surveillance upon the every move of her fellows.

She had approached close to the cave, which was quite evidently her destination, when one of those who followed her darted suddenly forward and clutched at Tarzan. With the quickness of a cat the woman dropped her burden, turned upon the temerarious one, and swinging her bludgeon with lightninglike celerity felled her with a heavy blow to the head, and then, standing astride the prostrate Tarzan, she glared about her like a lioness at bay, questioning dumbly who would be next to attempt to wrest her prize from her; but the others slunk back to their caves, leaving the vanquished one lying, unconscious, in the hot sand and the victor to shoulder her burden, undisputed, and continue her way to her cave, where she dumped the ape-man unceremoniously upon the ground just within the shadow of the entranceway, and squatting beside him, facing outward that she might not be taken unaware by any of her fellows, she proceeded to examine her find minutely. Tarzan's clothing either piqued her curiosity or aroused her disgust, for she began almost immediately to divest him of it, and having had no former experience of buttons and buckles, she tore it away by main force. The heavy, cordovan boots troubled her for a moment, but finally their seams gave way to her powerful muscles.

Only the diamond-studded, golden locket that had been his mother's she left untouched upon its golden chain about his neck.

For a moment she sat contemplating him and then she arose and tossing him once more to her shoulder she walked toward the center of the amphitheater, the greater portion of which was covered by low buildings constructed of enormous slabs of stone, some set on edge to form the walls while others, lying across these, constituted the roofs. Joined end to end, with occasional wings at irregular intervals running out into the amphitheater, they enclosed a rough oval of open ground that formed a large courtyard.

The several outer entrances to the buildings were closed with two slabs of stone, one of which, standing on edge, covered the aperture, while the other, leaning against the first upon the outside, held it securely in place against any efforts that might be made to dislodge it from the interior of the building.

To one of these entrances the woman carried her unconscious captive, laid him on the ground, removed the slabs that closed the aperture and dragged him into the dim and gloomy interior, where she deposited him upon the floor and clapped her palms together sharply three times with the result that there presently slouched into the room six or seven children of both sexes, who ranged in age from one year to sixteen or seventeen. The very youngest of them walked easily and seemed as fit to care for itself as the young of most lower orders at a similar age. The girls, even the youngest, were armed with clubs, but the boys carried no weapons either of offense or defense. At sight of them the woman pointed to Tarzan, struck her head with her clenched fist and then gestured toward herself, touching her breast several times with a calloused thumb. She made several other motions with her hands, so eloquent of meaning that one entirely unfamiliar with her sign language could almost guess their purport, then she turned and left the building, replaced the stones before the entrance, and slouched back to her cave, passing, apparently without notice, the woman she had recently struck down and who was now rapidly regaining consciousness.

As she took her seat before her cave-mouth her victim suddenly sat erect, rubbed her head for a moment and then, after looking about dully, rose unsteadily to her feet. For just an instant she swayed and staggered, but presently she mastered herself, and with only a glance at the author of her hurt moved off in the direction of her own cave. Before she had reached it her attention, together with that of all the others of this strange community, or at least of all those who were in the open, was attracted by the sound of approaching footsteps. She halted in her tracks, her great ears up-pricked, listening, her eyes directed toward the trail leading up from the valley. The others were similarly watching and listening and a moment later their vigil was rewarded by sight of another of their kind as she appeared in the entrance of the amphitheater. A huge creature this, even larger than she who captured the ape-man—broader and heavier, though little, if any, taller—carrying upon one shoulder the carcass of an antelope and upon the other the body of a creature that might have been half-human and half-beast, yet, assuredly, not entirely either the one or the other.

The antelope was dead, but not so the other creature. It wriggled weakly—its futile movements could not have been termed struggles—as it hung, its middle across the bare brown shoulder of its captor, its arms and legs dangling limply before and behind, either in partial unconsciousness or in the paralysis of fear.

The woman who had brought Tarzan to the amphitheater rose and stood before the entrance of her cave. We shall have to call her The First Woman, for she had no name; in the muddy convolutions of her sluggish brain she never had sensed even the need for a distinctive specific appellation and among her fellows she was equally nameless, as were they, and so, that we may differentiate her from the others, we shall call her The First Woman, and, similarly, we shall know the creature that she felled with her bludgeon as The Second Woman, and she who now entered the amphitheater with a burden upon each shoulder, as The Third Woman. So The First Woman rose, her eyes fixed upon the newcomer, her ears up-pricked. And The Second Woman rose, and all the others that were in sight, and all stood glaring at The Third Woman who moved steadily along with her burden, her watchful eyes ever upon the menacing figures of her fellows. She was very large, this Third Woman, so for a while the others only stood and glared at her, but presently The First Woman took a step forward and turning, cast a long look at The Second Woman, and then she took another step forward and stopped and looked again at The Second Woman, and this time she pointed at herself, at The Second Woman, and then at The Third Woman who now quickened her pace in the direction of her cave, for she understood the menace in the attitude of The First Woman. The Second Woman understood, too, and moved forward now with The First Woman. No word was spoken, no sound issued from those savage lips; lips that never had parted to a smile; lips that never had known laughter, nor ever would.

As the two approached her The Third Woman dropped her spoils in a heap at her feet, gripped her cudgel more firmly and prepared to defend her rights. The others, brandishing their own weapons, charged her. The remaining women were now but onlookers, their hands stayed, perhaps, by some ancient tribal custom that gauged the number of attackers by the quantity of spoil, awarding the right of contest to whoever initiated it. When The First Woman had been attacked by The Second Woman the others had all held aloof, for it had been The Second Woman that had advanced first to try conclusively for the possession of Tarzan. And now The Third Woman had come with two prizes, and since The First Woman and The Second Woman had stepped out to meet her the others had held back.

As the three women came together it seemed inevitable that The Third Woman would go down beneath the bludgeons of the others, but she warded both blows with the skill and celerity of a trained fencer and stepping quickly into the opening she had dealt The First Woman a terrific blow upon the head that stretched her motionless upon the ground, where a little pool of blood and brains attested the terrible strength of the wielder of the bludgeon the while it marked the savage, unmourned passing of The First Woman.

And now The Third Woman could devote her undivided attention to The Second Woman, but The Second Woman seeing the fate of her companion did not wait to discuss the matter further, and instead of remaining to continue the fight she broke and ran for the cave, while the creature that The Third Woman had been carrying along with the carcass of the antelope apparently believing that it saw a chance for escape while its captor was engaged with her assailants was crawling stealthily away in the opposite direction. Its attempt might have proved successful had the fight lasted longer; but the skill and ferocity of The Third Woman had terminated the whole thing in a matter of seconds, and now, turning about, she espied a portion of her prey seeking to escape and sprang quickly after it. As she did so The Second Woman wheeled and darted back to seize the carcass of the antelope, while the crawling fugitive leaped to its feet and raced swiftly down the trail that led through the mouth of the amphitheater toward the valley.

As the thing rose to its feet it became apparent that it was a man, or at least a male, and evidently of the same species as the women of this peculiar race, though much shorter and of proportionately lighter build. It stood about five feet in height, had a few hairs on its upper lip and chin, a much lower forehead than the women, and its eyes were set closer together. Its legs were much longer and more slender than those of the women, who seemed to have been designed for strength rather than speed, and the result was that it was apparent from the start that The Third Woman could have no hope of overhauling her escaping quarry, and then it was that the utility of the strange skirt of thongs and pebbles and feathers became apparent. Seizing one of the thongs she disengaged it easily and quickly from the girdle that supported them about her hips, and grasping the end of the thong between a thumb and forefinger she whirled it rapidly in a vertical plane until the feathered pebble at its end was moving with great rapidity—then she let go the thong. Like an arrow the missile sped toward the racing fugitive, the pebble, a fairly good-sized one as large as an English walnut, struck the man upon the back of his head dropping him, unconscious, to the ground. Then The Third Woman turned upon The Second Woman who, by this time, had seized the antelope, and brandishing her bludgeon bore down upon her. The Second Woman, possessing more courage than good sense, prepared to defend her stolen flesh and took her stand, her bludgeon ready. As The Third Woman bore down upon her, a veritable mountain of muscle, The Second Woman met her with threatening cudgel, but so terrific was the blow dealt by her mighty adversary that her weapon, splintered, was swept from her hands and she found herself at the mercy of the creature she would have robbed. Evidently she knew how much of mercy she might expect. She did not fall upon her knees in an attitude of supplication—not she. Instead she tore a handful of the pebble-missiles from her girdle in a vain attempt to defend herself. Futilest of futilities! The huge, destroying bludgeon had not even paused, but swinging in a great circle fell crushingly upon the skull of The Second Woman.

The Third Woman paused and looked about questioningly as if to ask: "Is there another who wishes to take from me my antelope or my man? If so, let her step forward." But no one accepted the gage and presently the woman turned and walked back to the prostrate man. Roughly she jerked him to his feet and shook him. Consciousness was returning slowly and he tried to stand. His efforts, however, were a failure and so she threw him across her shoulder again and walked back to the dead antelope, which she flung to the opposite shoulder and, continuing her interrupted way to her cave, dumped the two unceremoniously to the ground. Here, in the cave-mouth, she kindled a fire, twirling a fire stick dexterously amidst dry tinder in a bit of hollowed wood, and cutting generous strips from the carcass of the antelope ate ravenously. While she was thus occupied the man regained consciousness and sitting up looked about, dazed. Presently his nostrils caught the aroma of the cooking meat and he pointed at it. The woman handed him the rude stone knife that she had tossed back to the floor of the cave and motioned toward the meat. The man seized the implement and was soon broiling a generous cut above the fire. Half-burned and half-raw as it was he ate it with seeming relish, and as he ate the woman sat and watched him. He was not much to look at, yet she may have thought him handsome. Unlike the women, who wore no ornaments, the man had bracelets and anklets as well as a necklace of teeth and pebbles, while in his hair, which was wound into a small knot above his forehead, were thrust several wooden skewers ten or twelve inches long, which protruded in various directions in a horizontal plane.

When the man had eaten his fill the woman rose and seizing him by the hair dragged him into the cave. He scratched and bit at her, trying to escape, but he was no match for his captor.

Upon the floor of the amphitheater, before the entrances to the caves, lay the bodies of The First Woman and The Second Woman and black upon them swarmed the circling scavengers of the sky. Ska, the vulture, was first always to the feast.

3

WITHIN THE DIM interior of the strange rocky chamber where he had been so ruthlessly deposited, Tarzan immediately became the center of interest to the several Alali young that crowded about him. They examined him carefully, turned him over, pawed him, pinched him, and at last one of the young males, attracted by the golden locket removed it from the ape-man's neck and placed it about his own. Lowest, perhaps, in the order of human evolution nothing held their interest overlong, with the result that they soon tired of Tarzan and trooped out into the sunlit courtyard, leaving the ape-man to regain consciousness as best he could, or not at all. It was immaterial to them which he did. Fortunately for the Lord of the Jungle the fall through the roof of the forest had been broken by the fortuitous occurrence of supple branches directly in the path of his descent, with the happy result that he suffered only from a slight concussion of the brain. Already he was slowly regaining consciousness, and not long after the Alali young had left him his eyes opened, rolled dully inspecting the dim interior of his prison, and closed again. His breathing was normal and when again he opened his eyes it was as though he had emerged from a deep and natural slumber, the only reminder of his accident being a dull aching of the head.

Sitting up, he looked about him, his eyes gradually accustoming themselves to the dim light of the chamber. He found himself in a rude shelter constructed of great slabs of rock. A single opening led into what appeared to be another similar chamber the interior of which, however, was much lighter than that in which he lay. Slowly he rose to his feet and crossed to the opening. Across the second chamber he beheld another doorway leading into the fresh air and the sunshine. Except for filthy heaps of dead grasses on the floor both the rooms were unfurnished and devoid of any suggestion that they were utilized as places of human habitation. From the second doorway, to which he crossed, he looked out upon a narrow courtyard walled by great slabs of stone, the lower ends of which, embedded in the ground, caused them to remain erect. Here he saw the young Alali squatting about, some in the sun, others in the shadow. Tarzan looked at them in evident puzzlement. What were they? What was this place in which he was, all too evidently, incarcerated? Were these his keepers or were they his fellow prisoners? How had he come hither?

Running his fingers through his shock of black hair in a characteristic gesture of perplexity, he shook his head. He recalled the unfortunate termination of the flight; he even remembered falling through the foliage of the great tree; but beyond that all was blank. He stood for a moment examining the Alali, who were all unconscious of his near presence or his gaze upon them, and then he stepped boldly out into the courtyard before them, as a lion, fearless, ignores the presence of jackals.

Immediately they saw him, they rose and clustered about him, the girls pushing the boys aside and coming boldly close, and Tarzan spoke to them, first in one native dialect and then in another, but they seemed not to understand, for they made no reply, and then, as a last resort, he addressed them in the primitive language of the great apes, the languages of Manu the monkey, the first language that Tarzan had learned when, as a babe, he suckled at the hairy breast of Kala, the she-ape, and listened to the gutturals of the savage members of the tribe of Kerchak; but again his auditors made no response—at least no audible response, though they moved their hands and shoulders and bodies, and jerked their heads in what the ape-man soon recognized as a species of sign language, nor did they utter any vocal sounds that might indicate that they were communicating with one another through the medium of a spoken language. Presently they again lost interest in the newcomer and resumed their indolent lounging about the walls of the courtyard while Tarzan paced to and fro its length, his keen eye searching for whatever avenue of escape chance might provide, and he saw it in the height of the walls, to the top of which a long, running jump would take his outstretched fingers, he was sure; but not yet—he must wait for darkness to shield his attempt from those within the enclosure and those without. And as darkness approached the actions of the other occupants of the courtyard became noticeably altered; they walked back and forth, constantly passing and repassing the entrance to the shelter at the end of the courtyard, and occasionally entering the first room and often passing to the second room where they listened for a moment before the great slab that closed the outer aperture; then back into the courtyard again and back and forth in restless movement. Finally one stamped a foot upon the ground and this was taken up by the others until, in regular cadence, the thud, thud, thud of their naked feet must have been audible for some distance beyond the confines of their narrow prison yard.

Whatever this procedure might have been intended to accomplish, nothing, apparently, resulted, and presently one of the girls, her sullen face snarling in anger, seized her bludgeon more firmly in her two hands and stepping close to one of the walls began pounding violently upon one of its huge stone slabs. Instantly the other girls followed her example, while the young males continued beating time with their heels.

For a while Tarzan was puzzled for an explanation of their behavior, but it was his own stomach that at last suggested an answer—the creatures were hungry and were attempting to attract the attention of their jailers; and their method of doing so suggested something else, as well, something of which his past brief experience with them had already partially convinced him—the creatures were without speech, even totally unvocal, perhaps.

The girl who had started the pounding upon the wall suddenly stopped and pointed at Tarzan. The others looked at him and then back at her, whereupon she pointed at her bludgeon and then at Tarzan again, after which she acted out a little pantomime, very quickly, very briefly, but nonetheless realistically. The pantomime depicted the bludgeon falling upon

Tarzan's head, following which the pantomimist, assisted by her fellows, devoured the ape-man. The bludgeons ceased to fall upon the wall; the heels no longer smote the earth; the assemblage was interested in the new suggestion. They eyed Tarzan hungrily. The mother who should have brought them food, The First Woman, was dead. They did not know this; all they knew was that they were hungry and that The First Woman had brought them no food since the day before. They were not cannibals. Only in the last stages of hunger would they have devoured one another, even as shipwrecked sailors of civilized races have been known to do; but they did not look upon the stranger as one of their own kind. He was as unlike them as some of the other creatures that The First Woman had brought them to feed upon. It was no more wrong to devour him than it would have been to devour an antelope. The thought, however, would not have occurred to most of them; the older girl it was who had suggested it to them, nor would it have occurred to her had there been other food, for she knew that he had not been brought her for that purpose—he had been brought as the mate of The First Woman, who in common with the other women of this primitive race hunted a new mate each season among the forests and the jungles where the timid males lived their solitary lives except for the brief weeks that they were held captive in the stone corrals of the dominant sex, and where they were treated with great brutality and contempt even by the children of their temporary spouses.

Sometimes they managed to escape, though rarely, but eventually they were turned loose, since it was easier to hunt a new one the following season than to feed one in captivity for a whole year. There was nothing approximating love in the family relations of these savage half-brutes. The young, conceived without love, knowing not their own fathers, possessed not even an elemental affection for one another, nor for any other living thing. A certain tie bound them to their savage mothers, at whose breasts they suckled for a few short months and to whom they looked for food until they were sufficiently developed to go forth into the forests and make their own kills or secure whatever other food bountiful Nature provided for them.

Somewhere between the ages of fifteen and seventeen the young males were liberated and chased into the forest, after which their mothers knew them not from any other male and at a similar age the females were taken to the maternal cave, where they lived, accompanying their mothers on the daily hunt, until they had succeeded in capturing a first mate. After that they took up their abodes in separate caves and the tie between parent and child was cut as cleanly as though it never had existed, and they might, the following season, even become rivals for the same man, or at any time quarrel to the death over the spoils of the chase.

The building of the stone shelters and corrals in which the children and the males were kept was the only community activity in which the women engaged and this work they were compelled to do alone, since the men would have escaped into the forest at the first opportunity had they been released from the corrals to take part in the work of construction, while the children as soon as they had become strong enough to be of any assistance would doubtless have done likewise; but the great shes were able to accomplish their titanic labors alone.

Equipped by nature with mighty frames and thews of steel they quarried the great slabs from a sidehill overlooking the amphitheater, slid them to the floor of the little valley and pulled and pushed them into position by main strength and awkwardness, as the homely saying of our forefathers has it.

Fortunately for them it was seldom necessary to add to the shelters and corrals already built since the high rate of mortality among the females ordinarily left plenty of vacant enclosures for maturing girls. Jealousy, greed, the hazards of the hunt, the contingencies of intertribal wars all took heavy toll among the adult shes. Even the despised male, fighting for his freedom, sometimes slew his captor.

The hideous life of the Alalus was the natural result of the unnatural reversal of sex dominance. It is the province of the male to initiate love and by his masterfulness to inspire first respect, then admiration in the breast of the female he seeks to attract. Love itself developed after these other emotions. The gradually increasing ascendency of the female Alalus over the male eventually prevented the emotions of respect and admiration for the male from being aroused, with the result that love never followed.

Having no love for her mate and having become a more

powerful brute, the savage Alalus woman soon came to treat the members of the opposite sex with contempt and brutality with the result that the power, or at least the desire, to initiate love ceased to exist in the heart of the male—he could not love a creature he feared and hated, he could not respect or admire the unsexed creatures that the Alali women had become, and so he fled into the forests and the jungles and there the dominant females hunted him lest their race perish from the earth.

It was the offspring of such savage and perverted creatures that Tarzan faced, fully aware of their cannibalistic intentions. The males did not attack him at once, but busily engaged themselves in fetching dry grass and small pieces of wood from one of the covered chambers, and while the three girls, one of them scarce seven years of age, approached the ape-man warily with ready bludgeons, they prepared a fire over which they expected soon to be broiling juicy cuts from the strange creature that their hairy dam had brought them.

One of the males, a lad of sixteen, held back, making excited signs with hands, head and body. He appeared to be trying to dissuade or prevent the girls from the carrying-out of their plan, he even appealed to the other boys for backing, but they merely glanced at the girls and continued their culinary preparations. At last however, as the girls were deliberately approaching the ape-man he placed himself directly in their path and attempted to stop them. Instantly the three little demons swung their bludgeons and sprang forward to destroy him. The boy dodged, plucked several of the feathered stones from his girdle and flung them at his assailants. So swift and so accurate did the missiles speed that two girls dropped, howling, to the ground. The third missed, striking one of the other boys on the temple, killing him instantly. He was the youth who had stolen Tarzan's locket, which, being like all his fellow males a timid creature, he had kept continually covered by a palm since the ape-man's return to consciousness had brought him out into the courtyard among them.

The older girl, nothing daunted, leaped forward, her face hideous in a snarl of rage. The boy cast another stone at her and then turned and ran toward the ape-man. What reception he expected he himself probably did not know. Perhaps it was the recrudescence of a long dead emotion of fellowship that prompted him to place himself at Tarzan's side—possibly Tarzan himself in whom loyalty to kind was strong had inspired this reawakening of an atrophied soul-sense. However that may be the fact remains that the boy came and stood at Tarzan's side while the girl, evidently sensing danger to herself in this strange, new temerity of her brother, advanced more cautiously.

In signs she seemed to be telling him what she would do to him if he did not cease to interpose his weak will between her and her gastronomic desires; but he signed back at her defiantly and stood his ground. Tarzan reached over and patted him on the back, smiling. The boy bared his teeth horribly, but it seemed evident that he was trying to return the ape-man's smile. And now the girl was almost upon them. Tarzan was quite at a loss as to how to proceed against her. His natural chivalry restrained him from attacking her and made it seem most repellant to injure her even in self-preservation; but he knew that before he was done with her he might even possibly have to kill her and so, while looking for an alternative, he steeled himself for the deed he loathed; but yet he hoped to escape without that.

The Third Woman, conducting her new mate from the cave to the corral where she would keep him imprisoned for a week or two, had heard the cadenced beating of naked heels and heavy bludgeons arising from the corral of The First Woman and immediately guessed their import. The welfare of the offspring of The First Woman concerned her not as an individual. Community instinct, however, prompted her to release them that they might search for food and their services not be lost to the tribe through starvation. She would not feed them, of course, as they did not belong to her, but she would open their prison gate and turn them loose to fend for themselves, to find food or not to find it, to survive or to perish according to the inexorable law of the survival of the fittest.

But The Third Woman took her time. Her powerful fingers entangled in the hair of her snarling spouse she dragged the protesting creature to her corral, removed the great slab from before the entrance, pushed the man roughly within, accelerating his speed with a final kick, replaced the slab and turned leisurely toward the nearby corral of The First Woman.

Removing the stone door she passed through the two chambers and entered the corral at the moment that the oldest girl was advancing upon Tarzan. Pausing by the entranceway she struck her bludgeon against the stone wall of the shelter, evidently to attract the attention of those within the corral. Instantly all looked in her direction. She was the first adult female, other than their own dam, that the children of The First Woman had seen. They shrunk from her in evident terror. The youth at Tarzan's side slunk behind the ape-man, nor did Tarzan wonder at their fear. The Third Woman was the first adult Alalus he had seen, since all of the time that he had been in the hands of The First Woman he had been unconscious.

The girl who had been threatening him with her great club seemed now to have forgotten him, and instead stood with snarling face and narrowed eyes confronting the newcomer. Of all the children she seemed the least terrified.

The ape-man scrutinized the huge, brutish female standing at the far end of the corral with her savage eyes upon him. She had not seen him before as she had been in the forest hunting at the time that The First Woman had brought her prize back to the amphitheater. She had not known that The First Woman had any male in her corral other than her own spawn. Here, indeed, was a prize. She would remove him to her own corral. With this idea in mind, and knowing that, unless he succeeded in dodging past her and reaching the entranceway ahead of her, he could not escape her, she moved very slowly toward him, ignoring now the other occupants of the corral.

Tarzan, not guessing her real purpose, thought that she was about to attack him as a dangerous alien in the sacred precincts of her home. He viewed her great bulk, her enormous muscular development and the huge bludgeon swinging in her hamlike hand and compared them with his own defenseless nakedness.

To the jungle-born flight from useless and uneven combat carries with it no stigma of cowardice, and not only was Tarzan of the Apes jungle-born and jungle-raised, but the stripping of his clothes from him had now, as always before, stripped also away the thin and unnatural veneer of his civilization. It was, then, a savage beast that faced the oncoming Alalus woman—a cunning beast as well as a powerful one—a beast that knew when to fight and when to flee.

Tarzan cast a quick glance behind him. There crouched the Alalus lad, trembling in fear. Beyond was the rear wall of the corral, one of the great stone slabs of which tilted slightly outward. Slow is the mind of man, slower his eye by comparison with the eye and the mind of the trapped beast seeking escape. So quick was the ape-man that he was gone before The Third Woman had guessed that he was contemplating flight, and with him had gone the eldest Alalus boy.

Wheeling, all in a single motion Tarzan had swung the young male to his shoulder, leaped swiftly the few paces that had separated him from the rear wall of the corral, and, catlike, run up the smooth surface of the slightly tilted slab until his fingers closed upon the top, drawn himself over without a single backward glance, dropped the youth to the ground upon the opposite side, following him so quickly that they alighted almost together. Then he glanced about. For the first time he saw the natural amphitheater and the caves before several of which women still squatted. It would soon be dark. The sun was dropping behind the crest of the western hills. Tarzan saw but a single avenue of escape—the opening at the lower end of the amphitheater through which the trail led down into the valley and the forest below. Toward this he ran, followed by the youth.

Presently a woman, sitting before the entrance of her cave, saw him. Seizing her cudgel she leaped to her feet and gave immediate chase. Attracted by her another and another took up the pursuit, until five or six of them thundered along the trail.

The youth, pointing the way, raced swiftly ahead of the ape-man, but swift as he was, he could not outdistance the lithe muscles that had so often in the past carried their master safely from the swift rush of a maddened Numa, or won him a meal against the fleetness of Bara the deer. The heavy, lumbering women behind them had no chance of overhauling this swift pair if they were to depend entirely upon speed, but that they had no intention of doing. They had their stone missiles with which, almost from birth, they had practiced until approximate perfection was attained by each in casting them at either stationary or moving targets. But it was growing dark, the trail twisted and turned and the speed of the quarry made them elusive marks at which to cast an accurate missile that would be so timed as to stun rather than to kill. Of course more often than not a missile intended to stun did actually kill, but the quarry must take that chance. Instinct warned the women against killing the males, though it did not warn them against treating them with the utmost brutality. Had Tarzan realized why the women were pursuing him he would have run even faster than he did, and when the missiles began to fly past his head perhaps he did accelerate his speed a trifle.

Soon the ape-man reached the forest and as though he had dissolved into thin air disappeared from the astonished view of his pursuers, for now, indeed, was he in his own element. While they looked for him upon the ground he swung swiftly through the lower terraces, keeping in view the Alalus boy racing along the trail beneath him.

But with the man escaped, the women stopped and turned back toward their caves. The youth they did not want. For two or three years he would roam the forests unmolested by his own kind, and if he escaped the savage beasts and the spears and arrows of the ant people he would come to man's estate and be fair prey for any of the great shes during the mating season. For the time being, at least, he would lead a comparatively safe and happy existence.

His chances of survival had been materially lessened by his early escape into the forest. Had The First Woman lived she would have kept him safely within the walls of her corral for another year at least, when he would have been better fitted to cope with the dangers and emergencies of the savage life of the forest and the jungle.

The boy, his keen ears telling him that the women had given up the pursuit, halted and looked back for the strange creature that had freed him from the hated corral, but he could see only a short distance through the darkness of the growing forest night. The stranger was not in sight. The youth pricked up his great ears and listened intently. There was no sound of human footsteps other than the rapidly diminishing ones of the retreating women. There were other sounds, however, unfamiliar forest sounds that filled his muddy brain with vague terrors—sounds that came from the surrounding underbrush; sounds that came from the branches above his head, and, too, there were terrifying odors.

Darkness, complete and impenetrable, had closed in upon him with a suddenness that left him trembling. He could almost feel it weighing down upon him, crushing him and at the same time leaving him exposed to nameless terrors. He looked about him and could see naught, so that it seemed to him that he was without eyes, and being without a voice he could not call out either to frighten his enemies or attract the attention of the strange creature that had befriended him, and whose presence had so strangely aroused in his own breast an inexplicable emotion—a pleasurable emotion. He could not explain it; he had no word for it who had no word for anything, but he felt it and it still warmed his bosom and he wished in his muddy way that he could make a noise that would attract that strange creature to him again. He was lonely and much afraid.

A crackling of the bushes nearby aroused him to new and more intimate terror. Something large was approaching through the black night. The youth stood with his back against a great tree. He dared not move. He sniffed but what movement of the air there was took course from him in the direction of the thing that was creeping upon him out of the terrible forest, and so he could not identify it; but his instinct told him that the creature had identified him and was doubtless creeping closer to leap upon him and devour him.

He knew naught of lions, unless instinct carries with it a picture of the various creatures of which the denizens of the wild are instinctively afraid. In all his life he had never been outside the corral of The First Woman and as his people are without speech his dam could have told him nothing of the outside world, yet when the lion roared he knew that it was a lion.

4

Esteban Miranda, clinging tightly to the wrist of little Uhha, crouched in the darkness of another forest twenty miles away and trembled as the thunderous notes of another lion reverberated through the jungle.

The girl felt the trembling of the body of the big man at her side and turned contemptuously upon him.

"You are not the river devil!" she cried. "You are afraid. You are not even Tarzan, for Khamis, my father, has told me that Tarzan is afraid of nothing. Let me go that I may climb a tree—only a coward or a fool would stand here dead with terror waiting for the lion to come and devour him. Let me go, I say!" and she attempted to wrench her wrist free from his grasp.

"Shut up!" he hissed. "Do you want to attract the lion to us?" But her words and struggles had aroused him from his paralysis and stooping he seized her and lifted her until she could grasp the lower branches of the tree beneath which they stood. Then, as she clambered to safety, he swung himself easily to her side.

Presently, higher up among the branches, he found a safer and more comfortable resting place, and there the two settled down to await the coming of the dawn, while below them Numa the lion prowled for a while, coughing and grunting, and occasionally voicing a deep roar that shook the jungle.

When daylight came at last the two, exhausted by a sleepless night, slipped to the ground. The girl would have delayed, hoping that the warriors of Obebe might overtake them; but the man harbored a fear rather than a hope of the same contingency and was, therefore, for hastening on as rapidly as possible that he might put the greatest possible distance between himself and the black cannibal chief.

He was completely lost, having not the remotest idea of where he should search for a reasonably good trail to the coast, nor, at present, did he care; his one wish being to escape recapture by Obebe, and so he elected to move northward, keeping always an eye open for any indication of a well-marked trail toward the west. Eventually, he hoped, he might discover a village of friendly natives who would aid him upon his journey toward the coast, and so the two moved as rapidly as they could in a northerly direction, their way skirting The Great Thorn Forest along the eastern edge of which they traveled.

The sun beating down upon the hot corral of The First Woman found it deserted of life. Only the corpse of a youth lay sprawled where it had fallen the previous evening. A speck appeared in the distant blue. It grew larger as it approached until it took upon itself the form of a bird gliding easily upon motionless wings. Nearer and nearer it came, now and again winging great, slow circles, until at last it swung above the corral of The First Woman. Once again it circled and then dropped to earth within the enclosure—Ska, the vulture, had come. Within the hour the body of the youth was hidden by a mantle of the great birds. It was a two-days feast, and when they left, only the clean picked bones remained, and entangled about the neck of one of the birds was a golden chain from which depended a diamond-encrusted locket. Ska fought the bauble that swung annoyingly beneath him when he flew and impeded his progress when he walked upon the ground, but it was looped twice about his neck and he was unable to dislodge it, and so he winged away across The Great Thorn Forest, the bright gems gleaming and scintillating in the sun.

Tarzan of the Apes, after eluding the women that had chased him and the Alalus youth into the forest, halted in the tree beneath which the frightened son of The First Woman had come to a terrified pause. He was there, close above him, when

Numa charged, and reaching quickly down had seized the youth by the hair and dragged him to safety as the lion's raking talons embraced thin air beneath the feet of the Alalus.

The following day the apè-man concerned himself seriously in the hunt for food, weapons, and apparel. Naked and un-armed as he was it might have gone hard with him had he been other than Tarzan of the Apes, and it might have gone hard with the Alalus had it not been for the ape-man. Fruits and nuts Tarzan found, and birds' eggs, but he craved meat and for meat he hunted assiduously, not alone because of the flesh of the kill, but for the skin and the gut and the tendons, that he could use in the fabrication of the things he required for the safety and comfort of his primitive existence.

As he searched for the spoor of his prey he searched also for the proper woods for a spear and for bow and arrows, nor were they difficult to find in this forest of familiar trees, but the day was almost done before the gentle wind, up which he had been hunting, carried to his sensitive nostrils the scent spoor of Bara the deer.

Swinging into a tree he motioned the Alalus to follow him, but so inept and awkward was the creature that Tarzan was compelled to drag him to a place among the branches, where, by signs, he attempted to impart to him the fact that he wished him to remain where he was, watching the materials that the ape-man had collected for his weapons, while the latter con-tinued the hunt alone.

That the youth understood him he was not at all sure, but at least he did not follow when Tarzan swung off silently through the branches of the forest along the elusive trail of the rumi-nant, the scent of which was always translated to the foster son of Kala, the she-ape as Bara the deer, though in fact, as practi-cally always, the animal was an antelope. But strong are the impressions of childhood and since that long-gone day upon which he had pored over the colored alphabet primer in the far-off cabin of his dead father beside the landlocked harbor on the West Coast, and learned that "D stands for Deer," and had admired the picture of the pretty animal, the thing that most closely resembled it, with which he was familiar in his daily life, the antelope, became for him then, and always remained, Bara the deer.

To approach sufficiently close to Bara to bring him down with spear or arrow requires cunning and woodcraft far beyond the limited range of civilized man's ability. The native hunter loses more often than he wins in this game of wits and percipience. Tarzan, however, must excel them both and the antelope, too, in the keenness of his perceptive faculties and in coordination of mind and muscles if he were to lay Bara low with only the weapons with which nature had endowed him.

As Tarzan sped silently through the jungle, guided by his nostrils, in the direction of Bara the deer increasing strength of the familiar effluvium apprised him that not far ahead Bara foregathered in numbers, and the mouth of the savage ape-man watered in anticipation of the feast that but awaited his coming. And as the strength of the scent increased, more warily went the great beast, moving silently, a shadow among the shadows of the forest, until he came at last to the verge of an opening in which he saw a dozen antelope grazing.

Squatting motionless upon a low-hanging limb the ape-man watched the movements of the herd against the moment that one might come close enough to the encircling trees to give a charge at least a shadow of a chance for success. To wait patiently, oftentimes hour upon hour, for the quarry to expose itself to more certain death is a part of the great game that the hunters of the wild must play. A single ill-timed or thoughtless movement may send the timorous prey scampering off into the far distance from which they may not return for days.

To avoid this Tarzan remained in statuesque immobility waiting for chance to send one of the antelope within striking distance, and while he waited there came to his nostrils, faintly, the scent of Numa the lion. Tarzan scowled. He was downwind from Bara and the lion was not between him and the antelope. It must, therefore, be upwind from the quarry as well as from himself; but why had not the sensitive nostrils of the Herbivora caught the scent of their arch-enemy before it had reached the ape-man; that they had not was evidenced by their placidity as they grazed contentedly, their tails switching and occasionally a head raised to look about with up-pricked ears though with no symptom of the terror that would immediately follow the discovery of Numa in their vicinity.

The ape-man concluded that one of those freaks of the air

currents that so often leaves a motionless pocket of air directly in the path of the flow had momentarily surrounded the antelope, insulating them, as it were, from their immediate surroundings. And while he was thinking these things and wishing that Numa would go away he was shocked to hear a sudden crashing in the underbrush upon the opposite side of the clearing beyond the antelope, who were instantly upon the alert and poised for flight. Almost simultaneously there broke into view a young lion which, upon coming in sight of the antelope, set up a terrific roaring as it charged. Tarzan could have torn his hair in rage and disappointment. The blundering stupidity of a young lion had robbed him of his meat—the ruminants were scattering in all directions. The lion, charging futilely, had lost his own meat and Tarzan's too; but wait! what was this? A terrified buck, blind to all save the single thought of escape from the talons of the dread carnivore, was bolting straight for the tree in which Tarzan sat. As it came beneath him a sleek brown body shot headforemost from the foliage, steel fingers gripped the throat of the buck, strong teeth fastened in its neck. The weight of the savage hunter carried the quarry to its knees and before it could stumble to its feet again a quick wrench with those powerful hands had twisted and broken its neck.

Without a backward glance the ape-man threw the carcass to his shoulder and leaped into the nearest tree. He had no need to waste time in looking back to know what Numa would be doing, for he realized that he had leaped upon Bara full in the sight of the king of beasts. Scarce had he drawn himself to safety ere the great cat crashed across the spot where he had stood.

Numa, baffled, roared terribly as he returned to glare up at the ape-man perched above him. Tarzan smiled.

"Son of Dango, the hyena," he taunted, "go hungry until you learn to hunt," and casting a broken branch contemptuously in the lion's face the ape-man vanished among the leafy branches bearing his kill lightly across one broad shoulder.

It was still daylight when Tarzan returned to where the Alalus was awaiting him. The youth had a small stone knife and with this the ape-man hacked off a generous portion of the antelope for the whelp of The First Woman and another for himself. Into the raw flesh, hungrily, sank the strong white teeth of the English lord, while the Alalus youth, gazing at him in surprise, sought materials for fire making. Amused, Tarzan watched him until the other had succeeded in preparing his food as he thought it should be prepared—the outside burned to a cinder, the inside raw, yet it was cooked food and doubtless imparted to its partaker a feeling of great superiority over the low beasts that devoured their meat raw, just as though he had been a civilized epicure eating decaying game and putrid cheeses at some fashionable club in London.

Tarzan smiled as he thought how vague, after all, the line that separates primitive from civilized man in matters pertaining to their instincts and their appetites. Some of his French friends, with whom he was dining upon a certain occasion, were horrified when they learned that in common with many of the African tribes and the apes he ate caterpillars, and they voiced their horror between mouthfuls of the snails they were eating with relish at the time. The provincial American scoffs at the French for eating frogs' legs, the while he munches upon the leg of a pig! The Esquimaux eat raw blubber, the Amazonians, both white and native, eat the contents of the stomachs of parrots and monkeys and consider them delicacies, the Chinese coolie asks not how his meat came by its death, nor how long since, and there is a man in New York, an estimable and otherwise harmless man, who eats Limburger cheese on Bartlett pears.

The following day, with sufficient meat to last them several days, Tarzan set to work upon his weapons and his loincloth. Showing the Alalus how to scrape the antelope hide with his stone knife, the ape-man set to work, with nothing more in the way of tools than bits of stone picked from the bed of a stream, to fashion weapons with which to cope successfully with the Alali women, the great carnivores, and whatever other enemies time might reveal to him.

And as he worked he watched the Alalus youth and wondered of what use the poor creature could be to him in finding his way through the encircling thorn forest that he must pass to reach familiar country and the trail for home. That the poor thing was timid had been evidenced by its manner when fleeing from the Alali women and its terror when confronted by Numa. Its speechlessness made it useless as a companion and it was entirely without woodcraft other than a certain crude, instinctive kind that was of no use to Tarzan. But it had placed itself at his side during the altercation in the corral and although it could not have been of any help to him yet it had won a right to his consideration by its act. Moreover it was evident, quite evident, that the creature had attached itself to Tarzan and intended to remain with him.

An idea occurred to Tarzan as he worked upon his weapons and thought upon the Alalus—he would make similar weapons for the youth and teach him how to use them. He had seen that the crude weapons of the Alali would be no match against one armed with a bow and arrows, or even a good spear. Accurately they could not hope to throw their missiles as far as a good bowman could speed his shaft and their bludgeons were helpless in the face of a well-thrown spear.

Yes, he would make weapons for the youth and train him in their use and then he could be made of service in the hunt and, if necessary, in the fight, and as Tarzan of the Apes thought upon the matter the Alalus suddenly paused in his work and bent an ear close to the ground, then he lifted his head and turned his eyes upon Tarzan, pointing at him, at his ear, and then at the ground. The ape-man understood that he was to listen as the other had and when he did so he distinctly heard approaching footsteps resounding upon the hard-worn trail.

Gathering up his belongings he carried them high among the trees to a safe cache with the remnants of Bara the deer and then returning helped the youth into the tree beside him.

Slowly, already, the Alalus was becoming more at ease in the trees and could help himself to a greater extent in climbing into them, but he was still practically helpless in Tarzan's estimation.

The two had not long to wait before there swung down the trail one of the terrible women of the amphitheater, and behind her at ten or fifteen paces another, and behind the second a third. It was not often that they traveled thus, for theirs was a solitary existence, the Alali being almost devoid of gregarious instincts, yet they did occasionally start out upon their hunts together, especially when they were hunting some dangerous beast that had encroached upon their rights, or when, failing to collect sufficient men from the forest during the mating season, the unfortunate ones banded together to make a raid upon the corrals of a neighboring tribe.

The three, slouching along the trail, passed directly beneath the tree from which Tarzan and the youth watched them. The great, flat ears flapped lazily, the dark eyes wandered from side to side, and from time to time they moved rapidly the skin upon some portions of their bodies as they sought to dislodge annoying insects.

The two in the tree remained motionless while the three brute-women passed along down the trail to be presently lost to their view at a turning of the forest highway, then, after a short interval of listening, they descended to the ground and resumed their interrupted labors. The ape-man smiled as he idly pondered the events of the past few minutes—Tarzan of the Apes, Lord of the Jungle, hiding among the trees to escape the notice of three women! But such women! He knew little about them or their ways as yet, but what he did know was sufficient to convince him that they were as formidable foes as ever he had encountered and that while he remained weaponless he was no match against their great bludgeons and swift-thrown missiles.

The days passed; the ape-man and his silent companion perfected the weapons that would more easily give them food, the latter working mechanically, following the instructions of his master, until at last the time came when Tarzan and the Alalus were fully equipped and then they hunted together, the man training the youth in the use of bow and spear and the long grass rope that from boyhood had formed a unique feature of the ape-man's armament.

During these days of hunting there came over the Alalus youth, quite suddenly, a great change. It had been his habit to glide stealthily through the forest, stopping often to look this way and that, fearful, apparently, of every creature that roamed the shadowed trails; his one great fear the ferocious females of his kind; but suddenly all this changed as by magic. Slowly he was mastering the bow and the spear; with deep interest and a sense of awe and respect he had watched Tarzan bring down many animals, great and small, for food, and once he had seen him dispatch Sabor the lioness with a single thrust of his great spear when Sabor had caught the ape-man in a clearing too far from the sanctuary of his beloved trees, and then his own day came. He and Tarzan were hunting when the former disturbed a small herd of wild pigs, bringing down two with his arrows. The others scattered in all directions and one of these, a boar, sighting the Alalus, charged him. The youth was of a mind to flee, for ages of inherited instinct prompted him to flight. Always the male Alalus fled from danger, and between fleeing from carnivorous animals and from their own women they had become very swift, so swift that no dangerous enemy could overtake them—an Alalus man could be captured only by craft. He could have escaped the boar by flight and for an instant he was upon the verge of flight, but a sudden thought checked him—back flew his spear hand as the ape-man had taught him and then forward with all the weight of his body behind the cast. The boar was coming straight for him. The spear struck in front of the left shoulder and ranged downward through the heart. Horta the boar dropped in his tracks.

A new expression came into the eyes and spread over the countenance of the Alalus. He no longer wore that hunted expression; he no longer slunk through the forest casting fearful glances from side to side. Now he walked erect, boldly and with fearless mien, and, perhaps, instead of dreading the appearance of a female he rather courted the event. He was the personification of avenging manhood. Within him rankled countless ages of contemptuous treatment and abuse at the hands of his shes. Doubtless he never thought of the matter in this way at all, but the fact remained, and Tarzan realized it, that the first woman unfortunate enough to stumble upon this youth was going to get the surprise of her life.

And while Tarzan and the Alalus roamed the strange land hemmed in by The Great Thorn Forest and the ape-man sought for an avenue of escape, Esteban Miranda and little Uhha, daughter of Khamis the witch doctor, wandered along the forest's outer verge in search of a trail toward the west and the coast.

5

WITH DOGLIKE DEVOTION the Alalus youth clung to Tarzan. The latter had mastered the meager sign language of his protégé giving them a means of communication that was adequate for all their needs. The former, gaining confidence with a growing familiarity with his new weapons, became more independent, with the result that the two more often separated for the hunt, thus insuring a more fully stocked larder.

It was upon one of these occasions that Tarzan came suddenly upon a strange sight. He had been following the scent spoor of Bara the deer when it was suddenly crossed by that of one of the great female Alali. That probably meant that another would attempt to rob him of his prey. The savage instinct of the jungle beast predominated in the guidance of the breech-clouted ape-man. It was not the polished Lord Greystoke of London whose snarling upper lip revealed two gleaming fighting fangs—it was a primordial hunting-brute about to be robbed of its quarry.

Taking to the trees he moved rapidly in the direction of the Alalus woman, but before he came within sight of her a new scent impinged upon his nostrils—a strange, new scent that puzzled him. It was the scent of man, yet strange and unfamiliar to a degree. Never before had anything like it arrested his attention. It was very faint and yet, somehow, he knew that it was close, and then, ahead of him, he heard voices, low musical voices, that came faintly to his ears; and though they were low and musical there was something in the quality and pitch of them that suggested excitement. Now Tarzan went more carefully, Bara, the deer, all but forgotten.

As he drew nearer he realized that there were many voices and much commotion and then he came upon a large plain that stretched away to distant hills, and in the foreground, not a hundred yards from him, he looked upon a sight that might well have caused him to doubt the veracity of his own eyes. The only familiar figure was a giant Alalus woman. Surrounding her was a horde of diminutive men—tiny white warriors—mounted upon what appeared to be a form of the Royal Antelope of the West Coast. Armed with lances and swords they repeatedly charged at the huge legs of the Alalus, who, backing slowly toward the forest, kicked viciously at her assailants and struck at them with her heavy bludgeon.

It quickly became evident to Tarzan that they were attempting to hamstring her and had they been successful they might easily have slain her then; but though there must have been fully a hundred of them their chances of success appeared small, since, with a single kick of her mighty foot the woman could lay low a dozen or more of her assailants at a time. Already fully half the force was *hors de combat*, their bodies with those of many of their mounts being scattered out onto the plain marking the trail of the combat up to the time that Tarzan had come upon the scene.

The courage of the survivors, however, filled Tarzan with admiration as he watched them hurl themselves upon almost certain death in their stubborn efforts to bring down the female, and then it was that the ape-man saw the reason, or the apparent reason, for the mad sacrifice of life—in her left hand the Alalus clutched one of the tiny warriors. It was to rescue him, evidently, that the others were maintaining this forlorn hope.

If the warriors filled Tarzan with admiration to scarcely a lesser extent did their courageous and agile mounts. Always had he thought of the Royal Antelope, the smallest known member of its family, as the most timid of creatures, but not so these cousins of theirs. Slightly larger, standing perhaps fifteen inches at the withers, they were in all other outward respects identical; yet, at the guidance of their riders, they leaped fearlessly into close range of those enormous feet and the great, slashing bludgeon. Perfectly reined were they, too; so perfectly that their muscles seemed to have coordinated with the minds of their riders. In and out they bounded, scarcely touching the ground before they were out of harm's way again. Ten or a dozen feet they covered at a leap, so that Tarzan wondered not only at their agility but at the almost marvelous riding ability of the warriors who could keep their seats so perfectly upon these leaping, bounding, turning, twisting mounts.

It was a pretty sight and an inspiring one, and however unreal it had at first appeared to him he was not long in realizing that he was looking upon a race of real pygmies—not members of the black tribe with which all African explorers are more or less familiar, but with that lost white race of diminutive men reference to which is occasionally to be found in ancient manuscript of travel and exploration, of myth and legend.

While the encounter interested him and he viewed it at first as a disinterested neutral he soon found his sympathies gravitating to the tiny warriors and when it became evident that the Alalus woman was going to make good her escape into the forest with her captive, the ape-man decided to take a hand in the affair himself.

As he stepped from the concealment of the forest the little warriors were the first to see him. Evidently they mistook him at first for another of their giant enemies, for a great cry of disappointment rose from them, and they fell back for the first time since Tarzan had been watching the unequal struggle. Wishing to make his intentions clear before the little men set upon him he moved quickly in the direction of the woman, who, the instant that her eyes fell upon him, made imperative signs for him to join her in dispatching the balance of the pygmies. She was accustomed to being feared and obeyed by her mankind, when she had them in her power. Perhaps she wondered a little at the temerity of this he, for as a rule they all ran from here; but she needed him badly and that was the idea that dominated her thoughts.

As Tarzan advanced he commanded her in the sign language he had learned from the youth that she was to release her captive and go away, molesting the little men no more. At this she made an ugly grimace and raising her bludgeon came forward to meet him. The ape-man fitted an arrow to his bow.

"Go back!" he signed her. "Go back, or I will kill you. Go back, and put down the little man."

She snarled ferociously and increased her pace. Tarzan raised the arrow to the level of his eye and drew it back until the bow bent. The pygmies, realizing that for the moment at least this strange giant was their ally, sat their mounts and awaited the outcome of the duel. The ape-man hoped that the woman would obey his commands before he was compelled to take her life, but even a cursory glance at her face revealed anything but an intention to relinquish her purpose, which now seemed to be to annihilate this presumptuous meddler as well.

On she came. Already she was too close to make further delay safe and the ape-man released his shaft. Straight into her savage heart it drove and as she stumbled forward Tarzan leaped to meet her, seizing the warrior from her grasp before she might fall upon the tiny body and crush it, and as he did so the other warriors, evidently mistaking his intentions, spurred forward with loud shouts and brandishing weapons; but before they had reached him he had set the rescued man upon the ground and released him.

Instantly the attitude of the charging pygmies changed again and from war cries their tones turned to cheers. Riding forward they drew rein before the warrior that Tarzan had rescued and several of their number leaped from their mounts and, kneeling, raised his hand to their lips. It was evident then to the ape-man that he had rescued one who stood high among them, their chief, perhaps; and now he wondered what would be their attitude toward him, as, with a look of amused tolerance upon his grim features, he watched them as one might watch the interesting doings of a swarm of ants.

As they felicitated their fellow upon his miraculous escape Tarzan had an opportunity to inspect them more closely. The tallest of them stood about eighteen inches in height, their white skins were tanned by exposure to a shade a trifle darker than his own, yet there was no question but that they were white men; their features were regular and well proportioned, so that by any standards of our race they would have been considered handsome. There were, of course, variations and exceptions; but on the whole those that he saw before him were fine-looking men. All were smooth-faced and there seemed to be no very old men among them, while he whom Tarzan had saved from the Alalus woman was apparently younger than the average, and much younger than those who had dismounted to do him homage.

As Tarzan watched them the young man bade the others rise and then addressed them for a moment after which he turned toward the ape-man and directed his remarks to him, none of which, of course, Tarzan could understand. By his manner, however, he guessed that the other was thanking him and possibly too asking his further intentions toward them and in reply the ape-man endeavored to assure them that he desired their friendship. Further to emphasize his peaceful intentions he cast his weapons aside and took a step toward them, his arms thrown slightly outward, his open palms in their direction.

The young man seemed to understand his friendly overtures, for he too advanced, offering his hand to Tarzan. The ape-man knew that the other meant that he should kiss it, but this he did not do, preferring to assume a role of equality with their highest. Instead, he kneeled upon one knee that he might more easily reach the proffered hand of the pygmy and pressing the tiny fingers gently, inclined his head slightly in a formal bow which carried no suggestion of servility. The other seemed satisfied, returned the bow with equal dignity and then attempted to convey to the ape-man that he and his party were about to ride off across the plain, inviting him to accompany them.

Rather curious to see more of these remarkable little people Tarzan was nothing loath to accept the invitation. Before the party set out, however, they dispersed to gather up their dead and wounded and to put out of their misery any of the injured antelope that were too severely hurt to travel. This they did with the relatively long, straight sword which was part of the armament of each. Their lances they left resting in cylindrical boots attached to the right side of their saddles. For other weapons Tarzan could discover nothing but a tiny knife carried in a scabbard at the right side by each warrior. The blade, like the blade of the rapier, was two edged but only about an inch and a half long, with a very sharp point.

Having gathered the dead and wounded, the latter were examined by the young leader of the party, who was accompanied by the five or six who had gathered about him at the time that Tarzan had released him. These Tarzan took to be lieutenants, or underchiefs. He saw them question the wounded and in three cases, each evidently a hopeless one, the leader ran his sword quickly through the hearts of the unhappy men.

While this seemingly cruel, yet unquestionably sound, military measure was being carried out, the balance of the warriors, directed by underofficers, were excavating a long trench beside the dead, of which there were twenty, their tool being a stout shovel blade carried attached to the saddle and which could be quickly fitted to the butt of the spear or lance. The men worked with extreme rapidity and under a plan that seemed to abhor lost motion, of which there was the absolute minimum, until in an incredibly short time they had excavated a trench fifty inches in length, eighteen inches wide and nine inches deep, the equivalent of which to men of normal size would have been nearly seventeen feet long, six feet wide and three feet deep. Into this they packed the dead like sardines and in two layers. They then shoveled back sufficient earth to fill the interstices between the bodies and to come to a level with the top of the upper layer, after which loose stones were rolled in until the bodies were entirely covered by two inches of stones. The remaining earth from the excavation was then piled over all.

By the time this work was completed the loose antelope had been caught and the wounded strapped to their backs. At a word from their commander the party formed with military precision, a detail started ahead with the wounded and a moment later the balance of the troop was mounted and on the way. The method of mounting and taking up the march was unique and a source of considerable interest to Tarzan. The dismounted warriors were standing in line facing the young leader who was mounted, as were the several officers who accompanied him. Each warrior held his mount by the bridle. The commander made a rapid signal with the raised point of his sword—there was no spoken word of command—immediately after which he dropped the point quickly at his side simultaneously wheeling his mount, which leaped quickly off in the direction that the troop was facing, the mounts of his officers wheeling with him as though actuated by a single brain, and at the same instant the mount of each alternate warrior in the line leaped forward and as it leaped its rider swung to his saddle, vaulting to his seat as lightly as a feather. The instant the first line had cleared them the antelopes of the second line leaped in pursuit, their riders mounted as had the others before them and with a second and longer leap the intervals were closed and the whole troop raced forward in a compact line. It was a most clever and practical evolution and one that made it possible to put mounted troops in motion as rapidly as foot troops; there was no long delay caused by taking distance, mounting, and closing ranks.

As the troop galloped away ten warriors wheeled from the left flank and, following one of the officers who had detached himself from the party of the commander of the troop, returned to Tarzan. By signs the officer conveyed to the ape-man the intelligence that he was to follow this party which would guide him to their destination. Already the main body was far away across the open plain, their lithe mounts clearing as many as five or six feet in a single bound. Even the swift Tarzan could not have kept pace with them.

As the ape-man started away under the guidance of the detachment his thoughts reverted for an instant to the Alalus youth who was hunting alone in the forest behind them, but he soon put the creature from his mind with the realization that it was better equipped to defend itself than any of its kind, and that when he had made his visit to the country of the pygmies he could doubtless return and find the Alalus, if he so desired.

Tarzan, inured to hardship and to long and rapid marches, fell into a dogtrot such as he could keep up for hours at a time without rest, while his guides, trotting their graceful mounts, kept just ahead of him. The plain was more rolling than it had appeared from the verge of the forest, with here and there a clump of trees; the grass was plentiful and there were occasional bands of the larger species of antelope grazing at intervals. At sight of the approaching riders and the comparatively giantlike figure of Tarzan they broke and ran. Once they passed a rhinoceros, the party making only a slight detour to avoid it, and later, in a clump of trees, the leader halted his detachment suddenly and seizing his lance advanced again slowly toward a clump of bushes at the same time transmitting an order to his men which caused them to spread and surround the thicket.

Tarzan halted and watched the proceedings. The wind was

blowing from him in the direction of the thicket, so that he could not determine what manner of creature, if any, had attracted the attention of the officer; but presently, when the warriors had completely surrounded the bushes and those upon the other side had ridden into it, their spears couched and ready, he heard an ugly snarl issuing from the center of the thicket and an instant later an African wildcat sprang into view, leaping directly at the officer waiting with ready spear to receive it. The weight and momentum of the beast all but unseated the rider, the point of whose spear had met the cat full in the chest. There were a few spasmodic struggles before death ensued, during which, had the spear broken, the man would have been badly mauled and perhaps killed, for the cat was relatively as formidable a beast as is the lion to us. The instant that it died four warriors leaped forward and with their sharp knives removed the head and skin in an incredibly short time.

Tarzan could not but note that everything these people did was accomplished with maximum efficiency. Never did there seem to be any lost motion, never was one at a loss as to what to do, never did one worker get in the way of another. Scarcely ten minutes had elapsed from the moment that they had encountered the cat before the detachment was again moving, the head of the beast fastened to the saddle of one of the warriors, the skin to that of another.

The officer who commanded the detachment was a young fellow, not much, if any, older than the commander of the troop. That he was courageous Tarzan could bear witness from the manner in which he had faced what must have been, to so diminutive a people, a most deadly and ferocious beast; but then, the entire party's hopeless attack upon the Alalus woman had proved that they all were courageous, and the ape-man admired and respected courage. Already he liked these little men, though it was at times still difficult for him to accept them as a reality, so prone are we to disbelieve in the possibility of the existence of any form of life with which we are not familiar by association or credible repute.

They had been traveling for almost six hours across the plain, the wind had changed and there was borne to Tarzan's nostrils clearly the scent of Bara the deer, ahead. The ape-man, who had tasted no food that day, was ravenous, with the result that the odor of meat aroused all the savage instincts fostered by his strange upbringing. Springing forward abreast the leader of the detachment that was escorting him he signed them to halt and then as clearly as he could through the comparatively laborious and never quite satisfactory medium of further signs explained that he was hungry, that there was meat ahead and that they should remain in the rear until he had stalked his prey and made his kill.

The officer having understood and signified his assent, Tarzan crept stealthily forward toward a small clump of trees beyond which his keen scent told him there were several antelope, and behind Tarzan followed the detachment, so noiselessly that even the keen ears of the ape-man heard them not.

Sheltered by the trees Tarzan saw a dozen or more antelope grazing a short distance beyond, the nearest being scarce a hundred feet from the small grove. Unslinging his bow and taking a handful of arrows from his quiver, the ape-man moved noiselessly to the tree nearest the antelope. The detachment was not far behind him, though it had stopped the moment the officer saw the game that Tarzan was stalking, lest it be frightened away.

The pygmies knew naught of bows and arrows and so they watched with deep interest every move of the ape-man. They saw him fit an arrow to his bow, draw it far back and release it almost all in a single movement, so quick with this weapon was he, and they saw the antelope leap to the impact of the missile which was followed in rapid succession by a second and a third, and as he shot his bolts Tarzan leaped forward in pursuit of his prey; but there was no danger that he would lose it. With the second arrow the buck was upon his knees and when Tarzan reached him he was already dead.

The warriors who had followed close behind Tarzan the instant that there was no further need for caution were already surrounding the antelope, where they were talking with much more excitement than Tarzan had seen them display upon any previous occasion, their interest seemingly centered about the death-dealing projectiles that had so easily laid the great animal low, for to them this antelope was as large as would be the largest elephant to us; and as they caught the ape-man's eye they smiled and rubbed their palms together very rapidly with a circular motion, an act which Tarzan assumed to be in the nature of applause.

Having withdrawn his arrows and returned them to his quiver Tarzan signed to the leader of the detachment that he would borrow his rapier. For an instant the man seemed to hesitate and all his fellows watched him intently, but he drew the sword and passed it hilt foremost to the ape-man. If you are going to eat flesh raw while it is still warm you do not bleed the carcass, nor did Tarzan in this instance. Instead he merely cut off a hindquarter, sliced off what he wanted and fell to devouring it hungrily.

The little men viewed his act with surprise not unmixed with horror and when he offered them some of the flesh they refused it and drew away. What their reaction was he could not know, but he guessed that they held a strong aversion to the eating of raw meat. Later he was to learn that their revulsion was due to the fact that within the entire range of their experience, heretofore, the only creatures that devoured raw meat devoured the pygmies as well. When, therefore, they saw this mighty giant eating the flesh of his kill raw they could not but draw the conclusion that should he become sufficiently hungry he would eat them.

Wrapping some of the meat of the antelope in its own skin Tarzan secured it to his back and the party resumed its journey. The warriors now seemed troubled and as they conversed in low tones they cast many backward glances in the direction of the ape-man. They were not afraid for themselves, for these warriors scarcely knew the meaning of fear. The question that caused them apprehension related to the wisdom of leading among their people such a huge devourer of raw flesh, who, at a single hurried meal, had eaten the equivalent of a grown man.

The afternoon was drawing to a close when Tarzan discerned in the far distance what appeared to be a group of symmetrical, dome-shaped hillocks and later, as they approached these, he saw a body of mounted warriors galloping to meet them. From his greater height he saw these before the others saw them, and attracting the officer's attention made signs apprising the latter of his discovery, but the oncoming warriors were hidden from the view of their fellows by the inequalities of the ground.

Realizing this Tarzan stooped and, before the officer could

guess his intention, had gathered antelope and rider gently in his powerful hands and lifted them high above the ground. For an instant consternation held the remaining warriors. Swords flashed and a warning cry arose and even the plucky pygmy in his grasp drew his own diminutive weapon; but a smile from the ape-man reassured them all, and an instant later the officer saw why Tarzan had raised him aloft. He called down to the others below him then and from their manner as from that of him whom he held the ape-man guessed that the approaching party was composed of friends of his escort, and so, a few minutes later, it proved when he was surrounded by several hundreds of the pygmies, all friendly, eager, and curious. Among them was the leader whom he had rescued from the Alalus woman and him he greeted with a handshake.

A consultation now took place between the leader of the detachment that had escorted the ape-man, the young commander of the larger party and several older warriors. By the expressions of their faces and the tone of their voices Tarzan judged that the matter was serious and that it concerned him he was sure from the numerous glances that were cast in his direction. He could not know, though, that the subject of their discussion was based upon the report of the commander of the escort that their mighty guest was an eater of raw flesh and the consequent danger of bringing him among their people.

The chief among them, the young commander, settled the question, however, by reminding them that though the giant must have been very hungry to have devoured as much flesh as they told him he had, nevertheless he had traveled for many hours with only a small number of their warriors always within easy reach of him and had not offered to molest them. This seemed a conclusive argument of his good intentions and consequently the cavalcade set forth without further delay in the direction of the hillocks that were now in plain view a mile or two away.

As they neared them Tarzan saw what appeared to be literally innumerable little men moving about among the hillocks, and as he came nearer still he realized that these seeming hillocks were symmetrical mounds of small stones quite evidently built by the pygmies themselves and that the hordes of pygmies moving about among them were workers, for here was a long line all moving in one direction, emerging from a hole in the ground and following a well-defined path to a half-completed hillock that was evidently in course of construction. Another line moved, empty-handed, in the opposite direction, entering the ground through a second hole, and upon the flanks of each line and at frequent intervals, marched armed warriors, while other similar lines of guarded workers moved in and out of openings in each of the other domelike structures, carrying to the mind of the ape-man a suggestion of ants laboring about their hills.

6

SKA, THE VULTURE, winged his way leisurely in great circles far above the right bank of the Ugogo. The pendant locket, sparkling in the sunlight, had ceased to annoy him while on the wing, only when he alighted and walked upon the ground did it become an encumbrance; then he stepped upon it and tripped, but long since had he ceased to fight it, accepting it now as an inescapable evil. Beneath him he presently descried the still, recumbent form of Gorgo, the buffalo, whose posture proclaimed that he was already fit food for Ska. The great bird dropped, alighting in a nearby tree. All was well, no foes were in evidence. Satisfied of this, Ska flapped down to the fallen beast.

Miles away a giant white man crouched in the concealment of a dense thicket with a little black girl. The fingers of one of the man's hands were across her mouth, those of the other held a knife at her heart. The man's eyes were not upon the girl, but were straining through the dense foliage toward a game trail along which two ebon warriors were advancing. Succor was close at hand for Uhha, the daughter of Khamis the witch doctor, for the two approaching were hunters from the village of Obebe, the chief; but she dared not call aloud to attract them lest the sharp point of Miranda's knife slip into her young heart, and so she heard them come and go until, their voices lost in the distance, the Spaniard arose and dragged her back upon the trail, where they took up, what seemed to Uhha, their endless and fruitless wanderings through the jungle.

In the village of the ant men Tarzan found a warm welcome and having decided to remain for a while that he might study them and their customs he set to work, as was his wont when thrown among strange peoples, to learn their language as quickly as possible. Having already mastered several languages and numerous dialects the ape-man never found it difficult to add to his linguistic attainments, and so it was only a matter of a comparatively short time before he found it possible to understand his hosts and to make himself understood by them. It was then that he learned that they had at first thought that he was some form of Alalus and had consequently believed that it ever would be impossible to communicate with him by other means than signs. They were greatly delighted therefore when it had become apparent that he could utter vocal sounds identical to theirs, and when they comprehended that he desired to learn their tongue, Adendrohahkis, the king, placed several instructors at his disposal and gave orders that all his people, with whom the giant stranger might come in contact, should aid him to an early understanding of their language.

Adendrohahkis was particularly well inclined toward the ape-man because of the fact that it had been the king's son, Komodoflorensal, whom Tarzan had rescued from the clutches of the Alalus woman, and so it was that everything was done to make the giant's stay among them a pleasant one. A hundred slaves brought his food to him where he had taken up his abode beneath the shade of a great tree that grew in lonely majesty just outside the city. When he walked among the group of dome-houses a troop of cavalry galloped ahead to clear a path for him, lest he trod upon some of the people of the city; but always was Tarzan careful of his hosts, so that no harm ever befell one of them because of him.

As he mastered the language he learned many things concerning these remarkable people. Prince Komodoflorensal almost daily took it upon himself to assist in the instruction of his colossal guest and it was from him that Tarzan learned most. Nor were his eyes idle as he strolled around the city. Particularly interesting was the method of construction used in erecting the comparatively gigantic dome-houses which towered high above even the great Tarzan. The first step in the construction was to outline the periphery of the base with boulders of uniform size and weighing, perhaps, fifty pounds each. Two slaves easily carried such a boulder when it was slung in a rope hammock and as thousands of slaves were employed the work progressed with rapidity. The circular base, with a diameter of one hundred and fifty to two hundred feet, having been outlined, another, smaller circle was laid about ten feet inside the first, four openings being left in each circle to mark the location of the four entrances to the completed building and corresponding to the four principal cardinal points of the compass. The walls of the entrances were then outlined upon the ground with similar large boulders, these being a little more carefully selected for uniformity, after which the four enclosures thus formed were packed closely with boulders. The corridors and chambers of the first floor were then outlined and the spaces between filled with boulders, each being placed with the utmost care and nicety in relation to those touching it and those that should rest upon it when the second course was laid, for these were to support a tremendous weight when the edifice was completed. The corridors were generally three feet wide, the equivalent of twelve feet by our standards, while the chambers varied in dimensions according to the uses to which they were to be put. In the exact center of the building a circular opening was left that measured ten feet in diameter and this was carried upward as the building progressed until the whole formed an open shaft from ground floor to roof in the completed edifice.

The lower course having been built up in this manner to a height of six inches wooden arches were placed at intervals the lengths of the corridors which were now ceiled over by the simple expedient of fastening thin wooden strips lengthways of the corridors from arch to arch until the corridors were entirely roofed. The strips, or boards, which overlapped one another, were fastened in place by wooden dowels driven through them into the peripheries of the arches. As this work was progressing the walls of the various chambers and the outer wall of the building were raised to a height of twenty-four inches, bringing them to the level of the ceilings of the arched corridors, and the spaces between chambers and corridors were packed with boulders, the interstices between which were filled with smaller stones and gravel. The ceiling beams were then placed across the other chambers, timbers six inches square hewn from a hard, tough wood being used, and in the larger chambers these were further supported, at intervals, by columns of the same dimensions and material. The ceiling beams being in place they were covered over with tight-fitting boards, doweled to place. The ceilings of the chambers now projected six inches above the surrounding course of the structure, and at this juncture hundreds of cauldrons were brought in which a crude asphaltum was heated until it became liquid and the interstices of the next six inch course were filled with it, bringing the entire completed course to the same level at a height of thirty inches, over all of which a second six inch course of rock and asphaltum was laid, and the second story laid out and completed in a similar manner.

The palace of Adendrohahkis, constructed in this way, was two hundred twenty feet in diameter, and one hundred ten feet high, with thirty-six floors capable of housing eighty thousand people, a veritable anthill of humanity. The city consisted of ten similar domes, though each slightly smaller than the king's, housing a total of five hundred thousand people, two-thirds of whom were slaves; these being for the most part the artisans and body servants of the ruling class. Another half million slaves, the unskilled laborers of the city, dwelt in the subterranean chambers of the quarries from which the building material was obtained. The passageways and chambers of these mines were carefully shored and timbered as the work progressed, resulting in fairly commodious and comfortable quarters for the slaves upon the upper levels at least, and as the city was built upon the surface of an ancient ground moraine, on account of the accessibility of building material, the drainage was perfect, the slaves suffering no inconvenience because of their underground quarters.

The domes themselves were well ventilated through the large central air shaft and the numerous windows that pierced the outer walls at frequent intervals at each level above the ground floor, in which, as previously explained, there were but four openings. The windows, which were six and one-quarter inches wide by eighteen and a half inches high, admitted a certain amount of light as well as air; but the interior of the dome, especially the gloomy chambers midway between the windows and the central light and air shaft, was illuminated by immense, slow-burning, smokeless candles.

Tarzan watched the construction of the new dome with keenest interest, realizing that it was the only opportunity that he ever would have to see the interior of one of these remarkable, human hives, and as he was thus engaged Komodoflorensal and his friends hastened to initiate him into the mysteries of their language; and while he learned the language of his hosts he learned many other things of interest about them. The slaves, he discovered, were either prisoners of war or the descendants of prisoners of war. Some had been in bondage for so many generations that all trace of their origin had become lost and they considered themselves as much citizens of Trohanadalmakus, the city of King Adendrohahkis, as did any of the nobility. On the whole they were treated with kindness and were not overworked after the second generation. The recent prisoners and their children were, for the most part, included in the caste of unskilled labor from which the limit of human endurance was exacted. They were the miners, the quarriers, and the builders and fully fifty percent of them were literally worked to death. With the second generation the education of the children commenced, those who showed aptitude for any of the skilled crafts being immediately transferred from the quarries to the domes, where they took up the relatively easy life of a prosperous and indulged middle class. In another manner might an individual escape the quarries—by marriage, or rather by selection as they choose to call it, with a member of the ruling class. In a community where class consciousness was such a characteristic of the people and where caste was almost a fetish it was rather remarkable that such connections brought no odium upon the inferiors, but, on the contrary, automatically elevated the lesser to the caste of the higher contracting party.

"It is thus, Deliverer of the Son of Adendrohahkis," explained Komodoflorensal, in reply to Tarzan's inquiry relative to this rather peculiar exception to the rigid class distinctions the king's son had so often impressed upon him: "Ages ago, during the reign of Klamataamorosal in the city of Trohanadalmakus, the warriors of Veltopishago, king of the city of Veltopismakus, marched upon our fair Trohanadalmakus and in the battle that ensued the troops of our ancestors were all but annihilated. Thousands of our men and women were carried away into slavery and all that saved us from being totally wiped out was the courageous defense that our own slaves waged for their masters. Klamataamorosal, from whom I am descended, fighting in the thick of the fray noted the greater stamina of the slaves; they were stronger than the warriors of either city and seemed not to tire at all, while the high caste nobility of the fighting clans, though highly courageous, became completely exhausted after a few minutes of fighting.

"After the battle was over Klamataamorosal called together all the chief officers of the city, or rather all who had not been killed or taken prisoner, and pointed out to them that the reason our city had been defeated was not so much because of the greater numbers of the forces of the king Veltopishago as due to the fact that our own warriors were physical weaklings, and he asked them why this should be and what could be done to remedy so grievous a fault. The youngest man among them, wounded and weak from loss of blood, was the only one who could offer a reasonable explanation, or suggest a means of correcting the one obvious weakness of the city.

"He called their attention to the fact that of all the race of Minunians the people of the city of Trohanadalmakus were the most ancient and that for ages there had been no infusion of new blood, since they were not permitted to mate outside their own caste, while their slaves, recruited from all the cities of Minuni, had interbred, with the result that they had become strong and robust while their masters, through inbreeding, had grown correspondingly weaker.

"He exhorted Klamataamorosal to issue a decree elevating to the warrior class any slave that was chosen as mate by either a man or woman of that class, and further to obligate each and every warrior to select at least one mate from among their slaves. At first, of course, the objections to so iconoclastic a suggestion were loud and bitter; but Klamataamorosal was quick to sense the wisdom of the idea and not only did he issue the decree, but he was the first to espouse a slave woman, and what the king did all were anxious to do also.

"The very next generation showed the wisdom of the change and each succeeding generation has more than fulfilled the expectations of Klamataamorosal until now you see in the people of Trohanadalmakus the most powerful and warlike of the Minunians.

"Our ancient enemy, Veltopismakus, was the next city to adopt the new order, having learned of it through slaves taken in raids upon our own community, but they were several generations behind us. Now all the cities of Minuni wed their warriors with their slave women. And why not? Our slaves are all descended from the warrior class of other cities from which their ancestors were captured. We all are of the same race, we all have the same language and in all important respects the same customs.

"Time has made some slight changes in the manner of the selection of these new mates and now it is often customary to make war upon another city for the sole purpose of capturing their noblest born and most beautiful women.

"For us of the royal family it has been nothing less than salvation from extinction. Our ancestors were transmitting disease and insanity to their progeny. The new, pure, virile blood of the slaves has washed the taint from our veins and so altered has our point of view become that whereas, in the past, the child of a slave woman and a warrior was without caste, the lowest of the low, now they rank highest of the high, since it is considered immoral for one of the royal family to wed other than a slave."

"And your wife?" asked Tarzan. "You took her in a battle with some other city?"

"I have no wife," replied Komodoflorensal. "We are preparing now to make war upon Veltopismakus the daughter of whose king, we are told by slaves from that city, is the most beautiful creature in the world. Her name is Janzara, and as she is not related to me, except possibly very remotely, she is a fit mate for the son of Adendrohahkis."

"How do you know she is not related to you?" asked the ape-man.

"We keep as accurate a record of the royal families of Veltopismakus and several others of the nearer cities of Minuni as we do of our own," replied Komodoflorensal, "obtaining our information from captives, usually from those who are chosen in marriage by our own people. For several generations the kings of Veltopismakus have not been sufficiently powerful or fortunate to succeed in taking royal princesses from us by either force of arms or strategy, though they never have ceased attempting to do so, and the result has been that they have been forced to find their mates in other and oftentimes distant cities.

"The present king of Veltopismakus, Elkomoelhago, the father of the princess Janzara, took his mate, the mother of the princess, from a far distant city that has never, within historic times, taken slaves from Trohanadalmakus, nor have our warriors visited that city within the memory of any living man. Janzara, therefore, should make me an excellent mate."

"But what about love—suppose you should not care for one another?" asked Tarzan.

Komodoflorensal shrugged his shoulders. "She will bear me a son who will someday be king of Trohanadalmakus," he replied, "and that is all that can be asked."

While the preparations for the expedition against Veltopismakus were being carried on Tarzan was left much to his own devices. The activities of these diminutive people were a never ending source of interest to him. He watched the endless lines of slaves struggling with their heavy burdens toward the new dome that was rising with almost miraculous speed, or he strolled to the farmlands just beyond the city where other slaves tilled the rich soil, which they scratched with tiny plows drawn by teams of diadets, the diminutive antelope that was their only beast of burden. Always were the slaves accompanied by armed warriors if they were slaves of the first or second generation, lest they should attempt escape or revolution, as well as a protection against beasts of prey and human enemies, since the slaves were not permitted to bear arms and, consequently, could not protect themselves. These slaves of the first and second generations were always easily recognizable by the vivid green tunic, reaching almost to the knees, which was the single garment of their caste, and which carried upon both its front and back an emblem or character in black that denoted the city of the slave's birth and the individual to whom he now belonged. The slaves employed upon public works all belonged to the king, Adendrohahkis, but in the fields many families were represented by their chattels.

Moving about the city upon their various duties were thousands of white-tunicked slaves. They exercised the mounts of their masters, they oversaw much of the more menial and laborious work of the lower caste slaves, they plied their trades and sold their wares in perfect freedom; but like the other slaves they wore but a single garment, together with rough sandals which were common to both classes. On their breasts and backs in red were the emblems of their masters. The second generation slaves of the green tunics had a similar emblem, these having been born in the city and being consequently considered a part of it. There were other, though minor, distinguishing marks upon the tunics of the higher caste slaves; small insignia upon one shoulder or upon both, or upon a sleeve, denoting the occupation of the wearer. Groom, body servant, major-domo, cook, hairdresser, worker in gold and silver, potter—one could tell at a glance the vocation of each—and each belonged, body and soul, to his master, who was compelled to feed and clothe these dependents, the fruits of whose labors belonged exclusively to him.

The wealth of one warrior family might lie in the beauty and perfection of the gold and silver ornaments it sold to its wealthy fellows and in such an instance all its skilled slaves, other than those required for personal and household duties, would be employed in the designing and fabrication of these articles. Another family might devote its attention to agriculture, another to the raising of diadets; but all the work was done by the slaves, with the single exception of the breaking of the diadets that were bred for riding, an occupation that was not considered beneath the dignity of the warrior class, but rather, on the contrary, looked upon as a fitting occupation for nobles. Even the king's son broke his own diadets.

As an interested spectator Tarzan whiled the lazy days away. To his repeated queries as to the possibility of a way out of this bizarre, thorn-infested world, his hosts replied that it was naught to penetrate the forest of thorn trees, but that as it continued indefinitely to the uttermost extremities of matter it was quite useless to attempt to penetrate it at all, their conception of the world being confined to what they actually had seen—a land of hills, valleys and forest, surrounded by thorn trees. To creatures of their size the thorn forest was far from impenetrable, but Tarzan was not their size. Still he never ceased to plan on a means of escape, though he was in no great haste to attempt it, since he found the Minunians interesting and it suited his present primitive mood to loll in lazy ease in the city of Trohanadalmakus.

But of a sudden a change came, early of a morning, just as the first, faint promise of dawn was tinging the eastern sky.

7

THE ALALUS YOUTH, son of The First Woman, ranged the forest in search of the ape-man, the only creature that ever had stirred within his savage, primitive breast any emotion even slightly akin to affection; but he did not find him. Instead he fell in with two older males of his own species, and these three hunted together, as was occasionally the custom of these inoffensive creatures. His new acquaintances showed little interest in his strange armament—they were quite content with a stick and a stone knife. To the former an occasional rodent fell and the latter discovered many a luscious grub and insect beneath the mold that floored the forest or hidden under the bark of a tree. For the most part, however, they fed upon fruits, nuts, and tubers. Not so the son of The First Woman, however. He brought in many birds and an occasional antelope, for he was becoming daily more proficient with the bow and the spear, and as he often brought in more than he could eat and left the remainder to his two fellows, they were permanently attached to him, or at least until such time as some fearsome woman should appear upon the scene to shatter their idyllic existence and drag one of them away to her corral.

They wondered a little at him in their slow and stupid minds, for he seemed to differ in some vague, intangible way from them and all others of their sex that they had known. He held his chin higher for one thing and his gaze was far less shifty and apologetic. He strode with a firmer step and with less caution; but perhaps they smiled inwardly as they cogitated muddily upon that inevitable moment that would discover one of their coarse, brutal, hairy shes felling him with her bludgeon and dragging him off toward the caves by the hair of his head.

And then one day the thing happened, or at least a part of it happened—they met a huge she suddenly in an open place in the forest. The two who accompanied the son of The First Woman turned in flight, but when they had reached the vantage ground of close-growing timber they paused and looked back to see if the woman was pursuing them and what had become of their companion. To their relief they saw that the woman was not following them and to their consternation that their fellow had not fled, but was facing her defiantly, and motioning her to go away, or be killed. Such crass stupidity! He must have been whelped without brains. It never occurred to them to attribute his act to courage. Courage was for the shes; the male spent his life in fleeing danger and the female of his species.

But they were grateful to him, for his rash act would save them since the she would take but one of them and that one would be he who thus foolishly remained behind to defy her.

The woman, unaccustomed to having her rights challenged by mere man, was filled with surprise and righteous anger. Her surprise brought her to a sudden halt twenty paces from the man and her anger caused her to reach for one of the stone missiles hanging at her girdle. That was her undoing. The son of The First Woman, standing before her with an arrow already fitted to his bow, waited not to discover her further intentions, but even as the woman's fingers loosed the feathered messenger of defeat from the leather thong of her girdle, he drew the shaft to his cheek and released it.

His two companions, watching from the seclusion of the wood, saw the woman stiffen, her face contorted in a spasm of pain; they saw her clutch frantically at a feathered shaft protruding from her chest, sink to her knees and then sprawl to earth, where she lay kicking with her feet and clutching with her fingers for a brief moment before she relapsed into eternal quiet; then they emerged from their concealment, and as the son of The First Woman approached his victim and wrenched the arrow from her heart they joined him, half-stunned as they were by surprise, and gazed first at the corpse of the she with expressions of incredulity and then at him with what was closely akin to awe and reverence.

They examined his bow and arrows and again and again they returned to the wound in the woman's chest. It was all quite too amazing. And the son of The First Woman? He held his head high and his chest out and strutted proudly. Never before had he or any other man been cast in the role of hero and he enjoyed it. But he would impress them further. Seizing the corpse of the woman he dragged it to a nearby tree where he propped it in a sitting posture against the bole; then he walked away some twenty feet and, signing his fellows to observe him closely, he raised his heavy spear and hurled it at his realistic target, through which it passed to embed itself in the tree behind.

The others were greatly excited. One of them wanted to attempt this wondrous feat and when he had thrown, and missed, his fellow insisted upon having a turn. Later they craved practice with the bow and arrow. For hours the three remained before their grisly target, nor did they desist until hunger prompted them to move on and the son of The First Woman had promised to show them how to fashion weapons similar to his own—a momentous occurrence in the history of the Alali, though these three sensed it as little as did the hundreds of Alalus women repairing to their caves that night in blissful ignorance of the blow that had been struck at their supremacy by the militant suffragists of Minuni.

And as suddenly, with more immediate results, the even tenor of Tarzan's existence in the city of Trohanadalmakus was altered and a series of events initiated that were to lead to the maddest and most unbelievable denouement.

The ape-man lay upon a bed of grasses beneath a great tree that grew beside the city of King Adendrohahkis. Dawn was flushing the sky above the forest to the east of Trohanadalmakus, when Tarzan, his ear close to the ground, was suddenly awakened by a strange reverberation that seemed to come faintly from the bowels of the earth. It was such a dim and distant sound that it would scarce have been appreciable to you or to me had we placed an ear flat against the ground after having been told that the noise existed; but to Tarzan it was an interruption of the ordinary noises of the night and, therefore, however slight, of sufficient import to impinge upon his consciousness even in sleep.

Awakened, he still lay listening intently. He knew that the sound did not come from the bowels of the earth, but from the surface and he guessed that it originated at no great distance, and also, he knew, that it was coming closer rapidly. For just a moment it puzzled him and then a great light dawned upon him and he sprang to his feet. The dome of the king, Adendrohahkis, lay a hundred yards away and toward it he bent his steps. Just before the south entrance he was challenged by a tiny sentinel.

"Take word to your king," the ape-man directed him, "that Tarzan hears many diadets galloping toward Trohanadalmakus and that unless he is much mistaken each carries a hostile warrior upon its back."-

The sentinel turned and hallooed down the corridor leading from the entrance, and a moment later an officer and several other warriors appeared. At sight of Tarzan they halted.

"What is wrong?" demanded the officer.

"The King's Guest says that he heard many diadets approaching," replied the sentinel.

"From what direction?" demanded the officer, addressing Tarzan.

"From that direction the sounds appeared to come," replied the ape-man, pointing toward the west.

"The Veltopismakusians!" exclaimed the officer, and then, turning to those who had accompanied him from the interior of the king's dome: "Quick! arouse Trohanadalmakus—I will warn the king's dome and the king," and he wheeled and ran quickly within, while the others sped away to awaken the city.

In an incredibly short space of time Tarzan saw thousands of warriors streaming from each of the ten domes. From the north and the south doors of each dome rode mounted men, and from the east and west marched the foot soldiers. There was no confusion; everything moved with military precision and evidently in accordance with a plan of defense in which each unit had been thoroughly drilled.

Small detachments of cavalry galloped quickly to the four points of the compass—these were scouts each detail of which spread fanwise just beyond the limits of the domes until the city was encircled by a thin line of mounted men that would halt when it had reached a predetermined distance from the city, and fall back with information before an advancing enemy. Following these, stronger detachments of mounted men moved out to north and south and east and west to take positions just inside the line of scouts. These detachments were strong enough to engage the enemy and impede his progress as they fell back upon the main body of the cavalry which might by this plan be summoned in time to the point at which the enemy was making his boldest effort to reach the city.

And then the main body of the cavalry moved out, and in this instance toward the west, from which point they were already assured the foe was approaching; while the infantry, which had not paused since it emerged from the domes, marched likewise toward the four points of the compass in four compact bodies of which by far the largest moved toward the west. The advance foot troops took their stations but a short distance outside the city, while within the area of the domes the last troops to emerge from them, both cavalry and infantry, remained evidently as a reserve force, and it was with these troops that Adendrohahkis took his post that he might be centrally located for the purpose of directing the defense of his city to better advantage.

Komodoflorensal, the prince, had gone out in command of the main body of cavalry that was to make the first determined stand against the oncoming foe. This body consisted of seven thousand five hundred men and its position lay two miles outside the city, half a mile behind a cavalry patrol of five hundred men, of which there were four, one at each point of the compass, and totaling two thousand men. The balance of the ten thousand advance troops consisted of the five hundred mounted scouts or vedettes who, in turn, were half a mile in advance of the picket patrols, at two hundred foot intervals, entirely surrounding the city at a distance of three miles. Inside the city fifteen thousand mounted men were held in reserve.

In the increasing light of dawn Tarzan watched these methodical preparations for defense with growing admiration for the tiny Minunians. There was no shouting and no singing, but on the face of every warrior who passed close enough for the ape-man to discern his features was an expression of exalted rapture. No need here for war cries or battle hymns to bolster the questionable courage of the weak—there were no weak.

The pounding of the hoofs of the advancing Veltopismakusian horde had ceased. It was evident that their scouts had discovered that the intended surprise had failed. Were they altering the plan or point of attack, or had they merely halted the main body temporarily to await the result of a reconnaissance? Tarzan asked a nearby officer if, perchance, the enemy had abandoned his intention of attacking at all. The man smiled and shook his head.

"Minunians never abandon an attack," he said.

As Tarzan's eyes wandered over the city's ten domes, illuminated now by the rays of the rising sun, he saw in each of the numerous windows embrasures, that pierced the domes at regular intervals at each of their thirty odd floors, a warrior stationed at whose side lay a great bundle of short javelins, while just to his rear was piled a quantity of small, round stones. The ape-man smiled.

"They overlook no possible contingency," he thought. "But the quarry slaves! what of them? Would they not turn against their masters at the first opportunity for escape that an impending battle such as this would be almost certain to present to them?" He turned again to the officer and put the question to him.

The latter turned and pointed toward the entrance to the nearest quarry, where Tarzan saw hundreds of white-tunicked slaves piling rocks upon it while a detachment of infantry leaned idly upon their spears as their officers directed the labor of the slaves.

"There is another detachment of warriors bottled up inside the quarry entrance," explained the officer to Tarzan. "If the enemy gains the city and this outer guard is driven into the domes or killed or captured, the inner guard can hold off an entire army, as only one man can attack them at a time. Our slaves are safe, therefore, unless the city falls and that has not happened to any Minunian city within the memory of man. The best that the Veltopismakusians can hope for now is to pick up a few prisoners, but they will doubtless leave behind as many as they take. Had their surprise been successful they might have forced their way into one of the domes and made way with many women and much loot. Now, though, our forces are too well disposed to make it possible for any but a greatly superior force to seriously threaten the city itself. I even doubt if our infantry will be engaged at all."

"How is the infantry disposed?" asked Tarzan.

"Five thousand men are stationed within the windows of the domes," replied the officer; "five thousand more comprise the reserve which you see about you, and from which detachments have been detailed to guard the quarries. A mile from the city are four other bodies of infantry; those to the east, north, and south having a strength of one thousand men each, while the one to the west, facing the probable point of attack, consists of seven thousand warriors."

"Then you think the fighting will not reach the city?" asked Tarzan.

"No. The lucky men today are in the advance cavalry—they will get whatever fighting there is. I doubt if an infantryman draws a sword or casts a spear; but that is usually the case—it is the cavalry that fights, always."

"I take it that you feel unfortunate in not being attached to a cavalry unit. Could you not be transferred?"

"Oh, we must all take our turns of duty in each branch,"

explained the officer. "We are all mounted except for defense of the city and for that purpose we are assigned to the foot troops for four moons, followed by five moons in the cavalry"—the word he used was *diadetax*—"five thousand men being transferred from one to the other the night of each new moon."

Tarzan turned and looked out across the plain toward the west. He could see the nearer troops standing at ease, awaiting the enemy. Even the main body of cavalry, two miles away, he could discern, because there were so many of them; but the distant pickets and vedettes were invisible. As he stood leaning upon his spear watching this scene, a scene such as no other man of his race ever had witnessed, and realized the seriousness of these little men in the business of war that confronted them, he could not but think of the people of his own world lining up their soldiers for purposes usually far less momentous to them than the call to arms that had brought the tough little warriors of Adendrohahkis swarming from their pallets in the defense of home and city.

No chicanery of politics here, no thinly veiled ambition of some potential tyrant, no mad conception of hair-brained dreamers seized by the avaricious criminal for self-aggrandizement and riches; none of these, but patriotism of purest strain energized by the powerful urge of self-preservation. The perfect fighters, the perfect warriors, the perfect heroes these. No need for blaring trumpets; of no use to them the artificial aids to courage conceived by captains of the outer world who send unwilling men to battle for they know not what, deceived by lying propaganda, enraged by false tales of the barbarity of the foe, whose anger has been aroused against them by similar means.

During the lull that followed the departure from the city of the last of the advance troops Tarzan approached Adendrohahkis where he sat astride his diadet surrounded by a number of his high officers. The king was resplendent in golden jerkin, a leathern garment upon which small discs of gold were sewn, overlapping one another. About his waist was a wide belt of heavy leather, held in place by three buckles of gold, and of such dimensions as to have almost the appearance of a corset. This belt supported his rapier and knife, the scabbards of which were heavily inlaid with gold and baser metals in intricate and beautiful designs. Leather cuisses protected his upper legs in front covering the thighs to the knees, while his forearms were encased in metal armlets from wrists almost to elbows. Upon his feet were strapped tough sandals, with a circular golden plate protecting each anklebone. A well-shaped leather casque fitted his head closely.

As Tarzan stopped before him the king recognized the ape-man with a pleasant greeting. "The captain of the guard reports that it is to you we owe the first warning of the coming of the Veltopismakusians. Once again have you placed the people of Trohanadalmakus under deep obligation. However are we to repay our debt?"

Tarzan gestured deprecatively. "You owe me nothing, King of Trohanadalmakus," he replied. "Give me your friendship and tell me that I may go forward and join your noble son, the prince; then all the obligations shall be upon my head."

"Until the worms of death devour me I shall be your friend always, Tarzan," returned the king graciously. "Go where you will and that you choose to go where there should be fighting surprises me not."

It was the first time that any Minunian had addressed him by his name. Always had he been called Savior of the Prince, Guest of the King, Giant of the Forest, and by other similar impersonal appellations. Among the Minunians a man's name is considered a sacred possession, the use of which is permitted only his chosen friends and the members of his family, and to be called Tarzan by Adendrohahakis was equivalent to an invitation, or a command, to the closest personal friendship with the king.

The ape-man acknowledged the courtesy with a bow. "The friendship of Adendrohahakis is a sacred honor, ennobling those who wear it. I shall guard it always with my life, as my most treasured possession," he said in a low voice; nor was the Lord of the Jungle moved by any maudlin sentimentality as he addressed the king. For these little people he had long since · acknowledged to himself a keen admiration and for the personal character of Adendrohahakis he had come to have the most profound respect. Never since he had learned their language had he ceased his inquiries concerning the manners and the customs of these people, and he had found the personality of Adendrohahkis so inextricably interwoven with the lives of his subjects that in receiving the answers to his questions he could not but absorb unquestionable evidence of the glories of the king's character.

Adendrohahkis seemed pleased with his words, which he acknowledged graciously, and then the ape-man withdrew and started toward the front. On the way he tore a leafy branch from a tree that grew beside his path for the thought had occurred to him that such a weapon might be useful against Minunians and he knew not what the day might hold.

He had just passed the advanced infantry when a courier sped by him on a mad race toward the city. Tarzan strained his eyes ahead, but he could see no sign of battle and when he reached the main cavalry advance there was still no indication of an enemy as far ahead as he could see.

Prince Komodofloresal greeted him warmly and looked a little wonderingly, perhaps, at the leafy branch he carried across one shoulder.

"What news?" asked Tarzan.

"I have just sent a messenger to the king," replied the prince, "reporting that our scouts have come in touch with those of the enemy, who are, as we thought, the Veltopismakusians. A strong patrol from the outpost in our front pushed through the enemy's scout line and one courageous warrior even managed to penetrate as far as the summit of the Hill of Gartolas, from which he saw the entire main body of the enemy forming for attack. He says there are between twenty and thirty thousand of them."

As Komodofloresal ceased speaking, a wave of sound came rolling toward them from the west.

"They are coming!" announced the prince.

8

Ska, perched upon the horn of dead Gorgo, became suddenly aware of a movement in a nearby thicket. He turned his head in the direction of the sound and saw Sabor the lioness emerge from the foliage and walk slowly toward him. Ska was not terrified. He would leave, but he would leave with dignity. He crouched to spring upward, and extended his great wings to aid him in taking off. But Ska, the vulture, never rose. As he essayed to do so, something pulled suddenly upon his neck and held him down. He scrambled to his feet and, violently this time, strove to fly away. Again he was dragged back. Now Ska was terrified. The hateful thing that had been dangling about his neck for so long was holding him to earth—the swinging loop of the golden chain had caught around the horn of Gorgo, the buffalo. Ska was trapped.

He struggled, beating his wings. Sabor stopped to regard him and his wild antics. Ska was flopping around in a most surprising manner. Sabor had never seen Ska behave thus before, and lions are sensitive, temperamental animals; so Sabor was not surprised only, she was inclined to be frightened. For another moment she watched the unaccountable antics of Ska and then she turned tail and slunk back into the undergrowth, turning an occasional growling countenance back upon the vulture, as much as to say; "Pursue me at your peril!" But Ska had no thought of pursuing Sabor. Never again would Ska, the vulture, pursue aught.

* * *

"They are coming!" announced Komodoflorensal prince of Trohanadalmakus.

As Tarzan looked out across the rolling country in the direction of the enemy, he presently saw, from his greater height, the advance of the Veltopismakusians.

"Our scouts are falling back," he announced to Komodoflorensal.

"You can see the enemy?" demanded the prince.

"Yes."

"Keep me advised as to their movements."

"They are advancing in several long lines, deployed over a considerable front," reported the ape-man. "The scouts are falling back upon the outpost which seems to be standing its ground to receive them. It will be overwhelmed—if not by the first line then by those that succeed it."

Komodoflorensal gave a short command. A thousand mounted men leaped forward, urging their diadets into bounding leaps that cleared five, six, and even seven feet at a time. Straight for the outpost ahead of them they raced, deploying as they went.

Another thousand moved quickly toward the right and a third toward the left of the advance cavalry's position following Tarzan's announcement that the enemy had divided into two bodies just before it engaged the outpost, and that one of these was moving as though with the intention of turning the right flank of the main cavalry of Trohanadalmakus, while the other circled in the direction of the left flank.

"They are striking boldly and quickly for prisoners," said the prince to Tarzan.

"Their second and third lines are ploying upon the center and moving straight for us," said Tarzan. "They have reached the outpost, which is racing forward with them, giving battle vigorously with rapiers."

Komodoflorensal was dispatching messengers toward the rear. "It is thus that we fight," he said, evidently in explanation of the action of the outpost. "It is time that you returned to the rear, for in another few moments you will be surrounded by the enemy if you remain. When they reach us we, too, will turn and fight them hand-to-hand back toward the city. If it still is their intention to enter the city the battle will resemble more a race than aught else, for the speed will be too great for effective fighting; but it they have abandoned that idea and intend contenting themselves with prisoners there will be plenty of fighting before we reach the infantry, past which I doubt if they will advance.

"With their greatly superior numbers they will take some prisoners, and we shall take some—but, quick! you must get back to the city, if already it is not too late."

"I think I shall remain here," replied the ape-man.

"But they will take you prisoner, or kill you."

Tarzan of the Apes smiled and shook his leafy branch. "I do not fear them," he said, simply.

"That is because you do not know them," replied the prince. "Your great size makes you overconfident, but remember that you are only four times the size of a Minunian and there may be thirty thousand seeking to overthrow you."

The Veltopismakusians were driving swiftly forward. The prince could give no more time to what he saw was but a futile attempt to persuade Tarzan to retreat, and while he admired the strange giant's courage he likewise deplored his ignorance. Komodoflorensal had grown fond of their strange guest and he would have saved him had it been possible, but now he must turn to the command of his troops, since the enemy was almost upon them.

Tarzan watched the coming of the little men on their agile, wiry mounts. Line after line poured across the rolling country toward him, carrying to his mind a suggestion of their similarity to the incoming rollers of the ocean's surf, each drop of which was soft and harmless, but in their countless numbers combined into a relentless and terrifying force of destruction, and the ape-man glanced at his leafy bough and smiled, albeit a trifle ruefully.

But now his whole attention was riveted by the fighting in the first two lines of the advancing horde. Racing neck and neck with the Veltopismakusian warriors were the men of the Adendrohahkis outpost and the thousands who had reinforced them. Each had selected an enemy rider whom he sought to strike from his saddle, and at top speed each duel was carried on with keen rapiers, though here and there was a man wielding his spear, and sometimes to good effect. A few riderless diadets

leaped forward with the vanguard, while others, seeking to
break back or to the flanks, fouled the racing ranks, often
throwing beasts and riders to the ground; but more frequently
the warriors leaped their mounts entirely over these terrified
beasts. The riding of the Minunians was superb, and their
apparently effortless control of their swift and nervous steeds
bordered upon the miraculous. Now a warrior, lifting his mount
high into the air, cleared an adversary and as he rose above him
cut down viciously with his rapier at his foeman's head, striking
him from the saddle; but there was scarce time to catch more
than a fleeting, kaleidoscopic impression of the swift-moving
spectacle before the great horde swarmed down upon him.

With his leafy bough, Tarzan had thought to sweep the
little men from his path, but now friend and foe were so intermingled that he dared not attempt if for fear of unseating and
injuring some of the warriors of his hosts. He raised the bough
above their heads and waited until the first lines should have
passed him and then, with only the enemies of Adendrohahkis
about him, he would brush them aside and break the center of
their charge.

He saw the surprised expressions upon the faces of the men
of Veltopismakus as they passed near him—surprise, but no
fear—and he heard their shouts as one more fortunate than his
fellows was able to rein closer to him and cut viciously at his
legs as he sped past. Then indeed it became naught other than
a matter of self-preservation to attempt to fend these off with
his bough, nor was this impossible as the first lines moved past
in loose ranks; but presently the solid mass of the Veltopismakusian cavalry was upon him. There was no veering aside to
avoid him. In unbroken ranks, file after file, they bore down
upon him. He threw his useless bough before him to impede
their progress and grappled them with his fingers, tearing the
riders from their mounts and hurling them back upon their
onrushing fellows; but still they came.

They jumped their diadets over every obstruction. One rider,
leaping straight for him, struck him head-on in the pit of the
stomach, half winding him and sending him back a step.
Another and another struck his legs and sides. Again and again
the needlelike points of their rapiers pierced his brown hide
until from hips to feet he was red with his own blood, and

always there were more thousands bearing down upon him. His weapons, useless against them, he made no attempt to use and though he wrought havoc among them with his bare hands there were always a hundred to take the place of each that he disposed of.

He smiled grimly as he realized that in these little people, scarce one-fourth his size, he, the incomparable Tarzan, the Lord of the Jungle, had met his Wellington. He realized that he was entirely surrounded by the Veltopismakusians now, the warriors of Trohanadalmakus having engaged the advancing enemy were racing onward with them toward the seven thousand dismounted men who were to receive the brunt of that terrific charge. Tarzan wished that he might have witnessed this phase of the battle, but he had fighting enough and to spare to engage all his attention where he was.

Again he was struck in the stomach by a charging rider and again the blow staggered him. Before he could recover himself another struck him in the same place and this time he went down, and instantly he was covered, buried by warriors and diadets, swarming over him, like ants, in countless numbers. He tried to rise and that was the last he remembered before he sank into unconsciousness.

Uhha, daughter of Khamis the witch doctor of the tribe of Obebe the cannibal, lay huddled upon a little pile of grasses in a rude thorn shelter in an open jungle. It was night but she was not asleep. Through narrowed lids she watched a giant white man who squatted just outside the shelter before a tiny fire. The girl's lids were narrowed in hate as her smoldering eyes rested upon the man. There was no fear of the supernatural in her expression—just hate, undying hate.

Long since had Uhha ceased to think of Esteban Miranda as the river devil. His obvious fear of the greater beasts of the jungle and of the black men-beasts had at first puzzled and later assured her that her companion was an impostor; river devils do not fear anything. She was even commencing to doubt that the fellow was Tarzan, of whom she had heard so many fabulous stories during her childhood that she had come to look upon him as almost a devil himself—her people had no gods, only devils—which answer just as good a purpose among the ignorant and superstitious as do gods among the educated and superstitious.

And when Esteban Miranda quite conclusively proved by his actions that he feared lions and that he was lost in the jungle these things did not square at all with her preconceived estimate of the powers and attributes of the famous Tarzan.

With the loss of her respect for him she lost, also, nearly all her fear. He was stronger than she and brutal. He could and would hurt her if she angered him, but he could not harm her in any other way than physically and not at all if she could keep out of his clutches. Many times had she rehearsed plans for escape, but always she had hesitated because of the terrible fear she had of being alone in the jungle. Recently, however, she had been coming to realize more and more clearly that the white man was little or no protection to her. In fact, she might be better off without him, for at the first hint of danger it had been Miranda's habit to bolt for the nearest tree, and where trees were not numerous this habit of hers had always placed Uhha under a handicap in the race for self-preservation, since Esteban, being stronger, could push her aside if she impeded his progress toward safety.

Yes, she would be as well off alone in the jungle as in the company of this man whom she thoroughly despised and hated, but before she left him she must, her savage little brain assured her, revenge herself upon him for having tricked her into aiding him in his escape from the village of Obebe the chief as well as for having forced her to accompany him.

Uhha was sure that she could find her way to the village, albeit they had traveled long and far, and she was sure too that she could find the means for subsistence along the way and elude the fiercer beasts of prey that might beset the way. Only man she feared; but in this she was not unlike all other created things. Man alone of all the creations of God is universally hated and feared and not only by the lower orders but by his own kind, for of them all man alone joys in the death of others—the great coward who, of all creation, fears death the most.

And so the little Negro girl lay watching the Spaniard and her eyes glittered, for in his occupation she saw a means to her revenge. Squatting before his fire, leaning far forward, Esteban Miranda gloated over the contents of a small buckskin bag which he had partially emptied into the palm of one of his hands. Little Uhha knew how highly the white man prized these glittering stones, though she was entirely ignorant of their intrinsic worth. She did not even know them for diamonds. All she knew was that the white man loved them, that he valued them more highly than his other possessions, and that he had repeatedly told her that he would die sooner than he would part with them.

For a long time Miranda played with the diamonds and for a long time Uhha watched him; but at last he returned them to their bag, which he fastened securely inside his loincloth. Then he crawled beneath the thorn shelter, dragged a pile of thorns into the entrance to close it against the inroads of prowling beasts, and lay down upon the grasses beside Uhha.

How was this little girl going to accomplish the theft of the diamonds from the huge, Tarzanian Spaniard? She could not filch them by stealth, for the bag that contained them was so fastened inside his loincloth that it would be impossible to remove it without awakening him; and certainly this frail child could never wrest the jewels form Esteban by physical prowess. No, the whole scheme must die where it was born— inside Uhha's thick little skull.

Outside the shelter the fire flickered, lighting the jungle grasses about it and casting weird, fantastic shadows that leaped and danced in the jungle night. Something moved stealthily among the lush vegetation a score of paces from the tiny camp. It was something large, for the taller grasses spread to its advance. They parted and a lion's head appeared. The yellow-green eyes gazed uneasily at the fire. From beyond came the odor of man and Numa was hungry; too, upon occasion he had eaten of man and found him good—also of all his prey the slowest and the least able to protect himself; but Numa did not like the looks of things here and so he turned and disappeared from whence he had come. He was not afraid of the fire. Had he been he would have been afraid of the sun by day, for the sun he could not even look at without discomfort, and to Numa the fire and the sun might have been one, for he had no way of knowing which was sixty feet away and which ninety-three million miles. It was the dancing shadows that caused his nervous apprehension. Huge, grotesque creatures of which he had had no experience seemed to be leaping all about him, threatening him from every side.

But Uhha paid no attention to the dancing shadows and she had not seen Numa the lion. She lay very still now, listening. The fire flared less high as the slow minutes dragged their leaden feet along. It was not so very long that she lay thus, but it seemed long to Uhha, for she had her plan all matured and ready for execution. A civilized girl of twelve might have conceived it, but it is doubtful that she would have carried it to its conclusion. Uhha, however, was not civilized and being what she was she was not hampered by any qualms of conscience.

Presently the Spaniard's breathing indicated that he was asleep. Uhha waited a little longer to make assurance doubly sure, then she reached beneath the grasses just beside her and when she withdrew her hand again she brought forth a short, stout cudgel. Slowly and cautiously she rose until she kneeled beside the recumbent form of the sleeping Spaniard. Then she raised her weapon above her head and brought it down once, heavily, upon Esteban's skull. She did not continue to beat him—the one blow was enough. She hoped that she had not killed him, for he must live if her scheme of revenge was to be realized; he must live and know that Uhha had stolen the bag of pebbles that he so worshiped. Uhha appropriated the knife that swung at Miranda's hip and with it she cut away his loincloth and took possession of the buckskin bag and its contents. Then she removed the thorns from the entrance to the shelter, slipped out into the night and vanished into the jungle. During all her wanderings with the Spaniard she had not once lost her sense of the direction which pointed toward her home, and now, free, she set her face resolutely toward the southwest and the village of Obebe the cannibal. An elephant trail formed a jungle highway along which she moved at a swinging walk, her way lighted by the rays of a full moon that filtered through the foliage of a sparse forest. She feared the jungle night and the nocturnal beasts of prey, but she knew that she must take this chance that she might put as great a distance as possible between herself and the white man before he regained consciousness and started in pursuit.

A hundred yards ahead of her, in the dense thicket that bordered the trail, Numa the lion sniffed, and listened with up-pricked ears bent in her direction. No dancing shadows here to suggest menacing forms to Numa's high-strung nervous system—only the scent of man coming closer and closer—a young she-man, most tender of its kind. Numa licked his slavering jowls and waited.

The girl came rapidly along the trail. Now she was abreast the lion, but the king of beasts did not spring. There is something in the scent of the man-thing and the sight of the man-thing that awakens strange terrors in the breast of Numa. When he stalks Horta the boar or Bara the deer there is nothing in the near presence of either that arouses a similar sensation in the savage carnivore; then he knows no hesitancy when the instant comes to spring upon his prey. It is only the man-thing, helpless and leaden-footed, that causes him to pause in indecision at the crucial moment.

Uhha passed, ignorant of the fact that a great lion, hunting and hungry, stood within two paces of her. When she had passed Numa slunk into the trail behind her, and there he followed, stalking his tender quarry until the moment should come when the mists of his indecision should be dispelled. And so they went through the jungle night—the great lion, creeping on stealthy, noiseless pads, and just ahead of him the little black girl, unconscious of the grim death stalking her through the dappled moonlight.

9

WHEN TARZAN OF the Apes regained consciousness he found himself lying upon an earthen floor in a large chamber. As he first opened his eyes, before complete consciousness returned, he noticed that the room was well, but not brilliantly, lighted, and that there were others there besides himself. Later, as he commenced to collect and dominate his faculties of thought he saw that the room was lighted by two immense candles that appeared to be fully three feet in diameter and, though evidently partially melted away, yet at least five feet tall. Each supported a wick fully as large as a man's wrist and though the manner of their burning was similar to the candles with which he was familiar, yet they gave off no smoke, nor were the beams and boards of the ceiling directly above them smoke-blackened.

The lights, being the most noticeable things in the room, had been the first to attract the ape-man's attention, but now his eyes wandered to the other occupants of the room. There were fifty or a hundred men of about his own height; but they were garbed and armed as had been the little men of Trohanadal-makus and Veltopismakus. Tarzan knit his brows and looked long and steadily at them. Who were they? Where was he?

As consciousness spread slowly throughout his body he realized that he was in pain and that his arms felt heavy and numb. He tried to move them, only to discover that he could not—they were securely bound behind his back. He moved his feet—they were not secured. At last, after considerable effort, for he found that he was very weak, he raised himself to a sitting posture and looked about him. The room was filled with warriors who looked precisely like the little Veltopismaku-sians, but they were as large as normal men, and the room itself was immense. There were a number of benches and tables standing about the floor and most of the men either were seated upon the benches or lay stretched upon the hard earth. A few men moved about among them and seemed to be working over them. Then it was that Tarzan saw that nearly all within the chamber were suffering from wounds, many of them severe ones. The men who moved about among them were evidently attending to the wounded, and those, who might have been the nurses, were garbed in white tunics like the high caste slaves of Trohanadalmakus. In addition to the wounded and the nurses there were a half dozen armed warriors who were uninjured. One of these was the first to espy Tarzan after he had raised himself to a sitting posture.

"Ho!" shouted he. "The giant has come into his senses," and crossing the room he approached the ape-man. Standing before him, his feet widespread, he eyed Tarzan with a broad grin upon his face. "Your great bulk availed you little," he taunted, "and now we are as large as you. We, too, are giants, eh?" and he turned to his fellows with a laugh in which they joined him.

Seeing that he was a prisoner, surrounded by enemies, the ape-man fell back upon that lifelong characteristic of the wild beast—sullen silence. He made no reply, but only sat there regarding them with the savage, level gaze of the brute at bay.

"He is dumb like the great beast-women of the caves," said the warrior to his fellows.

"Perhaps he is one of them," suggested another.

"Yes," seconded a third, "perhaps he is one of the Zertalacolols."

"But their men are all cowards," urged the first speaker; "and this one fought like a warrior born."

"Yes, with his bare hands he fought till he went down."

"You should have seen how he threw diadets and warriors as one might pick up tiny pebbles and hurl them afar."

"He would not give a step, or run; and always he smiled."

"He does not look like the men of the Zertalacolols; ask him if he is."

He who had first addressed him put the question to Tarzan, but the ape-man only continued to glare at them.

"He does not understand me," said the warrior. "I do not think that he is a Zertalacolol, though. What he is, however, I do not know."

He approached and examined Tarzan's wounds. "These will soon be healed. In seven days, or less, he will be fit for the quarries."

They sprinkled a brown powder upon his wounds and brought him food and water and the milk of antelopes, and when they found that his arms were swelling badly and becoming discolored they brought an iron chain and, fastening one end about his waist with a clumsy padlock, secured him to a ring in the stone wall of the chamber, and cut the bonds from his wrists.

As they believed that he did not understand their language they spoke freely before him, but as their tongue was almost identical with that employed by the Trohanadalmakusians Tarzan understood everything that they said, and thus he learned that the battle before the city of Adendrohahkis had not gone as well for the Veltopismakusians as Elkomoelhago, their king, had desired. They had lost many in killed and prisoners and in return had not killed near so many of the enemy and had taken comparatively few prisoners, though Elkomoelhago, he learned, considered him worth the entire cost of the brief war.

How they had changed themselves into men of his own stature Tarzan could not comprehend, nor did any of the remarks he overheard shed any light upon this mystery of mysteries. But the climax of improbability was attained a few days later when he saw pass through the corridor, upon which the room of his incarceration was located, a file of warriors as large as he, each of whom was mounted upon a huge antelope fully as tall at the shoulder as the great eland, though obviously, from its contour and markings, a Royal Antelope, which is the smallest known. Tarzan ran his brown fingers through his thatch of black hair and gave up attempting to solve the enigmas that surrounded him.

His wounds healed quickly, as did those of the Veltopismakusians who were convalescing about him, and upon the seventh day a half-dozen warriors came for him and the chain was removed from about his waist that he might accompany them. His captors had long since ceased to address him, believing that he was ignorant of their language, which meant to them that he was as speechless as an Alalus, since they could conceive of no language other than their own; but from their conversation, as they led him from the chamber and along a circular corridor, he discovered that he was being taken before their king, Elkomoelhago, who had expressed a desire to see this remarkable captive after he had recovered from his wounds.

The long corridor, through which they were proceeding, was lighted partially by small candles set in niches and by the light from illuminated chambers the doors of which opened upon it. Slaves and warriors moved in two continuous and opposing lines through this corridor and every one that crossed it. There were high caste slaves in white tunics with the red emblems of their owners and their own occupation insignia upon them; there were green-tunicked slaves of the second generation with their master's insignia upon breast and back in black, and green-tunicked slaves of the first generation with a black emblem upon their breasts denoting the city of their nativity and their master's emblem upon their backs; there were warriors of every rank and position; there were the plain leather trappings of the young and poor, and the jewel-studded harness of the rich; and passing all these in both directions and often at high speed were other warriors mounted upon the mighty antelopes that were still the greatest wonder that had confronted Tarzan since his incarceration in the city of Veltopismakus.

At intervals along the corridor Tarzan saw ladders extending to a floor above, but as he never saw one descending to a lower level he assumed that they were then upon the lowest floor of the structure. From the construction that he noted he was convinced that the building was similar to the dome he had seen in the course of construction in the city of Adendrohahkis; but when he permitted his mind to dwell upon the tremendous proportions of such a dome capable of housing men of his own size he was staggered. Had Adendrohahkis's dome been duplicated in these greater dimensions, though in the same proportions, it would have been eight hundred eighty feet in diameter and four hundred forty feet high. It seemed preposterous to think that any race existed capable of accomplishing such an architectural feat with only the primitive means that these people might be able to command, yet here were the corridors with the arched roofs, the walls of neatly laid boulders and the great chambers with their heavy ceiling beams and stout columns, all exactly as he had seen the dome in Trohanadalmakus, but on a vastly larger scale.

As his eyes and mind dwelt upon these enigmas which confronted them his escort led him from the circular corridor into one that ran at right angles to it where presently they stopped at the entrance to a chamber filled with row upon row of shelving packed full with all manner of manufactured articles. There were large candles and small candles, candles of every conceivable size and shape; there were helmets, belts, sandals, tunics, bowls, jars, vases, and the thousand other articles of the daily life of the Minunians with which Tarzan had become more or less familiar during his sojourn among the Trohanadalmakusians.

As they halted before the entrance to this room a white-tunicked slave came forward in response to the summons of one of the warriors of the escort.

"A green tunic for this fellow from Trohanadalmakus," he ordered.

"Whose insignia upon his back?" inquired the slave.

"He belongs to Zoanthrohago," replied the warrior.

The slave ran quickly to one of the shelves from which he selected a green tunic. From another he took two large, wooden blocks upon the face of each of which was carved a different device. These he covered evenly with some sort of paint or ink, slipped a smooth board inside the tunic, placed one of the dies face downward upon the cloth, tapped it smartly with a wooden mallet several times and then repeated the operation with the other die upon the reverse side of the tunic. When he handed the garment to Tarzan with the instructions to don it the ape-man saw that it bore a device in black upon the breast and another upon the back, but he could not read them—his education had not progressed thus far.

The slave then gave him a pair of sandals and when he had strapped these to his feet the warriors motioned him on down the corridor, which, as they proceeded, he was aware changed rapidly in appearance. The rough boulder walls were plastered now and decorated with colored paintings portraying, most often, battle scenes and happenings of the hunt, usually framed in panels bordered in intricate, formal designs. Vivid colorings predominated. Many-hued candles burned in frequent niches. Gorgeously trapped warriors were numerous. The green-tunicked slave almost disappeared, while the white tunics of the higher caste bondsmen were of richer material and the slaves themselves were often resplendently trapped with jewels and fine leather.

The splendor of the scene, the brilliancy of the lighting, increased until the corridor came to an abrupt end before two massive doors of hammered gold in front of which stood gorgeously trapped warriors who halted them and questioned the commander of the escort as to their business.

"By the king's command we bring the slave of Zoanthrohago," replied the commander, "the giant who was taken prisoner at Trohanadalmakus."

The warrior who had challenged them turned to one of his fellows. "Go with this message and deliver it to the king!" he said.

After the messenger had departed the warriors fell to examining Tarzan and asking many questions concerning him, to few of which could his guard give more than speculative answers, and then, presently, the messenger returned with word that the party was immediately to be admitted to the king's presence. The heavy doors were swung wide and Tarzan found himself upon the threshold of an enormous chamber, the walls of which converged toward the opposite end, where a throne stood upon a dais. Massive wooden columns supported the ceiling, which was plastered between its beams. The beams as well as the columns were ornamented with carving, while the plastered portions of the ceiling carried gorgeous arabesques in brilliant colors. The walls were paneled to half their height, and above the paneling of wood were painted panels which Tarzan assumed depicted historical events from the history of Veltopismakus and her kings.

The room was vacant except for two warriors who stood before doors that flanked the throne dais, and as the party moved down the broad center aisle toward the throne one of these warriors signaled the leader and motioned to the door which he was guarding and which he now threw open before them, revealing a small antechamber in which were half a dozen handsomely trapped warriors seated on small, carved benches, while a seventh lolled in a high-backed chair, his fingers tapping upon its broad arms as he listened to the conversation of the others, into which he threw an occasional word that always was received with deepest attention. If he scowled when he spoke, the others scowled still more deeply; if he smiled, they broke into laughter, and scarcely for an instant did their eyes leave his face, lest they miss some fleeting index of his changing moods.

Just inside the doorway the warriors who were conducting Tarzan halted, where they remained in silence until the man in the high-backed armchair deigned to notice them, then the leader knelt upon one knee, raised his arms, palms forward, high above his head, leaned as far back as he could and in a monotonous dead level intoned his salutation.

"O, Elkomoelhago, King of Veltopismakus, Ruler of All Men, Master of Created Things, All-Wise, All-Courageous, All-Glorious! we bring these, as thou hast commanded, the slave of Zoanthrohago."

"Arise and bring the slave closer," commanded the man in the high-backed armchair, and then to his companions: "This is the giant that Zoanthrohago brought back from Trohanadalmakus."

"We have heard of him, All-Glorious," they replied.

"And of Zoanthrohago's wager?" questioned the king.

"And of Zoanthrohago's wager, All-Wise!" replied one.

"What think you of it?" demanded Elkomoelhago.

"Even as you think, Ruler of All Men," quickly spoke another.

"And how is that?" asked the king.

The six looked quickly and uneasily, one at the others. "How *does* he think?" whispered he who was farthest from Elkomoelhago to his neighbor, who shrugged his shoulders hopelessly and looked to another.

"What was that, Gofoloso?" demanded the king. "What was that you said?"

"I was about to remark that unless Zoanthrohago first consulted our august and all-wise ruler and is now acting upon his judgment he must, almost of necessity, lose the wager," replied Gofoloso glibly.

"Of course," said the king, "there is something in what you say, Gofoloso. Zoanthrohago did consult me. It was I who discovered the vibratory principle which made the thing possible. It was I who decided just how the first experiments were to be carried out. Heretofore it has not been enduring; but we believe that the new formula will have a persistency of thirty-nine moons at least—it is upon this that Zoanthrohago has made his wager. If he is wrong he loses a thousand slaves to Dalfastomalo."

"Wonderful!" exclaimed Gofoloso. "Blessed indeed are we above all other peoples, with a king so learned and so wise as Elkomoelhago."

"You have much to be thankful for, Gofoloso," agreed the king; "but nothing compared to what will follow the success of my efforts to apply this principle of which we have been speaking, but with results diametrically opposite to those we have so far achieved; but we work upon it, we work upon it! Someday it will come and then I shall give to Zoanthrohago the formula that will revolutionize Minuni—then with a hundred men might we go forth and conquer the world!"

Elkomoelhago now turned his attention suddenly upon the green-tunicked slave standing a short distance before him. He scrutinized him closely and in silence for several minutes.

"From what city do you come?" demanded the king, at last.

"O, All-Glorious Elkomoelhago," spoke up the leader of the escort, "the poor ignorant creature is without speech."

"Utters he any sound?" inquired the king.

"None since he was captured, Master of Men," replied the warrior.

"He is a Zertalacolol," stated Elkomoelhago. "Why all this silly excitement over one of these low, speechless creatures?"

"See now!" exclaimed Gofoloso, "how quickly and surely the father of wisdom grasps all things, probing to the bottom of all mysteries, revealing their secrets. Is it not marvelous!"

"Now that the Sun of Science has shone upon him even the dullest may see that the creature is indeed a Zertalacolol," cried another of the king's companions. "How simple, how stupid of us all! Ah, what would become of us were it not for the glorious intelligence of the All-Wise."

Elkomoelhago was examining Tarzan closely. He seemed not to have heard the eulogies of his courtiers. Presently he spoke again.

"He has not the features of the Zertalacolols," he pondered musingly. "See his ears. They are not the ears of the speechless ones, nor his hair. His body is not formed as theirs and his head is shaped for the storing of knowledge and the functioning of reason. No, he cannot be a Zertalacolol."

"Marvelous!" cried Gofoloso. "Did I not tell you! Elkomoelhago, our king, is always right."

"The most stupid of us may easily see that he is not a Zertalacolol, now that the king's divine intelligence has made it so plain," exclaimed the second courtier.

At this juncture a door, opposite that through which Tarzan had been brought into the apartment, opened and a warrior appeared. "O, Elkomoelhago, King of Veltopismakus," he droned, "thy daughter, the Princess Janzara, has come. She would see the strange slave that Zoanthrohago brought from Trohanadalmakus and craves the royal permission to enter."

Elkomoelhago nodded his assent. "Conduct the princess to us!" he commanded.

The princess must have been waiting within earshot immediately outside the door, for scarcely had the king spoken when she appeared upon the threshold, followed by two other young women, behind whom were a half dozen warriors. At sight of her the courtiers rose, but not the king.

"Come in, Janzara," he said, "and behold the strange giant who is more discussed in Veltopismakus than Veltopismakus's king."

The princess crossed the room and stood directly in front of the ape-man, who remained standing, as he had since he had entered the chamber, with arms folded across his broad chest, an expression of absolute indifference upon his face. He glanced at the princess as she approached him and saw that she was a very beautiful young woman. Except for an occasional distant glimpse of some of the women of Trohanadalmakus she was the first Minunian female Tarzan had seen. Her features were faultlessly chiseled, her soft, dark hair becomingly arranged beneath a gorgeous, jeweled headdress, her clear skin shaming the down of the peach in its softness. She was dressed entirely in white, befitting a virgin princess in the palace of her sire; her gown, of a soft, clinging stuff, fell in straight and simple lines to her arched insteps. Tarzan looked into her eyes. They were gray, but the shadows of her heavy lashes made them appear much darker than they were. He sought there an index to her character, for here was the young woman whom his friend, Komodoflorensal, hoped someday to espouse and make queen of Trohanadalmakus, and for this reason was the ape-man interested. He saw the beautiful brows knit into a sudden frown.

"What is the matter with the beast?" cried the princess. "Is it made of wood?"

"It speaks no language, nor understands any," explained her father. "It has uttered no sound since it was captured."

"It is a sullen, ugly brute," said the princess. "I'll wager to make it utter a sound, and that quickly," with which she snatched a thin dagger from her belt and plunged it into Tarzan's arm. With such celerity had she moved that her act had taken all who witnessed it by surprise; but she had given the Lord of the Jungle an instant's warning in the few words she had spoken before she struck and these had been sufficient for him. He could not avoid the blow, but he could and did avoid giving her the satisfaction of seeing her cruel experiment succeed, for he uttered no sound. Perhaps she would have struck again, for she was very angry now, but the king spoke sharply to her.

"Enough, Janzara!" he cried. "We would have no harm befall this slave upon whom we are conducting an experiment that means much to the future of Veltopismakus."

"He has dared to stare into my eyes," cried the princess, "and he has refused to speak when he knew that it would give me pleasure. He should be killed!"

"He is not yours to kill," returned the king. "He belongs to Zoanthrohago."

"I will buy him," and turning to one of her warriors, "Fetch Zoanthrohago!"

10

WHEN ESTEBAN MIRANDA regained consciousness, the fire before his rude shelter was but a heap of cold ashes and dawn had almost come. He felt weak and dizzy and his head ached. He put his hand to it and found his thick hair matted with coagulated blood. He found something else as well—a great wound in his scalp, that made him shudder and turn sick, so that he fainted. When again he opened his eyes it was quite daylight. He looked about him questioningly. Where was he? He called aloud in Spanish—called to a woman with a musical name. Not Flora Hawkes, but a soft, Spanish name that Flora never had heard.

He was sitting up now and presently he regarded his naked-ness in evident surprise. He picked up the loincloth that had been cut from his body. Then he looked all about him on the ground—his eyes dull, stupid, wondering. He found his weapons and picking them up examined them. For a long time he sat fingering them and looking at them, his brows puckered in thought. The knife, the spear, the bow and arrows he went over time and time again.

He looked out upon the jungle scene before him and the expression of bewilderment on his face but increased. He half-rose, remaining upon his knees. A startled rodent scurried across the clearing. At sight of it the man seized his bow and fitted an arrow, but the animal was gone before he could loose his shaft. Still kneeling, the bewildered expression upon his countenance deepening, he gazed in mute astonishment upon the weapon he held so familiarly in his hand. He arose, gath-ered up his spear and knife and the balance of his arrows and started off into the jungle.

A hundred yards from his shelter he came upon a lion feeding upon the carcass of its kill that it had dragged into the bushes beside the wide elephant trail along which the man made his way. The lion growled ominously. The man halted, listening intently. He was still bewildered; but only for an instant did he remain motionless in the trail. With the spring of a panther he gained the low-swinging limb of the nearest tree. There he squatted for a few minutes. He could see Numa the lion feeding upon the carcass of some animal—what the animal had been he could not determine. After a while the man dropped silently from the tree and went off into the jungle in the opposite direction from that he had at first chanced upon. He was naked, but he did not know it. His diamonds were gone, but he would not have known a diamond had he seen one. Uhha had left him, but he did not miss her, for he knew not that she ever had existed.

Blindly and yet well, his muscles reacted to every demand made upon them in the name of the first law of nature. He had not known why he leaped to a tree at the sound of Numa's growl, nor could he have told why he walked in the opposite direction when he saw where Numa lay up with his kill. He did not know that his hand leaped to a weapon at each new sound or movement in the jungle about him.

Uhha had defeated her own ends. Esteban Miranda was not being punished for his sins for the very excellent reason that he was conscious of no sins nor of any existence. Uhha had killed his objective mind. His brain was but a storehouse of memories that would never again be raised above the threshold of consciousness. When acted upon by the proper force they stimulated the nerves that controlled his muscles, with results seemingly identical with those that would have followed had he been able to reason. An emergency beyond his experience would, consequently, have found him helpless, though ignorant of his helplessness. It was almost as though a dead man walked through the jungle. Sometimes he moved along in silence, again he babbled childishly in Spanish, or, perhaps, quoted whole pages of Shakespeare in English.

Could Uhha have seen him now, even she, savage little cannibal, might have felt remorse at the horror of her handiwork, which was rendered even more horrible because its miserable object was totally unconscious of it; but Uhha was not there to see, nor any other mortal; and the poor clay that once had been a man moved on aimlessly through the jungle, killing and eating when the right nerves were excited, sleeping, talking, walking as though he lived as other men live; and thus, watching him from afar, we see him disappear amidst the riotous foliage of a jungle trail.

The Princess Janzara of Veltopismakus did not purchase the slave of Zoanthrohago. Her father, the king, would not permit it, and so, very angry, she walked from the apartment where she had come to examine the captive and when she had passed into the next room and was out of her royal sire's range of vision, she turned and made a face in his direction, at which all her warriors and the two handmaidens laughed.

"Fool!" she whispered in the direction of her unconscious father. "I shall own the slave yet and kill him, too, if I mind."

The warriors and the handmaidens nodded their heads approvingly.

King Elkomoelhago arose languidly from his chair. "Take it to the quarries," he said, indicating Tarzan with a motion of his thumb, "but tell the officer in charge that it is the king's wish that it be not overworked, nor injured," and as the ape-man was led away through one doorway, the king quitted the chamber by another, his six courtiers bowing in the strange, Minunian way until he was gone. Then one of them tiptoed quickly to the doorway through which Elkomoelhago had disappeared, flattened himself against the wall beside the door and listened for a moment. Apparently satisfied, he cautiously insinuated his head beyond the doorframe until he could view the chamber adjoining with one eye, then he turned back toward his fellows.

"The old half-wit has gone," he announced, though in a whisper that would have been inaudible beyond the chamber in which it was breathed, for even in Minuni they have learned that the walls have ears, though they express it differently, saying, instead: *Trust not too far the loyalty of even the stones of your chamber.*

"Saw you ever a creature endowed with such inordinate vanity!" exclaimed one.

"He believes that he is wiser than, not any man, but all men combined," said another. "Sometimes I feel that I can abide his arrogance no longer."

"But you will, Gefasto," said Gofoloso. "To be Chief of Warriors of Veltopismakus is too rich a berth to be lightly thrown aside."

"When one might simultaneously throw away one's life at the same time," added Torndali, Chief of Quarries.

"But the colossal effrontery of the man!" ejaculated another, Makahago, Chief of Buildings. "He has had no more to do with Zoanthrohago's success than have I and yet he claims the successes all for himself and blames the failures upon Zoanthrohago."

"The glory of Veltopismakus is threatened by his egotism," cried Throwaldo, Chief of Agriculture. "He has chosen us as his advisers, six princes, whose knowledge of their several departments should be greater than that of any other individuals and whose combined knowledge of the needs of Veltopismakus and the affairs of state should form a bulwark against the egregious errors that he is constantly committing; but never will he heed our advice. To offer it he considers a usurpation of his royal prerogatives, to urge it, little short of treason. To question his judgment spells ruin. Of what good are we to Veltopismakus? What must the people of the state think of us?"

"It is well known what they think of us," snapped Gofoloso. "They say that we were chosen, not for what we know, but for what we do not know. Nor can you blame them. I, a breeder of diadets, master of ten thousand slaves who till the soil and raise a half of all the food that the city consumes, am chosen Chief of Chiefs, filling an office for which I have no liking and no training, while Throwaldo, who scarce knows the top of a vegetable from its roots, is Chief of Agriculture. Makahago worked the quarry slaves for a hundred moons and is made Chief of Buildings, while Torndali, who is acclaimed the greatest builder of our time, is Chief of Quarries. Gefasto and Vestako, alone, are masters of their bureaus. Vestako the king chose wisely as Chief of the Royal Dome, that his royal comfort and security might be assured; but in Gefasto behold his greatest blunder! He elevated a gay young pleasure-seeker to the command of the army of Veltopismakus and discovered in his new Chief of Warriors as great a military genius as Veltopismakus has ever produced."

Gefasto bowed his acknowledgment of the compliment.

"Had it not been for Gefasto the Trohanadalmakusians would have trapped us fairly the other day," continued Gofoloso.

"I advised the king against pushing the assault," interjected Gefasto, "as soon as it became evident that we had failed to surprise them. We should have withdrawn. It was only after we had advanced and I was free from him that I could direct the affair without interference, and then, as you saw, I quickly extricated our troops and withdrew them with as little loss of men and prestige as possible."

"It was nobly done, Gefasto," said Torndali. "The troops worship you. They would like a king who led them in battle as you might lead them."

"And let them have their wine as of old," interjected Makahago.

"We would all rally around a king who permitted us the innocent pleasure of our wine," said Gofoloso. "What say you, Vestako?"

The Chief of the Royal Dome, the king's major-domo, who had remained silent throughout the arraignment of his master, shook his head.

"It is not wise to speak treason now," he said.

The three looked sharply at him and glanced quickly at one another.

"Who has spoken treason, Vestako?" demanded Gofoloso.

"You have all come too close to it for safety," said the oily Vestako. He spoke in a much louder voice than the others had spoken, as though, far from being fearful of being overheard, he rather hoped that he would be. "Elkomoelhago has been good to us. He has heaped honors and riches upon us. We are very powerful. He is a wise ruler. Who are we to question the wisdom of his acts?"

The others looked uneasily about. Gofoloso laughed nervously. "You were ever slow to appreciate a joke, my good Vestako," he said. "Could you not see that we were hoaxing you?"

"I could not," replied Vestako; "but the king has a fine sense of humor. I will repeat the joke to him and if he laughs then I shall laugh, too, for I shall know that it was indeed a joke. But I wonder upon whom it will be!"

"Oh, Vestako, do not repeat what we have said—not to the king. He might not understand. We are good friends and it was said only among friends." Gofoloso was evidently perturbed in spirit—he spoke rapidly. "By the way, my good Vestako, I just happened to recall that the other day you admired one of my slaves. I have intended giving him to you. If you will accept him he is yours."

"I admire a hundred of your slaves," said Vestako, softly.

"They are yours, Vestako," said Gofoloso. "Come with me now and select them. It is a pleasure to make my friend so trifling a present."

Vestako looked steadily at the other four. They shifted uneasily in momentary silence, which was broken by Throwaldo, Chief of Agriculture. "If Vestako would accept a hundred of my poor slaves I should be overwhelmed with delight," he said.

"I hope they will be slaves of the white tunic," said Vestako.

"They will," said Throwaldo.

"I cannot be outdone in generosity," said Torndali; "you must accept a hundred slaves from me."

"And from me!" cried Makahago, Chief of Buildings.

"If you will send them to my head slave at my quarters before the Sun enters the Warriors' Corridor I shall be over-whelmed with gratitude," said Vestako, rubbing his palms and smiling unctuously. Then he looked quickly and meaningly at Gefasto, Chief of Warriors of Veltopismakus.

"Best can I show my friendship for the noble Vestako," said Gefasto, unsmiling, "by assuring him that I shall, if possible, prevent my warriors from slipping a dagger between his ribs. Should aught of harm befall me, however, I fear that I cannot be responsible for the acts of these men, who, I am told, love me." For a moment longer he stood looking straight into the eyes of Vestako, then he turned upon his heel and strode from the room.

Of the six men who composed the Royal Council, Gefasto and Gofoloso were the most fearless, though even they flattered the vain and arrogant Elkomoelhago, whose despotic powers rendered him a most dangerous enemy. Custom and inherent loyalty to the royal family, in addition to that most potent of human instrumentalities—self-interest, held them to the service of their king, but so long had they been plotting against him, and so rife was discontent throughout the city, that each now felt that he might become bolder with impunity.

Torndali, Makahago, and Throwaldo, having been chosen by the king for their supposed pliability and having, unlike Gefasto and Gofoloso, justified his expectations, counted for little one way or another. Like the majority of the Veltopis-makusian nobles under the reign of Elkomoelhago they had become corrupt, and self-interest guided their every act and thought. Gefasto did not trust them, for he knew that they could be bought even while professing their virtue, and Gefasto had taken to the study of men since his success with the warriors of his city—a success that was fully as much a surprise to him as to others—and his knowledge of the mounting restlessness of the people had implanted in the fertile soil of a virile brain the idea that Veltopismakus was ripe for a new dynasty.

Vestako he knew for a self-acknowledged and shameless bribe-taker. He did not believe that there was an honest hair in the man's head, but he had been surprised at the veiled threat of exposure he had used to mulct his fellows.

"Low indeed have fallen the fortunes of Veltopismakus," he said to Gofoloso as the two walked along the Warriors' Corridor after quitting the council chamber of the king.

"As exemplified by—?" queried the Chief of Chiefs.

"By Vestako's infamy. He cares neither for king nor for people. For slaves or gold he would betray either, and Vestako is typical of the majority of us. No longer is friendship sacred, for even from Throwaldo he exacted the toll of his silence, and Throwaldo has ever been accounted his best friend."

"What has brought us to such a pass, Gefasto?" asked Gofoloso, thoughtfully. "Some attribute it to one cause and some to another, and though there should be no man in Veltopismakus better able than myself to answer my own question, I confess that I am at a loss. There are many theories, but I doubt me the right one has yet been expounded."

"If one should ask me, Gofoloso, and you have asked me, I should say to him as I am about to say to you that the trouble with Veltopismakus is too much peace. Prosperity follows peace—prosperity and plenty of idle time. Time must be occupied. Who would occupy it in labor, even the labor of preparing one's self to defend one's peace and prosperity, when it may so easily be occupied in the pursuit of pleasure? The material prosperity that has followed peace has given us the means to gratify our every whim. We have become satiated with the things we looked upon in the days of yesterday as luxuries to be sparingly enjoyed upon rare occasion. Consequently we have been forced to invent new whims to be gratified and you may rest assured that these have become more and more extravagant and exaggerated in form and idea until even our wondrous prosperity has been taxed to meet the demands of our appetites.

"Extravagance reigns supreme. It rests, like a malign incubus, upon the king and his government. To mend its inroads upon the treasury, the burden of the incubus is shifted from the back of the government to the back of the people in the form of outrageous taxes which no man can meet honestly and have sufficient remaining wherewith to indulge his appetites, and so by one means or another, he passes the burden on to those less fortunate or less shrewd."

"But the heaviest taxation falls upon the rich," Gofoloso reminded him.

"In theory, but not in fact," replied Gefasto. "It is true that the rich pay the bulk of the taxes into the treasury of the king, but first they collect it from the poor in higher prices and other forms of extortion, in the proportion of two *jetaks* for every one that they pay to the tax collector. The cost of collecting this tax added to the loss in revenue to the government by the abolition of wine and cost of preventing the unscrupulous from making and selling wine illicitly would, if turned back into the coffers of the government, reduce our taxes so materially that they would fall as a burden upon none."

"And that, you think, would solve our problems and restore happiness to Veltopismakus?" asked Gofoloso.

"No," replied his fellow prince. "We must have war. As we have found that there is no enduring happiness in peace or virtue, let us have a little war and a little sin. A pudding that is all of one ingredient is nauseating—it must be seasoned, it must be spiced, and before we can enjoy the eating of it to the fullest we must be forced to strive for it. War and work, the two most distasteful things in the world, are, nevertheless, the most essential to the happiness and the existence of a people. Peace reduces the necessity for labor, and induces slothfulness. War compels labor, that her ravages may be effaced. Peace turns us into fat worms. War makes men of us."

"War and wine, then, would restore Veltopismakus to her former pride and happiness, you think?" laughed Gofoloso. "What a firebrand you have become since you came to the command of all the warriors of our city!"

"You misunderstand me, Gofoloso," said Gefasto, patiently. "War and wine alone will accomplish nothing but our ruin. I have no quarrel with peace or virtue or temperance. My quarrel is with the misguided theorists who think that peace alone, or virtue alone, or temperance alone will make a strong, a virile, a contented nation. They must be mixed with war and wine and sin and a great measure of hard work—especially hard work— and with nothing but peace and prosperity there is little necessity for hard work, and only the exceptional man works hard when he does not have to.

"But come, you must hasten to deliver the hundred slaves to Vestako before the Sun enters the Warriors' Corridor, or he will tell your little joke to Elkomoelhago."

Gofoloso smiled ruefully. "Someday he shall pay for these hundred slaves," he said, "and the price will be very high."

"If his master falls," said Gefasto.

"*When* his master falls!" Gofoloso corrected.

The Chief of Warriors shrugged his shoulders, but he smiled contentedly, and he was still smiling after his friend had turned into an intersecting corridor and gone his way.

11

TARZAN OF THE Apes was led directly from the Royal Dome to the quarries of Veltopismakus, which lie a quarter of a mile from the nearer of the eight domes which constitute the city. A ninth dome was in course of construction and it was toward this that the line of burdened slaves wound from the entrance to the quarry to which the ape-man was conducted. Just below the surface, in a well-lighted chamber, he was turned over to the officer in charge of the quarry guard, to whom the king's instructions concerning him were communicated.

"Your name?" demanded the officer, opening a large book that lay upon the table at which he was seated.

"He is as dumb as the Zertalacolols," explained the commander of the escort that had brought him to the quarry. "Therefore he has no name."

"We will call him The Giant, then," said the officer, "for as such has he been known since his capture," and he wrote in his book, *Zuanthrol*, with Zoanthrohago as the owner, and Tro-hanadalmakus as the city of his origin, and then he turned to one of the warriors lolling upon a nearby bench. "Take him to the timbering crew in the extension of tunnel thirteen at the thirty-sixth level and tell the Vental in charge to give him light work and see that no harm befalls him, for such are the commands of the thagosto—go! But wait! here is his number. Fasten it upon his shoulder."

The warrior took the circular piece of fabric with black hieroglyphics stamped upon it and affixed it with a metal clasp to the left shoulder of Tarzan's green tunic and then, motioning the ape-man to precede him, quit the chamber.

Tarzan now found himself in a short, dark corridor which presently opened into a wider and lighter one along which innumerable, unladen slaves were moving in the same direction that his guard now escorted him. He noticed that the floor of the corridor had a constant downward gradient and that it turned ever to the right, forming a great spiral leading downward into the earth. The walls and ceiling were timbered and the floor paved with flat stones, worn smooth by the millions of sandaled feet that had passed over them. At sufficiently frequent intervals candles were set in niches in the left-hand wall, and, also at regular intervals, other corridors opened out of it. Over each of these openings were more of the strange hieroglyphics of Minuni. As Tarzan was to learn later, these designated the levels at which the tunnels lay and led to circular corridors which surrounded the main spiral runway. From these circular corridors ran the numerous horizontal tunnels leading to the workings at each level. Shafts for ventilation and emergency exit pierced these tunnels at varying distances, running from the surface to the lowest levels of the quarry.

At almost every level a few slaves turned off into these lateral tunnels which were well lighted, though not quite as brilliantly as the spiral. Shortly after they had commenced the descent, Tarzan, accustomed from infancy to keen observation, had taken note of the numbers of tunnel entrances they passed, but he could only conjecture at the difference in the depths of the levels into which they opened. A rough guess placed them at fifteen feet, but before they reached the thirty-sixth, into which they turned, Tarzan felt that there must be an error in his calculations, for he was sure that they could not be five hundred and forty feet below the earth's surface with open flames and no forced ventilation.

The horizontal corridor they now entered after leaving the spiral curved sharply to the right and then back to the left. Shortly afterward it crossed a wide, circular corridor in which were both laden and unladen slaves, beyond which were two lines, those laden with rock moving back in the direction from which Tarzan had come, while others, bearing lumber moved in the same direction that he did. With both lines there were unladen slaves.

After traversing the horizontal tunnel for a considerable distance they came at last upon the working party, and here Tarzan was turned over to the Vental, a warrior who, in the military organizations of the Minunians, commands ten men.

"So this is The Giant!" exclaimed the Vental. "And we are not to work him too hard." His tone was sneering and disagreeable. "Such a giant!" he cried. "Why, he is no larger than I and they are afraid to let him do any work into the bargain. Mark you, he will work here or get the lash. Kalfastoban permits no sluggards," and the fellow struck his chest vauntingly.

He who had brought Tarzan appeared disgusted. "You will do well, Kalfastoban," he said, as he turned away to retrace his steps to the guard room, "to heed the king's commands. I should hate to be wearing your harness if aught befell this speechless slave that has set every tongue in Veltopismakus going and made Elkomoelhago so jealous of Zoanthrohago that he would slip steel between his ribs were it not that he could then no longer steal the great wizard's applause."

"Kalfastoban fears no king," blustered the Vental, "least of all the sorry specimen that befouls the throne of Veltopishago. "He fools no one but himself. We all know that Zoanthrohago is his brain and Gefasto his sword."

"However," warned the other, "be careful of Zuanthrol," and he departed.

Kalfastoban Vental set the new slave to work upon the timbering of the tunnel as it was excavated from the great moraine that formed the quarry, the line of slaves coming from the surface empty-handed passed down one side of the tunnel to the end, loosened each a rock, or if heavy a rock to two men, and turned back to the tunnel's opposite side, carrying their burdens back to the spiral runway used by those leaving the workings and so up and out to the new dome. The earth, a light clay, that filled the interstices between the rocks in the moraine was tamped into the opening behind the wall timbers, the tunnel being purposely made sufficiently large to permit of this. Certain slaves were detailed for this work, others carried timbers cut to the right dimensions down to the timbering crew, of which Tarzan was one. It was only necessary for this crew of three to scoop a narrow, shallow trench in which to place the foot of each wall board, set them in place and slip the ceiling board on top of them. At each end of the ceiling boards was a cleat, previously attached at the surface, which kept the wall boards from falling in after being set in place. The dirt tamped behind them fastened them solidly in their places, the whole making a quickly erected and substantial shoring.

The work was light for the ape-man, though he still was weak from the effects of his wounds, and he had opportunities constantly to observe all that went on around him and to gather new information relative to the people in whose power he found himself. Kalfastoban he soon set down as a loud-mouthed braggart, from whom one need have nothing to fear during the routine of their everyday work, but who would bear watching if ever opportunity came for him to make a show of authority or physical prowess before the eyes of his superiors.

The slaves about him worked steadily, but seemed not to be overtaxed, while the guards, which accompanied them constantly, in the ratio of about one warrior to every fifty slaves, gave no indications of brutality in the treatment they accorded their charges, insofar as Tarzan was able to observe.

The fact that puzzled him most now as it had since the moment of his first return to consciousness, was the stature of these people. They were no pygmies, but men fully as large as the usual run of Europeans. There was none quite as tall as the ape-man, but there were many who missed it by but the scantiest fraction of an inch. He knew that they were Veltopismakusians, the same people he had seen battling with the Trohanadalmakusians; they spoke of having captured him in the battle that he had seen waged; and they called him Zuanthrol, The Giant, yet they were as large as he, and as he had passed from the Royal Dome to the quarry he had seen their gigantic dome dwellings rising fully four hundred feet above his head. It was all preposterous and impossible, yet he had the testimony of all his faculties that it was true. Contemplation of it but tended to confuse him more and so he gave over all attempts to solve the mystery and set himself to the gathering of information concerning his captors and his prison against that time which he well knew must someday come when the means of escape should offer itself to the alert and cunning instincts of the wild beast that, at heart, he always considered himself.

Wherever he had been in Veltopismakus, whoever he had heard refer to the subject, he had had it borne in upon him that the people were generally dissatisfied with their king and his government, and he knew that among a discontented people efficiency would be at low ebb and discipline demoralized to such an extent that, should he watch carefully, he must eventually discover the opportunity he sought, through the laxity of those responsible for his safekeeping. He did not expect it today or tomorrow, but today and tomorrow were the days upon which to lay the foundation of observation that would eventually reveal an avenue of escape.

When the long working day at last drew to a close the slaves were conducted to their quarters, which, as Tarzan discovered, were always on levels near to those in which they labored. He, with several other slaves, was conducted to the thirty-fifth level and into a tunnel the far end of which had been widened to the proportions of a large chamber, the narrow entrance to which had been walled up with stone except for a small aperture through which the slaves were forced to pass in and out of their chamber upon all fours, and when the last of them was within, this was closed and secured by a heavy door outside which two warriors watched throughout the night.

Once inside and standing upon his feet the ape-man looked about him to discover himself within a chamber so large that it seemed easy to accommodate the great throng of slaves that must have numbered fully five thousand souls of both sexes.

The women were preparing food over small fires the smoke of which found its way from the chamber through openings in the ceiling. For the great number of fires the amount of smoke was noticeably little, a fact which was, however, accounted for by the nature of the fuel, a clean, hard charcoal; but why the liberated gases did not asphyxiate them all was quite beyond the ape-man, as was still the riddle of the open flames and the pure air at the depth where the workings lay. Candles burned in niches all about the walls and there were at least half-a-dozen large ones standing upon the floor.

The slaves were of all ages from infancy to middle age, but there were no aged venerables among them. The skins of the women and children were the whitest Tarzan had ever seen and he marveled at them until he came to know that some of the former and all of the latter had never seen daylight since birth. The children who were born here would go up into the daylight sometime, when they were of an age that warranted beginning the training for the vocations their masters had chosen for them, but the women who had been captured from other cities would remain here until death claimed them, unless that rarest of miracles occurred—they should be chosen by a Veltopis-makusian warrior as his mate; but that was scarce even a remote possibility, since the warriors almost invariably chose their mates from the slaves of the white tunic with whom they came in daily contact in the domes above ground.

The faces of the women bore the imprint of a sadness that brought a spontaneous surge of sympathy to the breast of the savage ape-man. Never in his life had he seen such abject hopelessness depicted upon any face.

As he crossed the room many were the glances that were cast upon him, for it was obvious from his deep tan that he was a newcomer, and, too, there was that about him that marked him of different clay from them, and soon there were whispers running through the throng, for the slaves who had entered with him had passed the word of his identity to the others, and who, even in the bowels of the earth, had not heard of the wondrous giant captured by Zoanthrohago during the battle with the Trohanadalmakusians?

Presently a young girl, kneeling above a brazier over which she was grilling a cut of flesh, caught his eye and motioned him to her. As he came he saw that she was very beautiful, with a pale, translucent skin the whiteness of which was accentuated by the blue-black of a wealth of lustrous hair.

"You are The Giant?" she asked.

"I am Zuanthrol," he replied.

"He has told me about you," said the girl. "I will cook for you, too. I cook for him. Unless," she added with a trace of embarrassment, "there is another you would rather have cook for you."

"There is no one I would rather have cook for me," Tarzan told her; "but who are you and who is *he*?"

"I am Talaskar," she replied; "but I know him only by his number. He says that while he remains a slave he has no name, but will go always by his number, which is Eight Hundred Cubed, Plus Nineteen. I see that you are Eight Hundred Cubed, Plus Twenty-one." She was looking at the hieroglyphics that had been fastened upon his shoulder. "Have you a name?"

"They call me Zuanthrol."

"Ah," she said, "you are a large man, but I should scarcely call you a giant. He, too, is from Trohanadalmakus and he is about your height. I never heard that there were any giants in Minuni expect the people they call Zertalacolols."

"I thought you were a Zertalacolol," said a man's voice at Tarzan's ear.

The ape-man turned to see one of the slaves with whom he had been working eyeing him quizzically, and smiled.

"I am a Zertalacolol to my masters," he replied.

The other raised his brows. "I see," he said. "Perhaps you are wise. I shall not be the one to betray you," and passed on about his business.

"What did he mean?" asked the girl.

"I have never spoken, until now, since they took me prisoner," he explained, "and they think I am speechless, though I am sure that I do not look like a Zertalacolol, yet some of them insist that I am one."

"I have never seen one," said the girl.

"You are fortunate," Tarzan told her. "They are neither pleasant to see nor to meet."

"But I should like to see them," she insisted. "I should like to see anything that was different from these slaves whom I see all day and every day."

"Do not lose hope," he encouraged her, "for who knows but that it may be very soon that you will return to the surface."

" 'Return,' " she repeated. "I have never been there."

"Never been to the surface! You mean since you were captured."

"I was born in this chamber," she told him, "and never have I been out of it."

"You are a slave of the second generation and are still confined to the quarries—I do not understand it. In all Minunian cities, I have been told, slaves of the second generation are given the white tunic and comparative freedom above ground."

"It was not for me. My mother would not permit it. She would rather I had died than mated with a Veltopismakusian or another slave, as I must do if I go into the city above."

"But how do you avoid it? Your masters certainly do not leave such things to the discretion of their slaves."

"Where there are so many one or two may go unaccounted for indefinitely, and women, if they be ill-favored, cause no comment upon the part of our masters. My birth was never reported and so they have no record of me. My mother took a number for me from the tunic of one who died, and in this way I attract no attention upon the few occasions that our masters or the warriors enter our chamber."

"But you are not ill-favored—your face would surely attract attention anywhere," Tarzan reminded her.

For just an instant she turned her back upon him, putting her hands to her face and to her hair, and then she faced him again and the ape-man saw before him a hideous and wrinkled hag upon whose crooked features no man would look a second time.

"God!" ejaculated Tarzan.

Slowly the girl's face relaxed, assuming its normal lines of beauty, and with quick, deft touches she arranged her disheveled hair. An expression that was almost a smile haunted her lips.

"My mother taught me this," she said, "so that when they came and looked upon me they would not want me."

"But would it not be better to be mated with one of them and live a life of comfort above ground than to eke out a terrible

existence below ground?" he demanded. "The warriors of Veltopismakus are, doubtless, but little different from those of
your own country."

She shook her head. "It cannot be, for me," she said. "My
father is of far Mandalamakus. My mother was stolen from
him but a couple of moons before I was born in this horrid
chamber, far from the air and sunlight that my mother never
tired of telling me about."

"And your mother?" asked Tarzan. "Is she here?"

The girl shook her head sadly. "They came for her over
twenty moons since and took her away. I do not know what
became of her."

"And these others, they never betray you?" he inquired.

"Never! Whatever slave betrayed another would be torn to
pieces by his fellows. But come, you must be hungry," and she
offered him of the flesh she had been cooking.

Tarzan would have preferred his meat raw, but he did not
wish to offend her and so he thanked her and ate that which
she offered him, squatting on his haunches across the brazier
from her.

"It is strange that Aoponato does not come," she remarked,
using the Minunian form of Eight Hundred Cubed, Plus Nineteen. "Never before has he been so late."

A brawny slave, who had approached from behind her, had
halted and was looking scowlingly at Tarzan.

"Perhaps this is he," said Tarzan to the girl, indicating the
man with a gesture.

Talaskar turned quickly, an almost happy light in her eyes, but
when she saw who it was that stood behind her she rose quickly
and stepped back, her expression altered to one of disgust.

"No," she said, "it is not he."

"You are cooking for him?" demanded the fellow, pointing
at Tarzan. "But you would not cook for me," he accused, not
waiting for a reply to his question, the answer to which was all
too obvious. "Who is he that you should cook for him? Is he
better than I? You will cook for me, also."

"There are plenty to cook for you, Caraftap," replied
Talaskar, "and I do not wish to. Go to some other woman.
Until there are too many men we are permitted to choose those
whom we shall cook for. I do not choose to cook for you."

"If you know what is well for you, you will cook for me," growled the man. "You will be my mate, too. I have a right to you, because I have asked you many times before these others came. Rather than let them have you I will tell the Ventral tomorrow the truth about you and he will take you away. Have you ever seen Kalfastoban?"

The girl shuddered.

"I will see that Kalfastoban gets you," continued Caraftap. "They will not permit you to remain here when they find that you refuse to produce more slaves."

"I should prefer Kalfastoban to you," sneered the girl, "but neither one nor the other shall have me."

"Do not be too sure of that," he cried, and stepping forward, quickly, seized her by the arm before she could elude him. Dragging her toward him the man attempted to kiss her—but he did not succeed. Steel fingers closed upon his shoulder, he was torn roughly from his prey and hurled ruthlessly a dozen paces, stumbling and falling to the floor. Between him and the girl stood the gray-eyed stranger with the shock of black hair.

Almost roaring in his rage, Caraftap scrambled to his feet and charged Tarzan—charged as a mad bull charges, with lowered head and bloodshot eyes.

"For this you shall die," he screamed.

12

THE SON OF The First Woman strode proudly through the forest. He carried a spear, jauntily, and there were a bow and arrows slung to his back. Behind him came ten other males of his species, similarly armed, and each walked as though he owned the earth he trod. Toward them along the trail, though still beyond their sight, or hearing, or smell, came a woman of their kind. She, too, walked with fearless step. Presently her eyes narrowed and she paused, up-pricking her great, flat ears to listen; sniffing the air. Men! She increased her gait to a trot, bearing down upon them. There was more than one—there were several. If she came upon them suddenly they would be startled, filled with confusion, and no doubt she could seize one of them before they took to flight. If not—the feathered pebbles at her girdle would seek one out.

For some time men had been scarce. Many women of her tribe who had gone out into the forest to capture mates had never returned. She had seen the corpses of several of these herself, lying in the forest. She had wondered what had killed them. But here were men at last, the first she had discovered in two moons, and this time she would not return empty-handed to her cave.

At a sudden turning of the forest trail she came within sight of them, but saw, to her dismay, that they were still a long way off. They would be sure to escape if they saw her, and she was upon the point of hiding when she realized that already it was too late. One of them was pointing at her. Loosing a missile from her girdle and grasping her cudgel more firmly she started toward them at a rapid, lumbering run. She was both surprised and pleased when she saw that they made no attempt to escape. How terrified they must be to stand thus docilely while she approached them. But what was this? They were advancing to meet her! And now she saw the expressions upon their faces. No fear there—only rage and menace. What were the strange things they carried in their hands? One who was running toward her, the nearest, paused and hurled a long pointed stick at her. It was sharp and when it grazed her shoulder it brought blood. Another paused and holding a little stick across a longer stick, the ends of which were bent back with a piece of gut, suddenly released the smaller stick, which leaped through the air and pierced the flesh beneath one of her arms. And behind these two the others were rushing upon her with similar weapons. She recalled the corpses of women she had seen in the forest and the dearth of men for the past several moons, and though she was dull of wit yet she was not without reasoning faculties and so she compared these facts with the occurrences of the past few seconds with a resultant judgment that sent her lumbering away, in the direction from which she had come, as fast as her hairy legs could carry her, nor did she once pause in her mad flight until she sank exhausted at the mouth of her own cave.

The men did not pursue her. As yet they had not reached that stage in their emancipation that was to give them sufficient courage and confidence in themselves to entirely overcome their hereditary fear of women. To chase one away was sufficient. To pursue her would have been tempting Providence.

When the other women of the tribe saw their fellow stagger to her cave and sensed that her condition was the result of terror and the physical strain of long flight they seized their cudgels and ran forth, prepared to meet and vanquish her pursuer, which they immediately assumed to be a lion. But no lion appeared and then some of them wandered to the side of the woman who lay panting on her threshold.

"From what did you run?" they asked her in their simple sign language.

"Men," she replied.

Disgust showed plainly upon every face, and one of them kicked her and another spat upon her.

"There were many," she told them, "and they would have killed me with flying sticks. Look!" and she showed them the spear wound, and the arrow still embedded in the flesh beneath her arm. "They did not run from me, but came forward to attack me. Thus have all the women been killed whose corpses we have seen in the forest during the past few moons."

This troubled them. They ceased to annoy the prostrate woman. Their leader, the fiercest of them, paced to and fro, making hideous faces. Suddenly she halted.

"Come!" she signaled. "We shall go forth together and find these men, and bring them back and punish them." She shook her cudgel above her head and grimaced horribly.

The others danced about her, imitating her expression and her actions, and when she started off toward the forest they trooped behind her, a savage, bloodthirsty company—all but the woman who still lay panting where she had fallen. She had had enough of man—she was through with him forever.

* * *

"For this you shall die!" screamed Caraftap, as he rushed upon Tarzan of the Apes in the long gallery of the slaves' quarters in the quarry of Elkomeolhago, king of Veltopismakus.

The ape-man stepped quickly aside, avoiding the other, and tripped him with a foot, sending him sprawling, face downward, upon the floor. Caraftap, before he arose, looked about as though in search of a weapon and, his eyes alighting upon the hot brazier, he reached forth to seize it. A murmur of disapproval rose from the slaves who, having been occupied nearby, had seen the inception of the quarrel.

"No weapons!" cried one. "It is not permitted among us. Fight with your bare hands or not at all."

But Caraftap was too drunk with hate and jealousy to hear them or to heed, and so he grasped the brazier and, rising, rushed at Tarzan to hurl it in his face. Now it was another who tripped him and this time two slaves leaped upon him and wrenched the brazier from his hand. "Fight fair!" they admonished him, and dragged him to his feet.

Tarzan had stood smiling and indifferent, for the rage of others amused him where it was greater than circumstances warranted, and now he waited for Caraftap and when his adversary saw the smile upon his face it but increased his spleen, so that he fairly leaped upon the ape-man in his madness to destroy him, and Tarzan met him with the most surprising defense that Caraftap, who for long had been a bully among the slaves, ever had encountered. It was a doubled fist at the end of a straight arm and it caught Caraftap upon the point of his chin, stretching him upon his back. The slaves, who had by this time gathered in considerable numbers to watch the quarrel, voiced their approval in the shrill, "Ee-ah-ee-ah," that constituted one form of applause.

Dazed and groggy, Caraftap staggered to his feet once more and with lowered head looked about him as though in search of his enemy. The girl, Talaskar, had come to Tarzan's side and was standing there looking up into his face.

"You are very strong," she said, but the expression in her eyes said more, or at least it seemed to Caraftap to say more. It seemed to speak of love, whereas it was only the admiration that a normal woman always feels for strength exercised in a worthy cause.

Caraftap made a noise in his throat that sounded much like the squeal of an angry pig and once again he rushed upon the ape-man. Behind them some slaves were being let into the corridor and as the aperture was open one of the warriors beyond it, who chanced to be stooping down at the time, could see within. He saw but little, though what he saw was enough—a large slave with a shock of black hair raising another large slave high above his head and dashing him to the hard floor. The warrior, pushing the slaves aside, scrambled through into the corridor and ran forward toward the center. Before they were aware of his presence he stood facing Tarzan and Talaskar. It was Kalfastoban.

"What is the meaning of this?" he cried in a loud voice, and then: "Ah, ha! I see. It is The Giant. He would show the other slaves how strong he is, would he?" He glanced at Caraftap, struggling to rise from the floor, and his face grew very dark— Caraftap was a favorite of his. "Such things are not permitted here, fellow!" he cried, shaking his fist in the ape-man's face, and forgetting in his anger that the new slave neither spoke nor understood. But presently he recollected and motioned Tarzan to follow him. "A hundred lashes will explain to him that he must not quarrel," he said aloud to no one in particular, but he was looking at Talaskar.

"Do not punish him," cried the girl, still forgetful of herself. "It was all Caraftap's fault, Zuanthrol but acted in self-defense."

Kalfastoban could not take his eyes from the girl's face and presently she sensed her danger and flushed, but still she stood her ground, interceding for the ape-man. A crooked smile twisted Kalfastoban's mouth as he laid a familiar hand upon her shoulder.

"How old are you?" he asked.

She told him, shuddering.

"I shall see your master and purchase you," he announced. "Take no mate."

Tarzan was looking at Talaskar and it seemed that he could see her wilt, as a flower wilts in noxious air, and then Kalfastoban turned upon him.

"You cannot understand me, you stupid beast," he said; "but I can tell you, and those around you may listen and, perhaps, guide you from danger. This time I shall let you off, but let it happen again and you shall have a hundred lashes, or worse, maybe; and if I hear that you have had aught to do with this girl, whom I intend to purchase and take to the surface, it will go still harder with you," with which he strode to the entrance and passed through into the corridor beyond.

After the Vental had departed and the door of the chamber had been closed a hand was laid upon Tarzan's shoulder from behind and a man's voice called him by name: "Tarzan!" It sounded strange in his ears, far down in this buried chamber beneath the ground, in an alien city and among an alien people, not one of whom ever had heard his name, but as he turned to face the man who had greeted him a look of recognition and a smile of pleasure overspread his features.

"Kom—!" he started to ejaculate, but the other placed a finger to his lips. "Not here," he said. "Here I am Aoponato."

"But your stature! You are as large as I. It is beyond me. What has happened to swell the race of Minunians to such relatively gigantic proportions?"

Komodoflorensal smiled. "Human egotism would not permit you to attribute this change to an opposite cause from that to which you have ascribed it," he said.

Tarzan knit his brows and gazed long and thoughtfully at his royal friend. An expression that was of mingled incredulity and amusement crept gradually over his countenance.

"You mean," he asked slowly, "that I have been reduced in size to the stature of a Minunian?"

Komodoflorensal nodded. "Is it not easier to believe that than to think that an entire race of people and all their belongings, even their dwellings and the stones that they were built of, and all their weapons and their diadets, had been increased in size to your own stature?"

"But I tell you it is impossible!" cried the ape-man.

"I should have said the same thing a few moons ago," replied the prince. "Even when I heard the rumor here that they had reduced you I did not believe it, not for a long time, and I was still a bit skeptical until I entered this chamber and saw you with my own eyes."

"How was it accomplished?" demanded Tarzan.

"The greatest mind in Veltopismakus, and perhaps in all

Minuni, is Zoanthrohago," explained Komodoflorensal. "We have recognized this for many moons, for, during the occasional intervals that we are at peace with Veltopismakus, there is some exchange of ideas as well as goods between the two cities, and thus we heard of many marvels attributed to this greatest of walmaks."

"I have never heard a wizard spoken of in Minuni until now," said Tarzan, for he thought that that was the meaning of the word *walmak*, and perhaps it is, as nearly as it can be translated into English. A scientist who works miracles would be, perhaps, a truer definition.

"It was Zoanthrohago who captured you," continued Aoponato, "encompassing your fall by means at once scientific and miraculous. After you had fallen he caused you to lose consciousness and while you were in that condition you were dragged hither by a score of diadets hitched to a hastily improvised litter built of small trees tied securely one to the other, after their branches had been removed. It was after they had you safely within Veltopismakus that Zoanthrohago set to work upon you to reduce your stature, using apparatus that he has built himself. I have heard them discussing it and they say that it did not take him long."

"I hope that Zoanthrohago has the power to undo that which he has done," said the ape-man.

"They say that that is doubtful. He has never been able to make a creature larger than it formerly was, though in his numerous experiments he has reduced the size of many of the lower animals. The fact of the matter is," continued Aoponato, "that he has been searching for a means to enlarge the Veltopismakusians so that they may overcome all the other peoples of Minuni, but he has only succeeded in developing a method that gives precisely opposite results from that which they seek, so, if he cannot make others larger, I doubt if he can make you any larger than you now are."

"I would be rather helpless among the enemies of my own world," said Tarzan, ruefully.

"You need not worry about that, my friend," said the prince gently.

"Why?" asked the ape-man.

"Because you have very little chance of reaching your own

world again," said Komodoflorensal a trifle sadly. "I have no hope of ever seeing Trohanadalmakus again. Only by the utter overthrow of Veltopismakus by my father's warriors could I hope for rescue, since nothing less could overcome the guard in the quarry mouth. While we often capture slaves of the white tunic from the enemies' cities, it is seldom that we gather in any of the green tunic. Only in the rare cases of utter surprise attacks by daylight do any of us catch an enemies' green slaves above ground, and surprise day attacks may occur once in the lifetime of a man, or never."

"You believe that we will spend the rest of our lives in this underground hole?" demanded Tarzan.

"Unless we chance to be used for labor above ground during the daytime, occasionally," replied the prince of Trohanadalmakus, with a wry smile.

The ape-man shrugged. "We shall see," he said.

After Kalfastoban had left, Caraftap had limped away to the far end of the chamber, muttering to himself, his ugly face black and scowling.

"I am afraid that he will make you trouble," Talaskar said to Tarzan, indicating the disgruntled slave with a nod of her shapely head, "and I am sorry, for it is all my fault."

"Your fault?" demanded Komodoflorensal.

"Yes," said the girl. "Caraftap was threatening me when Aopontando interfered and punished him."

"Aopontando?" queried Komodoflorensal.

"That is my number," explained Tarzan.

"And it was on account of Talaskar that you were fighting? I thank you, my friend. I am sorry that I was not here to protect her. Talaskar cooks for me. She is a good girl." Komodoflorensal was looking at the girl as he spoke and Tarzan saw how her eyes lowered beneath his gaze and the delicate flush that mounted her cheeks, and he realized that he was downwind from an idea, and smiled.

"So this is the Aoponato of whom you told me?" he said to Talaskar.

"Yes, this is he."

"I am sorry that he was captured, but it is good to find a friend here," said the ape-man. "We three should be able to hit upon some plan of escape," but they shook their heads, smiling sadly.

For a while, after they had eaten, they sat talking together, being joined occasionally by other slaves, for Tarzan had many friends here now since he had chastised Caraftap and they would have talked all night had not the ape-man questioned Komodoflorensal as to the sleeping arrangements of the slaves.

Komodoflorensal laughed, and pointed here and there about the chamber at recumbent figures lying upon the hard earthen floor; men, women and children sleeping, for the most part, where they had eaten their evening meal.

"The green slaves are not pampered," he remarked laconically.

"I can sleep anywhere," said Tarzan, "but more easily when it is dark. I shall wait until the lights are extinguished."

"You will wait forever, then," Komodoflorensal told him.

"The lights are never extinguished?" demanded the ape-man.

"Were they, we should all be soon dead," replied the prince. "These flames serve two purposes—they dissipate the darkness and consume the foul gases that would otherwise quickly asphyxiate us. Unlike the ordinary flame, that consumes oxygen, these candles, perfected from the discoveries and inventions of an ancient Minunian scientist, consume the deadly gases and liberate oxygen. It is because of this even more than for the light they give that they are used exclusively throughout Minuni. Even our domes would be dark, ill-smelling, noxious places were it not for them, while the quarries would be absolutely unworkable."

"Then I shall not wait for them to be extinguished," said Tarzan, stretching himself at full length upon the dirt floor, with a nod and a "Tuano!"—a Minunian "Good night!"—to Talaskar and Komodoflorensal.

13

As TALASKAR WAS preparing their breakfast the following morning Komodoflorensal remarked to Tarzan that he wished they two could be employed upon the same work, that they might be always together.

"If there is ever the chance for escape that you seem to think will someday present itself," he said, "then it will be well if we are together."

"When we go," replied Tarzan, "we must take Talaskar with us."

Komodoflorensal shot a swift glance at the ape-man, but made no comment upon his suggestion.

"You would take me with you!" exclaimed Talaskar. "Ah, if such a dream could but be realized! I would go with you to Trohanadalmakus and be your slave, for I know that you would not harm me; but, alas, it can be nothing more than a pleasant daydream, enduring for a brief time, for Kalfastoban has spoken for me and doubtless my master will be glad to sell me to him, for I have heard it said among the slaves that he sells many of his each year to raise the money to pay his taxes."

"We will do what we can, Talaskar," said Tarzan, "and if Aoponato and I find a means of escape we will take you with us; but first he and I must find a way to be together more."

"I have a plan," said Komodoflorensal, "that might prove successful. They believe that you neither speak nor understand our language. To work a slave with whom they cannot communicate is, to say the least, annoying. I shall tell them that I can communicate with you, when it is quite probable that they will assign us to the same crew."

"But how will you communicate with me without using the Minunian language?" demanded the ape-man.

"Leave that to me," replied Komodoflorensal. "Until they discover in some other way that you speak Minunian I can continue to deceive them."

It was not long before the fruits of Komodoflorensal's plan ripened. The guards had come for the slaves and the various parties had gone forth from the sleeping chamber, joining in the corridors without the thousands of others wending their way to the scene of their daily labor. The ape-man joined the timbering crew at the extension of the thirteenth tunnel at the thirty-sixth level where he once more attacked the monotonous work of shoring the sides and roof of the shaft with an enthusiasm that elicited commendation from even the surly Kalfastoban, though Caraftap, who was removing rocks just ahead of Tarzan, often shot venomous looks at the ape-man.

The work had been progressing for perhaps two or three hours when two warriors descended the tunnel and halted beside Kalfastoban. They were escorting a green-tunicked slave, to whom Tarzan paid no more attention than he did to the warriors until a scrap of the conversation between the warriors and Kalfastoban reached his ears, then he shot a quick glance in the direction of the four and saw that the slave was Komodoflorensal, Prince of Trohanadalmakus, known in the quarries of Vetlopismakus as Slave Aoponato, or $800^3 + 19$,

which is written in Minunian hieroglyphics .

Tarzan's number Aopontando, $800^3 + 21$, appeared thus, upon the shoulder of his green tunic: Although the

Minunian form occupies less space than would our English equivalent of Tarzan's number, which is 512,000,021; it would be more difficult to read if expressed in English words, for it then would be, ten times ten times eight, cubed, plus seven times three; but the Minunians translate it in no such way. To them it is a whole number, Aopontando, which represents at first glance a single quantity as surely as do the digits 37 represent to our minds an invariable amount, a certain, definite measure of quantity which we never think of as three times ten plus seven, which, in reality, it is. The Minunian system of numerals, while unthinkably cumbersome and awkward from the European point of view, is, however, not without its merits.

As Tarzan looked up Komodoflorensal caught his eye and winked and then Kalfastoban beckoned to the ape-man, who crossed the corridor and stood in silence before the Vental.

"Let us hear you talk to him," cried Kalfastoban to Komodoflorensal. "I don't believe that he will understand you. How could he when he cannot understand us?" The fellow could not conceive of another language than his own.

"I will ask him in his own language," said Komodoflorensal, "if he understands me, and you will see that he nods his head affirmatively."

"Very good," cried Kalfastoban; "ask him."

Komodoflorensal turned toward Tarzan and voiced a dozen syllables of incomprehensible gibberish and when he was done the ape-man nodded his head.

"You see," demanded Komodoflorensal.

Kalfastoban scratched his head. "It is even as he says," he admitted, ruefully, "the Zertalacolol has a language."

Tarzan did not smile, though he should have liked to, at the clever manner in which Komodoflorensal had deceived the Veltopismakusians into believing that he had communicated with Tarzan in a strange language. As long as he could contrive to put all his communications into questions that could be answered by yes or no, the deception would be easily maintained; but under circumstances that made this impossible some embarrassments might be expected to arise, and he wondered how the resourceful Trohanadalmakusian would handle these.

"Tell him," said one of the warriors to Komodoflorensal, "that his master, Zoanthrohago, has sent for him, and ask him if he fully understands that he is a slave and that upon his good behavior depends his comfort; yes, even his life, for Zoanthrohago has the power of life and death over him; as much so as have the royal family. If he comes docilely to his master and is obedient he will not fare ill, but if he be lazy, impudent, or threatening he may expect to taste the point of a freeman's sword."

Komodoflorensal strung out, this time, a much longer series of senseless syllables, until he could scarce compose his features to comport with the seriousness of his mien.

"Tell them," said Tarzan, in English, which, of course, not one of them understood, "that at the first opportunity I shall break the neck of my master; that it would require but little incentive to cause me to seize one of these timbers and crack the skull of Kalfastoban and the rest of the warriors about us; and I shall run away at the first opportunity and take you and Talaskar with me."

Komodoflorensal listened intently until Tarzan had ceased speaking and then turned to the two warriors who had come with him to find the ape-man.

"Zuanthrol says that he fully understands his position and that he is glad to serve the noble and illustrious Zoanthrohago, from whom he claims but a single boon," translated the Trohanadalmakusian prince, rather freely.

"And what boon is that?" demanded one of the warriors.

"That I be permitted to accompany him that he may thus better fulfil the wishes of his master, since without me he could not even know what was desired of him," explained Aoponato.

Tarzan understood now how Komodoflorensal would surmount whatever difficulties of communication might arise and he felt that he would be safe in the hands of his quick-witted friend for as long a time as he cared to pretend ignorance of the Minunian tongue.

"The thought was even in our minds, slave, when we heard that you could communicate with this fellow," said the warrior to whom Komodoflorensal had addressed the suggestion. "You shall both be taken to Zoanthrohago, who will doubtless decide his wishes without consulting you or any other slave. Come! Kalfastoban Vental, we assume responsibility for the Slave Zuanthrol," and they handed the Vental a slip of paper upon which they had marked some curious hieroglyphics.

Then, with swords drawn, they motioned Komodoflorensal and Tarzan to precede them along the corridor, for the story of Tarzan's handling of Caraftap had reached even to the guard room of the quarry, and these warriors were taking no chances.

The way led through a straight corridor and up a winding spiral runway to the surface, where Tarzan greeted the sunlight and the fresh air almost with a sob of gratitude, for to be shut away from them for even a brief day was to the ape-man cruel punishment, indeed. Here he saw again the vast, endless multitude of slaves bearing their heavy burdens to and fro, the trim warriors who paced haughtily upon either flank of the long lines of toiling serfs, the richly trapped nobles of the higher castes and the innumerable white-tunicked slaves who darted hither and thither upon the errands of their masters, or upon their own business or pleasure, for many of these had a certain freedom and independence that gave them almost the standing of freemen. Always were these slaves of the white tunic owned by a master, but, especially in the case of skilled artisans, about the only allegiance they owed to this master was to pay him a certain percentage of their incomes. They constituted the bourgeoisie of Minuni and also the higher caste serving class. Unlike the green-tunicked slaves, no guard was placed over them to prevent their escape, since there was no danger that they would attempt to escape, there being no city in Minuni where their estate would be improved, for any other city than that of their birth would treat them as alien prisoners, reducing them immediately to the green tunic and lifelong hard labor.

The domes of Veltopismakus were as imposing as those of Trohanadalmakus. In fact, to Tarzan, they appeared infinitely larger since he now was one-fourth the size he had been when he had left Trohanadalmakus. There were eight of them fully occupied and another in course of construction, for the surface population of Veltopismakus was already four hundred and eighty thousand souls, and as overcrowding was not permitted in the king's dome the remaining seven were packed densely with humanity.

It was to the royal dome that Tarzan and Komodoflorensal were conducted, but they did not enter by way of the King's Corridor, before the gates of which fluttered the white and gold of the royal standards. Instead they were escorted to the Warrior's Corridor, which opens toward the west. Unlike the city of Trohanadalmakus, Veltopismakus was beautiful in the areas between the domes with flowers and shrubbery and trees, among which wound graveled walks and broad roadways. The royal dome faced upon a large parade where a body of mounted warriors was at drill. There were a thousand of them, forming an amak, consisting of four novands of two hundred fifty men each, the larger body being commanded by a kamak and the smaller by a novand. Five entex of fifty men each compose a novand, there being five entals of ten men each to an entex; these latter units commanded by a Vental and a Ventex, respectively. The evolutions of the amak were performed with kaleidoscopic rapidity, so quick upon their feet and so well trained were the tiny diadets. There was one evolution in particular, performed while he was passing, that greatly interested the ape-man. Two novands formed line at one end of the parade and two at the other and at the command of the kamak the thousand men charged swiftly down the field in two solid ranks that approached one another with the speed of an express train. Just when it seemed impossible that a serious accident could be averted, when it seemed that in another instant diadets and riders must crash together in a bloody jumble of broken bones, the warriors rushing so swiftly toward the east raised their agile mounts, which fairly flew above the heads of the opposing force and alighting upon the other side in an unbroken line continued to the far end of the field.

Tarzan was commenting on this maneuver and upon the beauties of the landscaping of the city of Veltopismakus to Komodoflorensal as they proceeded along the Warrior's Corridor, sufficiently ahead of their escort that Tarzan might speak in a low tone without the guard being cognizant of the fact that he was using the language of Minuni.

"It is a beautiful evolution," replied Komodoflorensal, "and it was performed with a precision seldom attained. I have heard that Elkomoelhago's troops are famous for the perfection of their drill, and as justly so as is Veltopismakus for the beauty of her walks and gardens; but, my friend, these very things constitute the weakness of the city. While Elkomoelhago's warriors are practicing to perfect their appearance upon parade, the warriors of my father, Adendrohahkis, are far afield, out of sight of admiring women and spying slaves, practicing the art of war under the rough conditions of the field and camp. The amaks of Elkomoelhago might easily defeat those of Adendrohahkis in a contest for the most beautiful; but it was not long since you saw less than fifteen thousand Trohanadalmakusians repulse fully thirty thousand warriors of Veltopismakus, for they never passed the infantry line that day. Yes, they can drill beautifully upon parade and they are courageous, all Minunians are that, but they have not been trained in the sterner arts of war—it is not the way of Elkomoelhago. He is soft and effeminate. He cares not for war. He listens to the advice he likes best—the advice of the weaklings and the women who urge him to refrain from war entirely, which would be not altogether bad if he could persuade the other fellow to refrain, also.

"The beautiful trees and shrubs that almost make a forest of Veltopismakus, and which you so admire! I, too, admire them—especially do I admire them in the city of an enemy. How easy it would be for a Trohanadalmakusian army to creep through the night, hidden by the beautiful trees and shrubs, to the very gateways of the domes of Veltopismakus! Do you understand now, my friend, why you saw less perfect maneuvers upon the parade grounds of my city than you have seen here, and why, though we love trees and shrubbery, we have none planted within the city of Trohanadalmakus?"

One of the guards who had approached him quickly from the rear touched Komodoflorensal upon the shoulder. "You said that Zuanthrol does not understand our language. Why then do you speak to him in this tongue which he cannot understand," the fellow demanded.

Komodoflorensal did not know how much the warrior had overheard. If he had heard Tarzan speak in Minuni it might be difficult to persuade the fellow that The Giant did not understand the language; but he must act on the assumption that he, alone, had been overheard.

"He wishes to learn it and I am trying to teach him," replied Komodoflorensal quickly.

"Has he learned anything of it?" asked the warrior.

"No," said Komodoflorensal, "he is very stupid."

And after this they went in silence, winding up long, gentle inclines, or again scaling the primitive ladders that the Minunians use to reach the upper levels of their dome-houses between the occasional levels that are not connected by the inclined runways, which are thus frequently broken for purposes of defense, the ladders being easily withdrawn upward behind hard-pressed defenders and the advance of the enemy thus more easily checked.

The royal dome of Elkomoelhago was of vast proportions, its summit rising to an equivalent of over four hundred feet, had it been built upon a scale corresponding to the relatively larger size of ordinary mankind. Tarzan ascended until he was almost as far above ground as he had been below ground in the quarry. Where the corridors on lower levels had been crowded with humanity, those which they now traversed were almost devoid of life. Occasionally they passed a tenanted chamber, but far more generally the rooms were utilized for storage purposes, especially for food, great quantities of which, cured, dried, and neatly wrapped, was packed ceiling-high in many large chambers.

The decorations of the walls were less ornate and the corridors narrower, on the whole, than those at lower levels. However, they passed through many large chambers, or halls, which were gorgeously decorated, and in several of which were many people of both sexes and all ages variously occupied, either with domestic activities or with the handiwork of one art or another.

Here was a man working in silver, perhaps fashioning a bracelet of delicate filigree, or another carving beautiful arabesques upon leather. There were makers of pottery, weavers of cloth, metal-stampers, painters, makers of candles, and these appeared to predominate, for the candle was in truth life to these people.

And then, at last, they reached the highest level, far above the ground, where the rooms were much closer to daylight because of the diminished thickness of the walls near the summit of the dome, but even here were the ever-present candles. Suddenly the walls of the corridor became gorgeously decorated, the number of candles increased, and Tarzan sensed that they were approaching the quarters of a rich or powerful noble. They halted, now, before a doorway where stood a sentinel, with whom one of the warriors conducting them communicated.

"Tell Zoanthrohago Zertol that we have brought Zuanthrol and another slave who can communicate with him in a strange tongue."

The sentinel struck a heavy gong with his lance and presently, from the interior of the chamber, a man appeared to whom the sentinel repeated the warrior's message.

"Let them enter," said the newcomer, who was a white-tunicked slave; "my glorious master, Zoanthrohago Zertol, expects his slave Zuanthrol. Follow me!"

They followed him through several chambers until at last he led them into the presence of a gorgeously garbed warrior who was seated behind a large table, or desk, upon which were numerous strange instruments, large, cumbersome looking volumes, pads of heavy Minunian writing paper, and the necessary implements for writing. The man looked up as they entered the room.

"It is your slave, Zuanthrol, Zertol," announced the fellow who had led them hither.

"But the other?" Prince Zoanthrohago pointed at Komodoflorensal.

"He speaks the strange language that Zuanthrol speaks, and he was brought along that you might communicate with Zuanthrol if you so wished." Zoanthrohago nodded.

He turned to Komodoflorensal. "Ask him," he ordered, "if he feels any differently since I reduced his size."

When the question was put to Tarzan by Komodoflorensal in the imaginary language with which they were supposed to communicate the ape-man shook his head, at the same time speaking a few words in English.

"He says no, illustrious prince," translated Komodoflorensal out of his imagination, "and he asks when you will restore him to his normal size and permit him to return to his own country, which is far from Minuni."

"As a Minunian he should know," replied the Zertol, "that he never will be permitted to return to his own country—Trohanadalmakus never will see him again."

"But he is not of Trohanadalmakus, nor is he a Minunian," explained Komodoflorensal. "He came to us and we did not make a slave of him, but treated him as a friend, because he is from a far country with which we have never made war."

"What country is that?" demanded Zoanthrohago.

"That we do not know, but he says that there is a great country beyond the thorns where dwell many millions as large as was he. He says that his people would not be unfriendly to ours and for this reason we should not enslave him, but treat him as a guest."

Zoanthrohago smiled. "If you believe this you must be a simple fellow, Trohanadalmakusian," he said. "We all know that there is naught beyond Minuni but impenetrable forests of thorn to the very uttermost wall of the blue dome within which we all dwell. I can well believe that the fellow is no Trohanadalmakusian, but he most certainly is a Minunian, since all creatures of whatever kind dwell in Minuni. Doubtless he is a strange form of Zertalacolol, a member of a tribe inhabiting some remote mountain fastness, which we have never previously discovered; but be that as it may, he will never—"

At this juncture the prince was interrupted by the clanging of the great gong at the outer entrance to his apartments. He paused to count the strokes and when they reached five and ceased he turned to the warriors who had conducted Tarzan and Komodoflorensal to his presence.

"Take the slaves into that chamber," he instructed, pointing to a doorway in the rear of the apartment in which he had received them. "When the king has gone I will send for them."

As they were crossing toward the doorway Zoanthrohago had indicated a warrior halted in the main entrance to the chamber. "Elkomoelhago," he announced, "Thagosto of Veltopismakus, Ruler of All Men, Master of Created Things, All-Wise, All-Courageous, All-Glorious! Down before the thagosto!"

Tarzan glanced back as he was quitting the chamber to see Zoanthrohago and the others in the room kneel and lean far back with arms raised high above their heads as Elkomoelhago entered with a guard of a dozen gorgeous warriors, and he could not but compare this ruler with the simple and dignified soldier who ruled Trohanadalmakus and who went about his city without show or pomp, and oftentimes with no other escort than a single slave; a ruler to whom no man bent his knee, yet to whom was accorded the maximum of veneration and respect.

And Elkomoelhago had seen the slaves and the warriors leave the chamber as he had entered it. He acknowledged the salutes of Zoanthrohago and his people with a curt wave of the hand and commanded them to arise.

"Who quitted the apartment as I entered?" he demanded, looking suspiciously at Zoanthrohago.

"The slave Zuanthrol and another who interprets his strange language for me," explained the Zertol.

"Have them back," commanded the thagosto; "I would speak with you concerning Zuanthrol."

Zoanthrohago instructed one of his slaves to fetch them and, in the few moments that it required, Elkomoelhago took a chair behind the desk at which his host had been sitting. When Tarzan and Komodoflorensal entered the chamber the guard who accompanied them brought them to within a few paces of the desk behind which the king sat, and here he bade them kneel and make their obeisance to the thagosto.

Familiar since childhood, was every tradition of slavery to Komodoflorensal the Trohanadalmakusian. Almost in a spirit of fatalism had he accepted the conditions of this servitude that the fortunes of war had thrust him into and so it was that, without question or hesitation, he dropped to one knee in servile salute to this alien king; but not so Tarzan of the Apes. He was thinking of Adendrohahkis. He had bent no knee to him and he did not propose to do greater honor to Elkomoelhago, whose very courtiers and slaves despised him, than he had done to the really great king of Veltopismakus.

Elkomoelhago glared at him. "The fellow is not kneeling," he whispered to Zoanthrohago, who had been leaning back so far that he had not noticed the new slave's act of disrespect.

The Zertol glanced toward Tarzan. "Down, fellow!" he cried, and then recalling that he understood no Minunian, he commanded Komodoflorensal to order him to kneel, but when the Trohanadalmakusian Zertolosto pretended to do so Tarzan but shook his head.

Elkomoelhago signaled the others to rise. "We will let it pass this time," he said, for something in the attitude of the slave told him that Zuanthrol never would kneel to him and as he was valuable because of the experiment of which he was the subject, the king preferred to swallow his pride rather than risk having the slave killed in an effort to compel him to kneel. "He is but an ignorant Zertalacolol. See that he is properly instructed before we see him again."

14

THE ALALI WOMEN, fifty strong, sallied forth into the forest to chastise their recalcitrant males. They carried their heavy bludgeons and many-feathered pebbles, but most formidable of all was their terrific rage. Never in the memory of one of them had man dared question their authority, never had he presumed to show aught but fear of them; but now, instead of slinking away at their approach, he had dared defy them, to attack them, to slay them! But such a condition was too preposterous, too unnatural, to exist, nor would it exist much longer. Had they had speech they would have said that and a number of other things. It was looking black for the men; the women were in an ugly mood—but what else could be expected of women who were denied the power of speech?

And in this temper they came upon the men in a large clearing where the renegades had built a fire and were cooking the flesh of a number of antelope. Never had the women seen their men so sleek and trim. Always before had they appeared skinny to the verge of cadaverousness, for in the past they had never fared so well as since the day that Tarzan of the Apes had given weapons to the son of The First Woman. Where before they had spent their lives fleeing in terror from their terrible women, with scarce time to hunt for decent food, now they had leisure and peace of mind and their weapons brought them flesh that otherwise they might not have tasted once in a year. From caterpillars and grubworms they had graduated to an almost steady diet of antelope meat.

But the women gave very little heed at the moment to the physical appearance of the men. They had found them. That was enough. They were creeping nearer when one of the men looked up and discovered them, and so insistent are the demands of habit that he forgot his new-found independence and leaping to his feet, bolted for the trees. The others, scarce waiting to know the cause of his precipitancy, followed close upon his heels. The women raced across the clearing as the men disappeared among the trees upon the opposite side. The former knew what the men would do. Once in the forest they would stop behind the nearest trees and look back to see if their pursuers were coming in their direction. It was this silly habit of the males that permitted their being easily caught by the less agile females.

But all the men had not disappeared. One had taken a few steps in the mad race for safety and had then halted and wheeled about, facing the oncoming women. He was the son of The First Woman, and to him Tarzan had imparted something more than knowledge of new weapons, for from the Lord of the Jungle, whom he worshipped with doglike devotion, he had acquired the first rudiments of courage, and so it now happened that when his more timorous fellows paused behind the trees and looked back they saw this one standing alone facing the charge of fifty infuriated shes. They saw him fit arrow to bow, and the women saw, too, but they did not understand—not immediately—and then the bowstring twanged and the foremost woman collapsed with an arrow in her heart; but the others did not pause, because the thing had been done so quickly that the full purport of it had not as yet penetrated their thick skulls. The son of The First Woman fitted a second arrow and sped it. Another woman fell, rolling over and over, and now the others hesitated—hesitated and were lost, for that momentary pause gave courage to the other men peering from behind the trees. If one of their number could face fifty women and bring them to halt what might not eleven men accomplish? They rushed forth then with spears and arrows just as the women renewed their assault. The feathered pebbles flew thick and fast, but faster and more accurately flew the feathered arrows of the men. The leading women rushed courageously forward to close quarters where they might use their bludgeons and lay hold of the men with their mighty hands, but they learned then that spears were more formidable weapons than bludgeons, with the result that those who did not fall wounded, turned and fled.

It was then that the son of The First Woman revealed possession of a spark of generalship that decided the issue for that day, and, perhaps, for all time. His action was epochal in the existence of the Zertalacolols. Instead of being satisfied with repulsing the women, instead of resting upon laurels gloriously won, he turned the tables upon the hereditary foe and charged the women, signaling his fellows to accompany him, and when they saw the women running from them, so enthused were they by this reversal of a custom ages old, they leaped swiftly in pursuit.

They thought that the son of The First Woman intended that they should slay all of the enemy and so they were surprised when they saw him overhaul a comely, young female and, seizing her by the hair, disarm her. So remarkable did it seem to them that one of their number, having a woman in his power, did not immediately slay her, they were constrained to pause and gather around him, asking questions in their strange sign language.

"Why do you hold her?" "Why do you not kill her?" "Are you not afraid that she will kill you?" were some of the many that were launched at him.

"I am going to keep her," replied the son of The First Woman. "I do not like to cook. She shall cook for me. If she refuses I shall stick her with this," and he made a jab toward the young woman's ribs with his spear, a gesture that caused her to cower and drop fearfully upon one knee.

The men jumped up and down in excitement as the value of this plan and the evident terror of the woman for the man sank into their dull souls.

"Where are the women?" they signed to one another; but the women had disappeared.

One of the men started off in the direction they had gone. "I go!" he signaled. "I come back with a woman of my own, to cook for me!" In a mad rush the others followed him, leaving the son of The First Woman alone with his she. He turned upon her.

"You will cook for me?" he demanded.

To his signs she but returned a sullen, snarling visage. The son of The First Woman raised his spear and with the heavy shaft struck the girl upon the head, knocking her down, and he stood over her, himself snarling and scowling, menacing her with further punishment, while she cowered where she had fallen. He kicked her in the side.

"Get up!" he commanded.

Slowly she crawled to her knees and embracing his legs gazed up into his face with an expression of doglike adulation and devotion.

"You will cook for me!" he demanded again.

"Forever!" she replied in the sign language of their people.

Tarzan had remained but a short time in the little room adjoining that in which Zuanthrohago had received Elkomoelhago, when he was summoned to appear before them alone, and as he entered the room his master motioned him to approach the desk behind which the two men sat. There was no other person in the room, even the warriors having been dismissed.

"You are quite positive that he understands nothing of our language?" demanded the king.

"He has not spoken a word since he was captured," replied Zoanthrohago. "We had supposed him some new form of Zertalalcolol until it was discovered that he possessed a language through which he was able to communicate with the other Trohanadalmakusian slave. It is perfectly safe to speak freely before him, All-Wise."

Elkomoelhago cast a quick, suspicious glance at his companion. He would have preferred that Zoanthrohago of all men address him as All-Glorious—it was less definite in its implication. He might deceive others, even himself, as to his wisdom, but he was perfectly aware that he could not fool Zoanthrohago.

"We have never discussed fully," said the king, "the details of this experiment. It was for this purpose that I came to the laboratory today. Now that we have the subject here let us go into the matter fully and determine what next step we should take."

"Yes, All-Wise," replied Zoanthrohago.

"Call me Thagosoto," snapped Elkomoelhago.

"Yes, Thagosoto," said the prince, using the Minunian word for Chief-Royal, or King, as Elkomoelhago had commanded. "Let us discuss the matter, by all means. It presents possibilities of great importance to your throne." He knew that what Elkomoelhago meant by *discussing* the matter consisted only in receiving from Zoanthrohago a detailed explanation of how he had reduced the stature of the slave Zuanthrol to one-quarter its original proportions; but he proposed, if possible, to obtain value received for the information, which he knew the king would use for his own aggrandizement, giving Zoanthrohago no credit whatever for his discoveries or all the long moons he had devoted to accomplishing this marvelous, scientific miracle.

"Before we enter into this discussion, O, Thagosoto," he said, "I beg that you will grant me one boon, which I have long desired and have hitherto hesitated to request, knowing that I did not deserve the recognition I crave for my poor talents and my mean service to thy illustrious and justly renowned rule."

"What boon do you wish?" demanded Elkomoelhago, crustily. At heart he feared this wisest of men, and, like the coward that he was, with him to fear was to hate. If he could have destroyed Zoanthrohago he would gladly have done so; but he could not afford to do this, since from this greatest of walmaks came whatever show of scientific ability the king could make, as well as all the many notable inventions for the safeguarding of the royal person.

"I would sit at the royal council," said Zoanthrohago, simply.

The king fidgeted. Of all the nobles of Veltopismakus here was the very last he would wish to see numbered among the royal councilors, whom he had chosen with especial reference to the obtuseness of their minds.

"There are no vacancies," he said, at last.

"The ruler of all men might easily make a vacancy," suggested Zoanthrohago, "or create a new post—Assistant Chief of Chiefs, for example, so that when Gofoloso was absent there would be one to take his place. Otherwise I should not have to attend upon your council meetings, but devote my time to the perfection of our discoveries and inventions."

Here was a way out and Elkomoelhago seized it. He had no

objection to Zoanthrohago being a royal councilor and thus escaping the burdensome income tax, which the makers of the tax had been careful to see proved no burden to themselves, and he knew that probably that was the only reason that Zoanthrohago wished to be a councilor. No, the king had no objection to the appointment, provided it could be arranged that the new minister was present at no council meetings, for even Elkomoelhago would have shrunk a bit from claiming as his own all the great discoveries of Zoanthrohago had Zoanthrohago been present.

"Very well," said the king, "you shall be appointed this very day—and when I want you at the council meetings I will send for you."

Zoanthrohago bowed. "And now," he said, "to the discussion of our experiments, which we hope will reveal a method for increasing the stature of our warriors when they go forth to battle with our enemies, and of reducing them to normal size once more when they return."

"I hate the mention of battles," cried the king, with a shudder.

"But we must be prepared to win them when they are forced upon us," suggested Zoanthrohago.

"I suppose so," assented the king; "but once we perfect this method of ours we shall need but a few warriors and the rest may be turned to peaceful and useful occupations. However, go on with the discussion."

Zoanthrohago concealed a smile, and rising, walked around the end of the table and stopped beside the ape-man. "Here," he said, placing a finger at the base of Tarzan's skull, "there lies, as you know, a small, oval, reddish gray body containing a liquid which influences the growth of tissues and organs. It long ago occurred to me that interference with the normal functioning of this gland would alter the growth of the subject to which it belonged. I experimented with small rodents and achieved remarkable results; but the thing I wished to accomplish, the increase of man's stature I have been unable to achieve. I have tried many methods and someday I shall discover the right one. I think I am on the right track, and that it is merely now a matter of experimentation. You know that stroking your face lightly with a smooth bit of stone produces a pleasurable sensation. Apply the same stone to the same face in the same manner, but with greatly increased force and you produce a diametrically opposite sensation. Rub the stone slowly across the face and back again many times, and then repeat the same motion rapidly for the same number of times and you will discover that the results are quite different. I am that close to a solution; I have the correct method but not quite, as yet, the correct application. I can reduce creatures in size, but I cannot enlarge them; and although I can reduce them with great ease, I cannot determine the period or endurance of their reduction. In some cases, subjects have not regained their normal size under thirty-nine moons, and in others, they have done so in as sort a period as three moons. There have been cases where normal stature was regained gradually during a period of seven suns, and others where the subject passed suddenly from a reduced size to normal size in less than a hundred heartbeats; this latter phenomenon being always accompanied by fainting and unconsciousness when it occurred during waking hours."

"Of course," commented Elkomoelhago. "Now, let us see. I believe the thing is simpler than you imagine. You say that to reduce the size of this subject you struck him with a rock upon the base of the skull. Therefore, to enlarge his size, the most natural and scientific thing to do would be to strike him a similar blow upon the forehead. Fetch the rock and we will prove the correctness of my theory."

For a moment Zoanthrohago was at a loss as to how best to circumvent the stupid intention of the king without humiliating his pride and arousing his resentment; but the courtiers of Elkomoelhago were accustomed to think quickly in similar emergencies and Zoanthrohago speedily found an avenue of escape from his dilemma.

"Your sagacity is the pride of your people, Thagosoto," he said, "and your brilliant hyperbole the despair of your courtiers. In a clever figure of speech you suggest the way to achievement. By reversing the manner in which we reduced the stature of Zuanthrol we should be able to increase it; but, alas, I have tried this and failed. But wait, let us repeat the experiment precisely as it was originally carried out and then, by reversing it, we shall, perhaps, be enabled to determine why I have failed in the past."

He stepped quickly across the room to one of a series of large cupboards that lined the wall and opening the door of it revealed a cage in which were a number of rodents. Selecting one of these he returned to the table, where, with wooden pegs and bits of cord he fastened the rodent securely to a smooth board, its legs spread out and its body flattened, the underside of the lower jaw resting firmly upon a small metal plate set flush with the surface of the board. He then brought forth a small wooden box and a large metal disc, the latter mounted vertically between supports that permitted it to be revolved rapidly by means of a hand crank. Mounted rigidly upon the same axis as the revolving disc was another which remained stationary. The latter disc appeared to have been constructed of seven segments, each of a different material from all the others, and from each of these segments a pad, or brush, protruded sufficiently to press lightly against the revolving disc.

To the reverse side of each of the seven segments of the stationary disc a wire was attached, and these wires Zoanthrohago now connected to seven posts projecting from the upper surface of the wooden box. A single wire attached to a post upon the side of the box had at its other extremity a small, curved metal plate attached to the inside of a leather collar. This collar Zoanthrohago adjusted about the neck of the rodent so that the metal plate came in contact with its skin at the base of the skull and as close to the hypophysis gland as possible.

He then turned his attention once more to the wooden box, upon the top of which, in addition to the seven binding posts, was a circular instrument consisting of a dial about the periphery of which were a series of hieroglyphics. From the center of this dial projected seven tubular, concentric shafts, each of which supported a needle, which was shaped or painted in some distinguishing manner, while beneath the dial seven small metal discs were set in the cover of the box so that they lay in the arc of a circle from the center of which a revolving metal shaft was so arranged that its free end might be moved to any of the seven metal discs at the will of the operator.

The connections having all been made, Zoanthrohago moved the free end of the shaft from one of the metal discs to another, keeping his eyes at all times intently upon the dial, the seven needles of which moved variously as he shifted the shaft from point to point.

Elkomoelhago was an intent, if somewhat bewildered, observer, and the slave, Zuanthrol, unobserved, had moved nearer the table that he might better watch this experiment which might mean so much to him.

Zoanthrohago continued to manipulate the revolving shaft and the needles moved hither and thither from one series of hieroglyphics to another, until at last the walmak appeared satisfied.

"It is not always easy," he said, "to attune the instrument to the frequency of the organ upon which we are working. From all matter and even from such incorporeal a thing as thought there emanate identical particles, so infinitesimal as to be scarce noted by the most delicate of my instruments. These particles constitute the basic structure of all things whether animate or inanimate, corporeal or incorporeal. The frequency, quantity, and rhythm of the emanations determine the nature of the substance. Having located upon this dial the coefficient of the gland under discussion it now becomes necessary, in order to so interfere with its proper functioning that the growth of the creature involved will be not only stopped but actually reversed, that we decrease the frequency, increase the quantity and compound the rhythm of these emanations. This I shall now proceed to do," and he forthwith manipulated several small buttons upon one side of the box, and grasping the crank handle of the free disc revolved it rapidly.

The result was instantaneous and startling. Before their eyes Elkomoelhago, the king, and Zuanthrol, the slave, saw the rodent shrink rapidly in size, while retaining its proportions unchanged. Tarzan, who had followed every move and every word of the walmak, leaned far over that he might impress indelibly upon his memory the position of the seven needles. Elkomoelhago glanced up and discovered his interest.

"We do not need this fellow now," he said, addressing Zoanthrohago. "Have him sent away."

"Yes, Thagosoto," replied Zoanthrohago, summoning a warrior whom he directed to remove Tarzan and Komodoflorensal to a chamber where they could be secured until their presence was again required.

15

THROUGH SEVERAL CHAMBERS and corridors they were conducted toward the center of the dome on the same level as the chamber in which they had left the king and the walmak until finally they were thrust into a small chamber and a heavy door was slammed and barred behind them.

There was no candle in the chamber. A faint light, however, relieved the darkness so that the interior of the room was discernible. The chamber contained two benches and a table—that was all. The light which faintly illuminated it entered through a narrow embrasure which was heavily barred, but it was evidently daylight.

"We are alone," whispered Komodoflorensal, "and at last we can converse; but we must be cautious," he added. " 'Trust not too far the loyalty of even the stones of your chamber!' " he quoted.

"Where are we?" asked Tarzan. "You are more familiar with Minunian dwellings than I."

"We are upon the highest level of the Royal Dome of Elkomoelhago," replied the prince. "With no such informality does a king visit the other domes of his city. You may rest assured that this is Elkomoelhago's. We are in one of the innermost chambers, next the central shaft that pierces the dome from its lowest level to its roof. For this reason we do not need a candle to support life—we will obtain sufficient air through this embrasure. And now, tell me what happened within the room with Elkomoelhago and Zoanthrohago."

"I discovered how they reduced my stature," replied Tarzan, "and, furthermore, that at almost any time I may regain my full size—an occurrence that may eventuate from three to thirty-nine moons after the date of my reduction. Even Zoanthrohago cannot determine when this thing will happen."

"Let us hope that it does not occur while you are in this small chamber," exclaimed Komodoflorensal.

"I would have a devil of a time getting out," agreed Tarzan.

"You would never get out," his friend assured him. "While you might, before your reduction, have crawled through some of the larger corridors upon the first level, or even upon many of the lower levels, you could not squeeze into the smaller corridors of the upper levels, which are reduced in size as the necessity for direct supports for the roof increase as we approach the apex of the dome."

"Then it behooves me to get out of here as quickly as possible," said Tarzan.

Komodoflorensal shook his head. "Hope is a beautiful thing, my friend," he said, "but if you were a Minunian you would know that under such circumstances as we find ourselves it is a waste of mental energy. Look at these bars," and he walked to the window and shook the heavy irons that spanned the embrasure. "Think you that you could negotiate these?"

"I haven't examined them," replied the ape-man, "but I shall never give up hope of escaping; that your people do is doubtless the principal reason that they remain forever in bondage. You are too much a fatalist, Komodoflorensal."

As he spoke Tarzan crossed the room and standing at the prince's side took hold of the bars at the window. "They do not seem overheavy," he remarked, and at the same time exerted pressure upon them. They bent! Tarzan was interested now and Komodoflorensal, as well. The ape-man threw all his strength and weight into the succeeding effort with the result that two bars, bent almost double, were torn from their setting.

Komodoflorensal gazed at him in astonishment. "Zoanthrohago reduced your size, but left you with your former physical prowess," he cried.

"In no other way can it be accounted for," replied Tarzan, who now, one by one, was removing the remaining bars from the window embrasure. He straightened one of the shorter ones and handed it to Komodoflorensal. "This will make a good weapon," he said, "if we are forced to fight for our liberty," and then he straightened another for himself.

The Trohandalmakusian gazed at him in wonder. "And you intend," he demanded, "to defy a city of four hundred and eighty thousand people, armed only with a bit of iron rod?"

"And my wits," added Tarzan.

"You will need them," said the prince.

"And I shall use them," Tarzan assured him.

"When shall you start?" asked Komodoflorensal, chaffingly.

"Tonight, tomorrow, next moon—who knows?" replied the ape-man. "Conditions must be ripe. All the time I shall be watching and planning. In that sense I started to escape the instant I regained consciousness and knew that I was a prisoner."

Komodoflorensal shook his head.

"You have no faith in me?" demanded Tarzan.

"That is precisely what I have—faith," replied Komodoflorensal. "My judgment tells me that you cannot succeed and yet I shall cast my lot with you, hoping for success, yes, believing in success. If that is not faith I do not know what it might be called."

The ape-man smiled. He seldom, if ever, laughed aloud. "Let us commence," he said. "First we will arrange these rods so that they will have the appearance, from the doorway, of not having been disturbed, for I take it we shall have an occasional visitor. Someone will bring us food, at least, and whoever comes must suspect nothing."

Together they arranged the rods so that they might be quickly removed and as quickly replaced. By that time it was getting quite dark within the chamber. Shortly after they had finished with the rods their door opened and two warriors, lighting their way with candles, appeared escorting a slave who bore food in bucketlike receptacles and water in bottles made of glazed pottery.

As they were going away again, after depositing the food and drink just inside the doorway, taking their candles with them, Komodoflorensal addressed them.

"We are without candles, warrior," he said to the nearer. "Will you not leave us one of yours?"

"You need no candle in this chamber," replied the man.

"One night of darkness will do you good, and tomorrow you return to the quarry. Zoanthrohago is done with you. In the quarry you will have plenty of candles," and he passed out of the chamber, closing the door behind him.

The two slaves heard the heavy bolt shot into place upon the opposite side of the door. It was very dark now. With difficulty they found the receptacles containing the food and water.

"Well?" inquired Komodoflorensal, dipping into one of the food jars. "Do you think it is going to be so easy now, when tomorrow you will be back in the quarry, perhaps five hundred huals below ground?"

"But I shall not be," replied Tarzan, "and neither shall you."

"Why not?" asked the prince.

"Because, since they expect to remove us to the quarries tomorrow, it follows that we must escape tonight," explained Tarzan.

Komodoflorensal only laughed.

When Tarzan had eaten his fill he arose and walked to the window, where he removed the bars and, taking the one that he had selected for himself, crawled through the passage that led to the opposite end of the embrasure, for even so close to the apex of the dome the wall was quite thick, perhaps ten huals. The hual, which is about three inches in length by our standards, constitutes the Minunian basic unit of measure, corresponding most closely to our foot. At this high level the embrasure was much smaller than those opening at lower levels, practically all of which were of sufficient size to permit a warrior to walk erect within them; but here Tarzan was forced to crawl upon all fours.

At the far end he found himself looking out into a black void above which the stars were shining and about the sides of which were dotted vague reflections of inner lights, marking the lighted chambers within the dome. Above him it was but a short distance to the apex of the dome, below was a sheer drop of four hundred huals.

Tarzan, having seen all that could be seen from the mouth of the embrasure, returned to the chamber. "How far is it, Komodoflorensal," he asked, "from the floor of this embrasure to the roof of the dome?"

"Twelve huals, perhaps," replied the Trohanadalmakusian.

Tarzan took the longest of the bars from the embrasure and measured it as best he could. "Too far," he said.

"What is too far?" demanded Komodoflorensal.

"The roof," explained Tarzan.

"What difference does it make where the roof is—you did not expect to escape by way of the roof of the dome, did you?"

"Most certainly—had it been accessible," replied the ape-man; "but now we shall have to go by way of the shaft, which will mean crossing entirely through the dome from the interior shaft to the outer periphery. The other route would have entailed less danger of detection."

Komodoflorensal laughed aloud. "You seem to think that to escape a Minunian city it is only necessary to walk out and away. It cannot be done. What of the sentries? What of the outer patrols? You would be discovered before you were halfway down the outside of the dome, provided that you could get that far without falling to your death."

"Then perhaps the shaft would be safer," said Tarzan. "There would be less likelihood of discovery before we reached the bottom, for from what I could see it is as dark as pitch in the shaft."

"Clamber down the inside of the shaft!" exclaimed Komodoflorensal. "You are mad! You could not clamber from this level to the next without falling, and it must be a full four hundred huals to the bottom."

"Wait!" Tarzan admonished him.

Komodoflorensal could hear his companion moving around in the dark chamber. He heard the scraping of metal on stone and presently he heard a pounding, not loud, yet heavy.

"What are you doing?" he asked.

"Wait!" said Tarzan.

And Komodoflorensal waited, wondering. It was Tarzan who spoke next.

"Could you find the chamber in which Talaskar is confined in the quarry?" he asked.

"Why?" demanded the prince.

"We are going after her," explained Tarzan. "We promised that we would not leave without her."

"I can find it," said Komodoflorensal, rather sullenly Tarzan thought.

For some time the ape-man worked on in silence, except for the muffled pounding and the scraping of iron on stone, or of iron on iron.

"Do you know everyone in Trohanadalmakus?" Tarzan asked, suddenly.

"Why, no," replied Komodoflorensal. "There are a million souls, including all the slaves. I could not know them all."

"Did you know by sight all those that dwelt in the royal dome?" continued the ape-man.

"No, not even those who lived in the royal dome," replied the Trohanadalmakusian; "though doubtless I knew practically all of the nobles, and the warrior class by sight if not by name."

"Did anyone?" asked Tarzan.

"I doubt it," was the reply.

"Good!" exclaimed Tarzan.

Again there was a silence, broken again by the Englishman.

"Can a warrior go anywhere without question in any dome of his own city?" he inquired.

"Anywhere, under ordinary circumstances, except into the king's dome, in daytime."

"One could not go about at night, then?" asked Tarzan.

"No," replied his companion.

"By day, might a warrior go and come in the quarries as he pleased?"

"If he appeared to be employed he would not be questioned, ordinarily."

Tarzan worked a little longer in silence. "Come!" he said presently; "we are ready to go."

"I shall go with you," said Komodoflorensal, "because I like you and because I think it would be better to be dead than a slave. At least we shall have some pleasure out of what remains to us of life, even though it be not a long life."

"I think we shall have some pleasure, my friend," replied Zuanthrol. "We may not escape; but, like you, I should rather die now than remain a slave for life. I have chosen tonight for our first step toward freedom, because I realize that once returned to the quarry our chances for a successful break for liberty will be reduced to almost nothing, and tonight is our only night above ground."

"How do you propose that we escape from this chamber?"

"By way of the central shaft," replied Tarzan; "but first tell me, may a white-tunicked slave enter the quarries freely by day?"

Komodoflorensal wondered what bearing all these seemingly immaterial questions had upon the problem of their escape; but he answered patiently:

"No, white tunics are never seen in the quarries."

"Have you the iron bar I straightened for you?"

"Yes."

"Then follow me through the embrasure. Bring the other rods that I shall leave in the opening. I will carry the bulk of them. Come!"

Komodoflorensal heard Tarzan crawling into the embrasure, the iron rods that he carried breaking the silence of the little chamber. Then he followed. In the mouth of the embrasure he found the rods that Tarzan had left for him to carry. There were four rods, the ends of each bent into hooks. It had been upon this work that Tarzan had been engaged in the darkness—Komodoflorensal wondered to what purpose. Presently his further advance was halted by Tarzan's body.

"Just a moment," said the ape-man. "I am making a hole in the window ledge. When that is done we shall be ready." A moment later he turned his head back toward his companion. "Pass along the rods," he said.

After Komodoflorensal had handed the hooked rods to Tarzan he heard the latter working with them, very quietly, for several minutes, and then he heard him moving his body about in the narrow confines of the embrasure and presently when the ape-man spoke again the Trohanadalmakusian realized that he had turned around and that his head was close to that of his companion.

"I shall go first, Komodoflorensal," he said. "Come to the edge of the embrasure and when you hear me whistle once, follow me."

"Where?" asked the prince.

"Down the shaft to the first embrasure that will give us foothold, and let us pray that there is one directly below this within the next eighteen huals. I have hooked the rods together, the upper end hooked into the hole I made in the ledge, the lower end dangling down a distance of eighteen huals."

"Good-bye, my friend," said Komodoflorensal.

Tarzan smiled and slipped over the edge of the embrasure. In one hand he carried the rod that he had retained as a weapon, with the other he clung to the window ledge. Below him for eighteen huals dangled the slender ladder of iron hooks, and below this, four hundred huals of pitchy darkness hid the stone flagging of the inner courtyard. Perhaps it roofed the great central throne room of the king, as was true in the royal dome of Adendrohahkis; perhaps it was but an open court. The truth was immaterial if the frail support slipped from the shallow hole in the ledge above, or if one of the hooks straightened under the weight of the ape-man.

Now he grasped the upper section of his ladder with the hand that held his improvised weapon, removed the hand from the ledge and grasped the rod again, still lower down. In this way he lowered his body a few inches at a time. He moved very slowly for two reasons, the more important of which was that he feared that any sudden strains upon his series of hooks might straighten one of them and precipitate him into the abyss below; the other was the necessity for silence. It was very dark even this close to the summit of the dome, but that was rather an advantage than otherwise, for it hid his presence from any chance observer who might glance through one of the embrasures in the opposite wall of the shaft. As he descended he felt in both directions for an embrasure, but he was almost at the end of his ladder before he felt himself swing slightly into one. When he had lowered himself still farther and could look into the opening he saw that it was dark, an indication that it did not lead into an inhabited chamber, a fact for which he was thankful. He hoped, too, that the inner end of the embrasure was not barred, nor the door beyond bolted upon the outside.

He whistled once, very low, for Komodoflorensal, and an instant later he felt the movement of the iron ladder that told him his companion had commenced the descent. The embrasure in which he stood was higher than the one they had just quitted, permitting him to stand erect. There he waited for the Trohanadalmakusian who was soon standing upon the ledge beside him.

"Whew!" exclaimed the prince, in a whisper. "I should hate to have had to do that in the daytime when I could have seen all the way to the bottom. What next? We have come farther already than ever I dreamed would be possible. Now I am commencing to believe that escape may lie within the realm of possibilities."

"We haven't started yet," Tarzan assured him; "but we are going to now. Come!"

Grasping their rude weapons the two walked stealthily the length of the embrasure. There were no bars to impede their progress and they stepped to the floor of the chamber beyond. Very carefully, feeling each step before he planted a foot and with his weapon extended before him, Tarzan groped his way about the chamber, which he found was fairly well filled with casks and bottles, the latter in wooden and wicker cases. Komodoflorensal was directly behind him.

"We are in one of the rooms where the nobles charged with enforcing the laws against wine have hidden confiscated liquor," whispered the Trohanadalmakusian. "I have heard much talk concerning the matter since I was made prisoner— the warriors and the slaves, too, seem to talk of nothing else but this and the high taxes. The chances are that the door is heavily barred—they guard these forbidden beverages as never they guarded their gold or jewels."

"I have found the passageway leading to the door," whispered Tarzan, "and I can see a light beneath it."

They crept stealthily the length of the passage. Each grasped his weapon more firmly as Tarzan gently tried the latch. It gave! Slowly the ape-man pushed the door ajar. Through the tiny aperture thus opened he could see a portion of the room. Its floor was strewn with gorgeous carpets, thick and soft. That portion of the wall that was revealed to him was hung with heavy fabrics woven in many colors and strange patterns— splendid, barbaric. Directly in the line of his vision the body of a man lay sprawled, facedown, upon the floor—a pool of red stained a white rug beneath his head.

Tarzan opened the door a little farther, revealing the bodies of three other men. Two lay upon the floor, the third upon a low divan. The scene, gorgeous in its coloring, tragic in its suggestion of mystery and violent death, held the eyes of the ape-man yet a moment longer before he opened the door still wider and leaped quickly to the center of the room, his weapon raised and ready, giving no possible skulking foe behind the door the opportunity to fell him that would have offered had he edged into the room slowly.

A quick glance about the apartment showed the bodies of six men that had not been visible from the partially opened door. These were lying in a pile in one corner of the room.

16

KOMODOFLORENSAL STOOD AT Tarzan's side, his weapon ready to take issue with any who might question their presence here; but presently the end of his iron rod dropped to the floor and a broad smile overspread his features.

Tarzan looked at him. "Who are they?" he demanded, "and why have they been killed?"

"They are not dead, my friend," replied Komodoflorensal. "They are the nobles whose duty it is to prevent the use of wine. They are not dead—they are drunk."

"But the blood beneath the head of this one at my feet!" demanded the ape-man.

"It is red wine, not blood," his companion assured him. Then Tarzan smiled.

"They could not have chosen a better night for their orgy," he said. "Had they remained sober the door through which we entered from the storeroom would have been securely fastened, I imagine."

"Assuredly, and we would have had a sober guard of warriors to deal with in this chamber, instead of ten drunken nobles. We are very fortunate, Zuanthrol."

He had scarcely ceased speaking when a door in the opposite side of the room swung open, revealing two warriors, who stepped immediately into the chamber. They eyed the two who faced them and then glanced about the room at the inert forms of its other occupants.

"What do you here, slaves?" demanded one of the newcomers.

"Sh-sh-sh!" cautioned Tarzan, placing a finger to his lips. "Enter and close the door, lest others hear."

"There is no one near to hear," snapped one of them, but they entered and he closed the door. "What is the meaning of this?"

"That you are our prisoners," cried the ape-man, leaping past them and placing himself before the door, his iron rod in readiness.

A sneer twisted the mouth of each of the two Veltopismaku-sians as they whipped out their rapiers and leaped toward the ape-man, ignoring for the moment the Trohanadalmakusian, who, seizing upon the opportunity thus afforded him, threw aside his iron rod and snatched a rapier from the side of one of the drunken nobles—a substitution of weapons that would render Komodoflorensal a dangerous opponent anywhere in Minuni, for there was no better swordsman among all the war-like clans of Trohanadalmakus, whose blades were famed throughout Minuni.

Facing, with only an iron rod, two skilled swordsmen placed Tarzan of the Apes at a disadvantage that might have proved his undoing had it not been for the presence of Komodoflo-rensal, who, no sooner than he had appropriated a weapon, leaped forward and engaged one of the warriors. The other pressed Tarzan fiercely.

"Your prisoner, eh, slave?" he sneered as he lunged for his opponent; but though less skilled, perhaps, in swordplay than his antagonist, the Lord of the Jungle had not faced Bol-gani and Numa for nothing. His movements were as light-ning, his strength as great as before Zoanthrohago had reduced his stature. At the first onslaught of the warriors he had leaped to one side to avoid the thrust of a blade, and as much to his own astonishment as to theirs, what he had intended for a nimble sidestep had carried him the length of the room, and then the man had been at him again, while the other was having his time well occupied with the Zertolosto of Trohanadalmakus.

Twice Tarzan parried cuts with his cumbersome bar and

then a thrust but missed him by a hairbreadth, his sidestep coming but in the nick of time. It was a close call, for the man had lunged at his abdomen—a close call for Tarzan and death for his opponent, for as the point slipped harmlessly by him the ape-man swung his rod upon the unguarded head of the Veltopismakusian, and with a grunt the fellow slumped to the floor, his skull crushed to the bridge of his nose.

Then Tarzan turned to aid Komodoflorensal, but the son of Adendrohahkis needed no aid. He had his man against the wall and was running him through the heart as Tarzan turned in their direction. As the man fell, Komodoflorensal swung toward the center of the room and as his eye fell upon the ape-man a smile crossed his face.

"With an iron bar you bested a swordsman of Minuni!" he cried. "I would not have believed it possible and so I hastened to dispatch my man that I might come to your rescue before it was too late."

Tarzan laughed. "I had the same thought in mind concerning you," he said.

"And you could have well held it had I not been able to secure this rapier," Komodoflorensal assured him. "But what now? We have again come much farther than it seems possible we can have. Naught will surprise me hereafter."

"We are going to trade apparel with these two unfortunate gentlemen," said Tarzan, divesting himself of the green tunic as he spoke.

Komodoflorensal chuckled as he followed the example of his companion.

"There are other peoples as great as the Minunians," he declared, "though until I met you, my friend, I should never have believed it."

A few moments later the two stood garbed in the habiliments of Veltopismakusian warriors and Tarzan was slipping his green tunic upon the corpse of him whom he had slain.

"But why are you doing that?" asked the prince.

"Do likewise with yours and you will see, presently," Tarzan replied.

Komodoflorensal did as the other bid him and when the change had been completed the ape-man threw one of the corpses across his shoulder and carried it into the storeroom, followed closely by Komodoflorensal with the other. Walking through the window embrasure to the edge of the shaft Tarzan hurled his burden out into space, and reaching back took Komodoflorensal's from him and pitched it after the first.

"If they do not examine them too closely," he said, "the ruse may serve to convince them that we died attempting to escape." As he spoke he detached two of the hooks from the ladder down which they had clambered from the window of their dungeon and dropped them after the corpses. "These will lend color to the suggestion," he added, in explanation.

Together they returned to the room where the drunken nobles lay, where Komodoflorensal began to rifle the fat money pouches of the unconscious men.

"We shall need all of this that we can get if we are to pose as Veltopismakusian warriors for any length of time," he said. "I know these people by reputation and that gold will buy many of the things that we may require—the blindness of guards and the complaisance of officials, if they do not guess too close to the truth concerning us."

"That part of it you must attend to, Komodoflorensal," said Tarzan, "for I am unfamiliar with the ways of your people; but we may not remain here. These gentlemen have served us well, and themselves, too, for their faithfulness and debauchery saved their lives, while the two who followed in sobriety the path of duty were destroyed."

"Matters are strangely ordered," commented Komodoflorensal.

"In Minuni as elsewhere," agreed Tarzan, leading the way to the door of the chamber which they found opened into a corridor instead of into another chamber as they had rather expected would be the fact at a point thus close to the central shaft.

In silence they proceeded along the passageway, which, at this hour of the morning, was deserted. They passed lighted chambers, where men and women were sleeping peacefully in the glare of many candles. They saw a sentry asleep before the door of a noble's quarters. No one discovered them and thus they passed down a series of inclined runways and along interminable corridors until they were far from that portion of the royal dome in which they had been incarcerated and where it would be most natural for the search for them to commence in the event that the bodies they had hurled into the shaft were not immediately discovered, or were identified for what they really were, rather than for what the two fugitives had tried to make them appear.

And now a white-tunicked slave was approaching them along the corridor. He passed without paying them any heed, and presently another and another appeared until the two realized that morning was approaching and the corridors would soon be filled with the inhabitants of the dome.

"It will be best," said Komodoflorensal, "to find a hiding place until there are more people abroad. We shall be safer in a crowd than among just a few where we shall be the more noticeable."

Nearly all the chambers they passed now were occupied by families, while those that were untenanted were without candles and therefore unsafe as hiding places for any length of time; but presently Komodoflorensal touched Tarzan's arm and pointed to the hieroglyphic beside a door they were approaching.

"Just the place," he said.

"What is it?" asked Tarzan, and as they came opposite the open door, "Why, it is filled with men! When they awake we shall be discovered."

"But not recognized," returned the Trohanadalmakusian, "or at least the chances are slight that we shall be. This is a common chamber where any man may purchase lodgings overnight. Doubtless there are visitors from other domes and strangers will not be particularly remarked on this account."

He entered the room, followed by Tarzan. A white-tunicked slave approached them. "Candles for two," demanded Komodoflorensal, handing the slave one of the smaller golden coins he had filched from the sleeping nobles.

The fellow led them to a far corner of the room where there was plenty of space upon the floor, lit two candles and left them. A moment later they were stretched at full length, their faces toward the wall as a further protection against recognition, and were soon asleep.

When Tarzan awoke he saw that he and Komodoflorensal were the only remaining occupants of the chamber, other than the slave who had admitted them, and he awoke his companion, believing that they should do nothing that might even in a slight degree call more than ordinary attention to them. A bucket of water was brought them and they performed their ablutions at a gutter which encircled the chamber, passing along the foot of each wall, as was the custom throughout Minuni, the waste water being carried away in pipes to the fields beyond the cities, where it was used for irrigating the crops. As all the water had to be carried into the domes and to the different levels in buckets, the amount used for ablutions was reduced to the minimum, the warrior and noble class getting the bulk of it, while the white-tunicked slaves depended principally upon the rivers, near which domes are always erected, for their baths. The green slaves fare the worst, and suffer a real hardship through lack of bathing facilities, for the Minunians are a cleanly people; but they managed to alleviate their plight to some extent, where the quarry masters are more kindly disposed, by the use of stagnant seepage water that accumulates in every quarry at the lower levels and which, not being fit for drinking purposes, may be used by the slaves for bathing when they are permitted the time to obtain it.

Having washed, Tarzan and Komodoflorensal passed out into the corridor, a broad thoroughfare of the dome city, where there were now passing two solid lines of humanity moving in opposite directions, the very numbers of the people proving their greatest safeguard against detection. Candles at frequent intervals diffused a brilliant light and purified the air. Open doorways revealed shops of various descriptions within which men and women were bartering for goods, and now Tarzan had his first real glimpse of Veltopismakusian life. The shops were all conducted by white-tunicked slaves, but slaves and warriors intermingled as customers, both sexes of each class being represented. It was Tarzan's first opportunity, also, to see the women of the warrior class outside their own homes. He had seen the Princess Janzara in the palace quarters and, through the doorways in various portions of the dome, he had seen other women of varying stations in life; but these were the first that he had seen abroad at close hand. Their faces were painted deep vermilion, their ears blue, and their apparel so arranged that the left leg and left arm were bare, though if even so much

as the right ankle or wrist became uncovered they hastily read-
justed their garments to hide them, giving every evidence of
confusion and embarrassment. As the ape-man watched them
he was reminded of fat dowagers he had seen at home whose
evening gowns left them naked to their kidneys, yet who
would rather have died than to have exposed a knee.

The front of the shops were covered with brilliant paintings,
usually depicting the goods that were on sale, together with
hieroglyphics describing the wares and advertising the name
of the proprietor. One of these finally held the attention of
the Trohanadalmakusian, and he touched Tarzan's arm and
pointed toward it.

"A place where food is served," he said. "Let us eat."

"Nothing would suit me better. I am famished," Tarzan
assured him, and so the two entered the little shop where several customers were already sitting upon the floor with small
benches pulled close to them, upon which food was being
served in wooden dishes. Komodoflorensal found a space near
the rear of the shop, not far from a doorway leading into
another chamber, which was also a shop of a different character, not all the places of business being fortunately located
upon a corridor, but having their entrances, like this one,
through another place of business.

Having seated themselves and dragged a bench before
them they looked about while waiting to be served. It was
evidently a poor shop, Komodoflorensal told Tarzan, catering
to the slave caste and the poorer warriors, of which there
were several sitting at benches in different parts of the room.
By their harness and apparel, which was worn and shabby,
one might easily guess at their poverty. In the adjoining shop
were several more of the same class of unfortunate warriors
mending their own clothes with materials purchased from the
poor shopkeeper.

The meal was served by a slave in a white tunic of very
cheap material, who was much surprised when payment for the
meal and the service was offered in gold.

"It is seldom," he said, "that warriors rich enough to possess gold come to our poor shop. Pieces of iron and bits of
lead, with much wooden money, pass into my coffers; but
rarely do I see gold. Once I did, and many of my customers

were formerly of the richest of the city. Yonder see that tall man with the heavily wrinkled face. Once he was rich—the richest warrior in his dome. Look at him now! And see them in the next room performing menial services, men who once owned slaves so prosperous that they, in turn, hired other slaves to do the meaner duties for them. Victims, all of them, of the tax that Elkomoelhago has placed upon industry.

"To be poor," he continued, "assures one an easier life than being rich, for the poor have no tax to pay, while those who work hard and accumulate property have only their labor for their effort, since the government takes all from them in taxes.

"Over there is a man who was very rich. He worked hard all his life and accumulated a vast fortune. For several years after Elkomoelhago's new tax law was enforced, he struggled to earn enough to insure that his income would be at least equal to his taxes and the cost of his living; but he found that it was impossible. He had one enemy, a man who had wronged him grievously. This man was very poor, and to him he gave all of what remained of his great fortune and his property. It was a terrible revenge. From being a contented man, this victim of another's spleen is now a haggard wreck, laboring unceasingly eighteen hours each day in a futile attempt to insure himself an income that will defray his taxes."

Having finished their meal the two fugitives returned to the corridor and continued their way downward through the dome toward the first level, keeping always to the more crowded corridors, where detection seemed least likely. Now, mounted men were more frequently encountered and so rapidly and recklessly did the warriors ride along the narrow corridors that it was with difficulty that the pedestrians avoided being ridden down and trampled, and it seemed to Tarzan but little less than a miracle that any of them arrived at their destinations uninjured. Having at last come to the lowest level, they were engaged in searching for one of the four corridors that would lead them from the dome, when their way was completely blocked by a great throng that had congregated at the intersection of two corridors. Those in the rear were stretching their necks to observe what was going on in the center of the gathering. Everyone was asking questions of his neighbor, but as yet no one upon the outskirts of the mob appeared to know what had occurred, until at last fragments of rumors filtered back to the farthermost. Tarzan and Komodoflorensal dared ask no questions, but they kept their ears open and presently they were rewarded by overhearing repeated what seemed to be an authoritative account of what had transpired to cause this congestion. In answer to a question put by one of the throng a fellow who was elbowing his way out from the center of the jam explained that those in front had halted to view the remains of two slaves who had been killed while trying to escape.

"They were locked in one of Zoanthrohago's slave cells at the very highest level," he told his questioner, "and they tried to escape by climbing down an improvised ladder into the central shaft. Their ladder broke and they were precipitated to the roof of the throne room, where their bodies, terribly mangled, were but just found. They are being carried out to the beasts, now. One of them was a great loss to Zoanthrohago as it was the slave Zuanthrol, upon whom he was experimenting."

"Ah," exclaimed a listener, "I saw them but yesterday."

"You would not know them today," vouchsafed the informer, "so terribly are their faces disfigured."

When the press of humanity had been relieved Tarzan and Komodoflorensal continued their way, finding that the Slaves' Corridor lay just before them, and that it was down this avenue that the bodies of their victims of the previous night were being carried.

"What," asked the ape-man, "did he mean by saying that they were being carried to the beasts?"

"It is the way in which we dispose of the bodies of slaves," replied the Trohanadalmakusian. "They are carried to the edge of the jungle, where they are devoured by wild beasts. There are old and toothless lions near Trohanadalmakus that subsist entirely upon slave meat. They are our scavengers and so accustomed are they to being fed that they often come to meet the parties who bring out the corpses, pacing beside them, roaring and growling, until the spot is reached where the bodies are to be deposited."

"You dispose of all your dead in this manner?"

"Only the slave dead. The bodies of warriors and nobles are burned."

"In a short time, then," continued Tarzan, "there will be no danger of there ever being a correct identification of those two." He jerked his thumb along the corridor ahead, where the bodies of the two dead warriors were being bounced and jolted along upon the backs of diadets.

17

"WHERE NOW?" DEMANDED Komodoflorensal as the two emerged from the mouth of the Slaves' Corridor and stood for a moment in the brilliant sunlight without.

"Lead the way to the quarry where we were confined and to the chamber in which we slept."

"You must be weary of your brief liberty," remarked the Trohanadalmakusian.

"We are returning for Talaskar, as I promised," Tarzan reminded him.

"I know," said the Zertolosto, "and I commend your loyalty and valor while deprecating your judgment. It will be impossible to rescue Talaskar. Were it otherwise I should be the first to her assistance; but I know, and she knows that, for her, escape is beyond hope. We will but succeed in throwing ourselves again into the hands of our masters."

"Let us hope not," said Tarzan; "but, if you feel as you say, that our effort is foredoomed to failure and that we shall but be recaptured, do not accompany me. My only real need of you is to guide me to the apartment where Talaskar is confined. If you can direct me to it that is all I ask."

"Think you I was attempting to evade the danger?" demanded Komodoflorensal. "No! Where you go, I will go. If you are captured I shall be captured. We shall fail, but let us not separate. I am ready to go wherever you go."

"Good," commented Tarzan. "Now lead the way to the quarry and use your knowledge of things Minunian and your best wits to gain us entrance without too much talking."

They passed, unchallenged, along the shaded walks between the domes of Veltopismakus and past the great parade where gorgeously caparisoned warriors were executing intricate evolutions with the nicest precision, and out beyond the domes along well-worn trails filled with toiling slaves and their haughty guards. Here they fell in beside the long column moving in the direction of the quarry in which they had been imprisoned, taking their places in the column of flanking guards, and thus they came to the entrance to the quarry.

Perfunctorily the numbers of the slaves were taken, as they passed in, and entered in a great book; but to Tarzan's relief he noted that no attention was paid to the guards, who moved along beside their charges and down into the interior without being checked or even counted, and with them went Komodoflorensal, Prince Royal of Trohanadalmakus, and Tarzan of the Apes.

Once inside the quarry and past the guard room the two fell gradually to the rear of the column, so that when it turned into a level above that which they wished to reach they were enabled to detach themselves from it without being noticed. To leave one column was but to join another, for there was no break in them and often there were several moving abreast; but when they reached the thirty-fifth level and entered the tunnel leading to the chamber in which Talaskar was confined they found themselves alone, since there is little or no activity in these corridors leading to slave quarters except early in the morning when the men are led forth to their labors and again at night when they are brought back.

Before the door of the chamber they found a single warrior on guard. He was squatting on the floor of the tunnel leaning against the wall, but at their approach he rose and challenged them.

Komodoflorensal, who was in the lead, approached him and halted. "We have come for the slave girl, Talaskar," he said.

Tarzan, who was just behind Komodoflorensal, saw a sudden light leap to the eyes of the warrior. Was it recognition?

"Who sent you?" demanded the warrior.

"Her master, Zoanthrohago," replied the Trohanadalmakusian.

The expression upon the face of the warrior changed to one of cunning.

"Go in and fetch her," he said, and unbolted the door, swinging it open.

Komodoflorensal dropped upon his hands and knees and crawled through the low aperture, but Tarzan stood where he was.

"Go in!" said the guard to him.

"I will remain where I am," replied the ape-man. "It will not require two of us to find a single slave girl and fetch her to the corridor."

For an instant the warrior hesitated, then he closed the door hurriedly and shot the heavy bolts. When he turned toward Tarzan again, who was now alone with him in the corridor, he turned with a naked sword in his hands; but he found Zuanthrol facing him with drawn rapier.

"Surrender!" cried the warrior. "I recognized you both instantly."

"I thought as much," said Zuanthrol. "You are clever, with the exception of your eyes—they are fools, for they betray you."

"But my sword is no fool," snapped the fellow, as he thrust viciously at the ape-man's breast.

Lieutenant Paul D'Arnot of the French navy had been recognized as one of the cleverest swordsmen in the service and to his friend Greystoke he had imparted a great measure of his skill during the many hours that the two had whiled away with the foils, and today Tarzan of the Apes breathed a prayer of gratitude to the far-distant friend whose careful training was, after many long years, to serve the ape-man in such good stead, for he soon realized that, though his antagonist was a master at the art of fence, he was not wholly outclassed, and to his skill was added his great strength and his agility.

They had fought for but a minute or two when the Veltopismakusian realized that he was facing no mean antagonist and that he was laboring at a disadvantage in being unable to fall back when Tarzan rushed him, while his foeman had at his back the whole length of the tunnel. He tried then to force Tarzan back, but in this he failed, receiving a thrust in the shoulder for his pains, and then he commenced to call for help and the ape-man realized that he must silence him and that quickly. Awaiting the opportunity that was presently afforded by a feint that evoked a wild lunge, Tarzan stepped quickly in and passed his sword through the heart of the Veltopismaku-sian and as he withdrew his blade from the body of his antago-nist he released the bolts that held the door and swung it open. Beyond it, white of face, crouched Komodoflorensal, but as his eyes fell upon Tarzan and the body of the guard behind him, a smile curved his lips and an instant later he was in the corridor beside his friend.

"How did it happen?" he demanded.

"He recognized us; but what of Talaskar? Is she not coming?"

"She is not here. Kalfastoban took her away. He has pur-chased her from Zoanthrohago."

Tarzan wheeled. "Rebolt the door and let us get out of here," he said.

Komodoflorensal closed and fastened the door. "Where now?" he asked.

"To find Kalfastoban's quarters," replied the ape-man.

Komodoflorensal shrugged his shoulders and followed on behind his friend. They retraced their steps toward the surface without incident until they were opposite the sixteenth level, when a face was suddenly turned toward them from a column of slaves crossing the runway from one lateral to another. Just for an instant did the eyes of the slave meet those of Tarzan, and then the fellow had passed into the mouth of the lateral and disappeared.

"We must hurry," whispered Tarzan to his companion.

"Why now more than before?" demanded Komodoflo-rensal.

"Did you not see the fellow who just passed us and turned to look a second time at me?"

"No; who was it?"

"Caraftap," replied Tarzan.

"Did he recognize you?"

"As to that I cannot say; but he evidently found something familiar in my appearance. Let us hope that he did not place me, though I fear that he did."

"Then we must lose no time in getting out of here, and out of Veltopismakus, as well."

They hurried on. "Where are Kalfastoban's quarters?" asked Tarzan.

"I do not know. In Trohanadalmakus warriors are detailed to the quarries for but short periods and do not transfer their quarters or their slaves during the time that they are there. I do not know the custom here. Kalfastoban may have finished his tour of duty in the quarries. On the other hand it may be for a long period that they are detailed for that service and his quarters may lie on the upper level of the quarry. We shall have to inquire."

Soon after this Tarzan stepped up to a warrior moving in the same direction as he and Komodoflorensal. "Where can I find Kalfastoban Vental?" he asked.

"They will tell you in the guard room, if it is any of your affair," he replied, shooting a quick glance at the two. "I do not know."

After that they passed the fellow and at the first turn that hid them from him they increased their speed, for both were becoming suspicious of every least untoward incident, and their own wish now was to escape the quarry in safety. Nearing the entrance they attached themselves to a column of slaves toiling upward with their heavy burdens of rocks for the new dome, and with them they came to the guard room where the slaves were checked out. The officer and the clerks labored in a mechanical manner, and it appeared that it was to be as easy to leave the quarry as it had been to enter it, when the officer suddenly drew his brow together and commenced to count.

"How many slaves in this crew?" he asked.

"One hundred," replied one of the warriors accompanying them.

"Then why four guards?" he demanded.

"There are but two of us," rejoined the warrior.

"We are not with them," Komodoflorensal spoke up quickly.

"What do you here?" demanded the officer.

"If we can see you alone we can explain that quickly," replied the Trohanadalmakusian.

The officer waved the crew of slaves upon their way and

beckoned to Komodoflorensal and Tarzan to follow him into an adjoining chamber, where they found a small anteroom in which the commander of the guard slept.

"Now," he said, "let me see your passes."

"We have none," replied Komodoflorensal.

"No passes! That will be difficult to explain, will it not?"

"Not to one of your discrimination," replied the prince, accidentally jingling the golden coins in his pouch. "We are in search of Kalfastoban. We understand that he owns a slave we wish to purchase and not being able to obtain a pass to the quarry in the short time at our disposal we ventured to come, upon so simple an errand, without one. Could you direct us to Kalfastoban?" Again he jingled the coins.

"I shall be delighted," replied the officer. "His quarters are upon the fifth level of the Royal Dome upon the central corridor and about midway between the King's Corridor and the Warrior's Corridor. As he was relieved from duty in the quarry this very morning I have no doubt but that you will find him there."

"We thank you," said Komodoflorensal, leaning far back in the Minunian bow. "And now," he added, as though it was an afterthought, "if you will accept it we shall be filled with gratitude if you will permit us to leave this slight token of our appreciation," and he drew a large coin from the pouch and proffered it to the officer.

"Rather than seem ungrateful," replied the officer, "I must accept your gracious gift, with which I may alleviate the sufferings of the poor. May the shadow of disaster never fall upon you!"

The three then bowed and Tarzan and Komodoflorensal quitted the guard room and a moment later were in the free, fresh air of the surface.

"Even in Minuni!" breathed Tarzan.

"What was that?" asked his friend.

"I was just thinking of my simple, honest jungle and God's creatures that men call beasts."

"What should they call them?" demanded Komodoflorensal.

"If judged by the standards that men themselves make, and fail to observe, they should be called demigods," replied the ape-man.

"I believe I get your point," laughed the other; "but think! Had a lion guarded the entrance to this quarry no gold piece would have let us pass. The frailties of man are not without their virtues; because of them right has just triumphed over wrong and bribery has worn the vestments of virtue."

Returning to the Royal Dome they passed around the east side of the structure to the north front, where lies the Slaves' Corridor in every dome. In quitting the dome they had come from the Warriors' Corridor on the west and they felt that it would be but increasing the chances of detection were they to pass too often along the same route where someone, half-recognizing them in one instance, might do so fully after a second or third inspection.

To reach the fifth level required but a few minutes after they had gained entrance to the dome. With every appearance of boldness they made their way toward the point in the central corridor at which the officer of the guard had told them they would find Kalfastoban's quarters, and perhaps Kalfastoban himself; but they were constantly on the alert, for both recognized that the greatest danger of detection lay through the chance that Kalfastoban might recall their features, as he of all Veltopismakusians would be most apt to do so, since he had seen the most of them, or at least the most of Tarzan since he had donned the slave's green.

They had reached a point about midway between the Slaves' Corridor and the Warriors' Corridor when Komodoflorensal halted a young, female slave and asked her where the quarters of Kalfastoban were located.

"It is necessary to pass through the quarters of Hamadalban to reach those of Kalfastoban," replied the girl. "Go to the third entrance," and she pointed along the corridor in the direction they had been going.

After they had left her Tarzan asked Komodoflorensal if he thought there would be any difficulty in gaining entrance to Kalfastoban's quarters.

"No," he replied, "the trouble will arise in knowing what to do after we get there."

"We know what we have come for," replied the ape-man. "It is only necessary to carry out our design, removing all obstacles as they intervene."

"Quite simple," laughed the prince.

Tarzan was forced to smile. "To be candid," he admitted, "I haven't the remotest idea what we are going to do after we get in there, or after we get out either, if we are successful in finding Talaskar and bringing her away with us, but that is not strange, since I know nothing, or practically nothing, of what conditions I may expect to confront me from moment to moment in this strange city of a strange world. All that we can do is to do our best. We have come thus far much more easily than I expected—perhaps we will go the whole distance with no greater friction—or we may stop within the next dozen steps, forever."

Pausing before the third entrance they glanced in, discovering several women squatting upon the floor. Two of them were of the warrior class, the others slaves of the white tunic. Komodoflorensal entered boldly.

"These are the quarters of Hamadalban?" he asked.

"They are," replied one of the women.

"And Kalfastoban's are beyond?"

"Yes."

"And beyond Kalfastoban's?" inquired the Trohanadalmakusian.

"A long gallery leads to the outer corridor. Upon the gallery open many chambers where live hundreds of people. I do not know them all. Whom do you seek?"

"Palastokar," replied Komodoflorensal quickly, choosing the first name that presented itself to his memory.

"I do not recall the name," said the woman, knitting her brows in thought.

"But I shall find him now, thanks to you," said Komodoflorensal, "for my directions were to pass through the quarters of Hamadalban and Kalfastoban, when I should come upon a gallery into which opened the quarters of Palastokar; but perhaps if Kalfastoban is in, he will be able to direct me more exactly."

"Kalfastoban has gone out with Hamadalban," replied the woman; "but I expect them back momentarily. If you will wait, they will soon be here."

"Thank you," said Komodoflorensal, hastily; "but I am sure that we shall have no trouble finding the quarters of Palastokar.

May your candles burn long and brilliantly!" and without waiting on further ceremony he crossed the room and entered the quarters of Kalfastoban, into which Tarzan of the Apes followed at his heels.

"I think, my friend," said the prince, "that we shall have to work rapidly."

Tarzan glanced quickly around the first chamber that they entered. It was vacant. Several doors opened from it. They were all closed either with wooden doors or with hangings. The ape-man stepped quickly to the nearer and tried the latch. It gave and he pushed the door ajar. All was darkness within.

"Bring a candle, Komodoflorensal," he said.

The prince brought two from their niches in the wall. "A storeroom," he said, as the rays of the candles illuminated the interior of the room. "Food and candles and raiment. Kalfastoban is no pauper. The tax collector has not ruined him yet."

Tarzan, standing in the doorway of the storeroom, just behind Komodoflorensal, turned suddenly and looked out across the other chamber. He had heard voices in the quarters of Hamadalban beyond—men's voices. One of them he recognized an instant later—it was the voice of Kalfastoban Vental.

"Come!" roared the bull voice of the Vental. "Come to my quarters, Hamadalban, and I will show you this new slave of mine."

Tarzan pushed Komodoflorensal into the storeroom and following him, closed the door. "Did you hear?" he whispered.

"Yes, it was Kalfastoban!"

The storeroom door was ornamented with a small, open grill covered with a hanging of some heavy stuff upon the inside. By drawing the hanging aside the two could obtain a view of most of the interior of the outer chamber, and they could hear all that was said by the two men who now entered from Hamadalban's quarters.

"I tell you she is the greatest bargain I have ever seen," cried Kalfastoban; "but wait, I'll fetch her," and he stepped to another door, which he unlocked with a key. "Come out!" he roared, flinging the door wide.

With the haughty bearing of a queen a girl stepped slowly into the larger room—no cowering servility of the slave here. Her chin was high, her gaze level. She glanced almost with contempt upon the Vental. And she was beautiful. It was Talaskar. Komodoflorensal realized that he had never before appreciated how really beautiful was the little slave girl, who had cooked for him. Kalfastoban had given her a white tunic of good quality, which set off the olive of her skin and the rich blackness of her hair to better effect than had the cheap green thing that he had always seen her in.

"She belonged to Zoanthrohago," Kalfastoban explained to his friend, "but I doubt that he ever saw her, else he never would have parted with her for the paltry sum I paid."

"You will take her for your own woman and raise her to our class?" asked Hamadalban.

"No," replied Kalfastoban, "for then she would no longer be a slave and I could not sell her. Women are too expensive. I shall keep her for a time and then sell her while her value is still high. I should make a pretty profit from her."

Tarzan's fingers closed tightly, as though upon the throat of an enemy, and the right hand of Komodoflorensal crept to the hilt of his rapier.

A woman came from the quarters of Hamadalban and stood in the doorway.

"Two of the guards from the quarry are here with a green slave inquiring for Kalfastoban," she said.

"Send them in," directed the Vental.

A moment later the three entered—the slave was Caraftap.

"Ah!" exclaimed Kalfastoban, "my good slave, Caraftap; the best in the quarry. Why is he brought here?"

"He says that he has information of great value," replied one of the guard; "but he will divulge it to none but you. He has staked his life against the worth of his information and the Novand of the guard ordered him brought hither."

"What information have you?" demanded Kalfastoban.

"It is of great moment," cried Caraftap. "Noble Zoanthrohago, and even the king, will be grateful for it; but were I to give it and have to return to the quarries the other slaves would kill me. You were always good to me, Kalfastoban Vental, and so I asked to be brought to you, for I know that if you promise that I shall be rewarded with the white tunic, if my service is considered worthy of it, I shall be safe."

"You know that I cannot do that," replied Kalfastoban.

"But the king can, and if you intercede with him he will not refuse."

"I can promise to intercede with the king in your behalf if the information you bring is of value; but that is all I can do."

"That is enough—if you promise," said Caraftap.

"Very well, I promise. What do you know that the king would like to know?"

"News travels fast in Veltopismakus," said Caraftap, "and so it was that we in the quarry heard of the death of the two slaves, Aoponato and Zuanthrol, within a short time after their bodies were discovered. As both had been slaves of Zoanthrohago we were all confined together in one chamber and thus I knew them both well. Imagine then my surprise when, while crossing one of the main spirals with a crew of other slaves, I beheld both Zuanthrol and Aoponato, in the habiliments of warriors, ascending toward the surface."

"What is the appearance of these two?" suddenly demanded one of the warriors who had accompanied Caraftap from the quarry.

The slave described them as fully as he could.

"The same!" cried the warrior. "These very two stopped me upon the spiral and inquired the whereabouts of Kalfastoban."

A crowd of women and men had gathered in the doorway of Kalfastoban's chamber, having been attracted by the presence of a green slave accompanied by members of the quarry guard. One of them was a young slave girl.

"I, too, was questioned by these very men," she exclaimed, "only a short time since, and they asked me the same question."

One of Hamadalban's women voiced a little scream. "They passed through our quarters but a moment since," she cried, "and entered Kalfastoban's, but they asked not where lay the quarters of Kalfastoban, the name they mentioned was unknown to me—a strange name."

"Palastokar," one of her companions reminded her.

"Yes, Palastokar, and they said he had his quarters upon the gallery leading from Kalfastoban's to the outer corridor."

"There is no one of such a name in the Royal Dome," said Kalfastoban. "It was but a ruse to enter my quarters."

"Or to pass through them," suggested one of the quarry guard.

"We must hurry after them," said the other.

"Keep Caraftap here until we return, Kalfastoban," said the first guard, "and also search your own quarters and those adjoining carefully. Come!" and motioning to the other guard he crossed the chamber and departed along the gallery that led to the outer corridor, followed not alone by his fellow but by Hamadalban and all the other men who had congregated in the chamber, leaving Kalfastoban and Caraftap, with the women, in the Vental's quarters.

18

KALFASTOBAN TURNED IMMEDIATELY to a search of the various chambers of his quarters, but Caraftap laid a restraining hand upon his arm.

"Wait, Vental," he begged. "If they be here would it not be best to insure their capture by fastening the doors leading from your quarters?"

"A good thought, Caraftap," replied Kalfastoban, "and then we may take our time searching for them. Out of here, all you women!" he cried, waving the females back into Hamadalban's quarters. A moment later the two doors leading from the chamber to Hamadalban's quarters and the gallery were closed and locked.

"And now, master," suggested Caraftap, "as there be two of them would it not be well to supply me with a weapon."

Kalfastoban smote his chest. "A dozen such could Kalfastoban overcome alone," he cried; "but for your own protection get you a sword from yonder room while I lock this proud she-cat in her cell again."

As Kalfastoban followed Talaskar to the room in which she had been confined, Caraftap crossed to the door of the store-room where the Vental had told him he would find a weapon.

The Vental reached the door of the room just behind the girl and reaching out caught her by the arm.

"Not so fast, my pretty!" he cried. "A kiss before you leave me; but fret not! The moment we are sure that those villainous slaves are not within these rooms I shall join you, so do not pine for your Kalfastoban."

Talaskar wheeled and struck the Vental in the face. "Lay not your filthy hands upon me, beast!" she cried, and struggled to free herself from his grasp.

"So-ho! a cat, indeed!" exclaimed the man, but he did not release her, and so they struggled until they disappeared from sight within the cell, and at the same moment Caraftap, the slave, laid his hand upon the latch of the storeroom door, and opening it stepped within.

As he did so steel fingers reached forth out of the darkness and closed upon his throat. He would have screamed in terror, but no sound could he force through his tight-closed throat. He struggled and struck at the thing that held him—a thing so powerful that he knew it could not be human, and then a low voice, cold and terrifying, whispered in his ear.

"Die, Caraftap!" it said. "Meet the fate that you deserve and that you well know you deserved when you said that you dared not return to the quarters of the slaves of Zoanthrohago after betraying two of your number. Die, Caraftap! and know before you die that he whom you would have betrayed is your slayer. You searched for Zuanthrol and—you have found him!" With the last word the terrible fingers closed upon the man's neck. Spasmodically the slave struggled, fighting for air. Then the two hands that gripped him turned slowly in opposite directions and the head of the traitor was twisted from his body.

Throwing the corpse aside Tarzan sprang into the main chamber of the Vental's quarters and ran quickly toward the door of Talaskar's cell, Komodoflorensal but half a pace behind him. The door of the little room had been pushed to by the struggles of the couple within, and as Tarzan pushed it open he saw the girl in the clutches of the huge Vental, who, evidently maddened by her resistance, had lost his temper completely and was attempting to rain blows upon her face, which she sought to ward off, clutching at his arms and hands.

A heavy hand fell upon the shoulder of the Vental. "You seek us!" a low voice whispered in his ear. "Here we are!"

Kalfastoban released the girl and swung around, at the same time reaching for his sword. Facing him were the two slaves and both were armed, though only Aoponato had drawn his weapon. Zuanthrol, who held him, had not yet drawn.

" 'A dozen such could Kalfastoban overcome alone,' " quoted Tarzan. "Here we are, braggart, and we are only two; but we cannot wait while you show us how mighty you be. We are sorry. Had you not molested this girl I should merely have locked you in your quarters, from which you would soon have been released; but your brutality deserves but one punishment—death."

"Caraftap!" screamed Kalfastoban. No longer was he a blusterer, deep-toned and swaggering. His voice was shrill with terror and he shook in the hands of the ape-man. "Caraftap! Help!" he cried.

"Caraftap is dead," said Tarzan. "He died because he betrayed his fellows. You shall die because you were brutal to a defenseless slave girl. Run him through, Komodoflorensal! We have not time to waste here."

As the Trohanadalmakusian withdrew his sword from the heart of Kalfastoban Vental and the corpse slid to the floor of the cell Talaskar ran forward and fell at the feet of the ape-man.

"Zuanthrol and Aoponato!" she cried. "Never did I think to see you again. What has happened? Why are you here? You have saved me, but now you will be lost. Fly—I know not where to you may fly—but go from here! Do not let them find you here. I cannot understand why you are here, anyway."

"We are trying to escape," explained Komodoflorensal, "and Zuanthrol would not go without you. He searched the quarry for you and now the Royal Dome. He has performed the impossible, but he has found you."

"Why did you do this for me?" asked Talaskar, looking wonderingly at Tarzan.

"Because you were kind to me when I was brought to the chamber of Zoanthrohago's slaves," replied the ape-man, "and because I promised that when the time for escape came we three should be together."

He had lifted her to her feet and led her into the main chamber. Komodoflorensal stood a little aside, his eyes upon the floor. Tarzan glanced at him and an expression of puzzlement came into the eyes of the ape-man, but whatever thought had caused it he must have put quickly aside for the consideration of more pressing matters.

"Komodoflorensal, you know best what avenues of escape should be the least beset by the dangers of discovery. Whether to go by way of Hamadalban's quarters or through the gallery they mentioned? These are questions I cannot answer to my own satisfaction; and look!" his eyes had been roving about the chamber, "there is an opening in the ceiling. Where might that lead?"

"It might lead almost anywhere, or nowhere at all!" replied the Trohanadalmakusian. "Many chambers have such openings. Sometimes they lead into small lofts that are not connected with any other chamber; again they lead into secret chambers, or even into corridors upon another level."

There came a pounding upon the door leading into Hamadalban's quarters and a woman's voice called aloud: "Kalfastoban, open!" she cried. "There has come an ental from the quarry guard in search of Caraftap. The sentry at the entrance to the quarters of the slaves of Zoanthrohago has been found slain and they wish to question Caraftap, believing that there is a conspiracy among the slaves."

"We must go by the gallery," whispered Komodoflorensal, stepping quickly to the door leading thereto.

As he reached it someone laid a hand upon the latch from the opposite side and attempted to open the door, which was locked.

"Kalfastoban!" cried a voice from the gallery beyond. "Let us in! The slaves went not this way. Come, open quickly!"

Tarzan of the Apes glanced quickly about. Upon his face was a half-snarl, for once again was he the cornered beast. He measured the distance from the floor to the trap in the ceiling, and then with a little run he sprang lightly upward. He had forgotten to what extent the reduction of his weight affected his agility. He had hoped to reach a handhold upon the upper edge of the opening, but instead he shot entirely through it, alighting upon his feet in a dark chamber. Turning he looked down at his friends below. Consternation was writ large upon the countenance of each; but at that he could not wonder. He was almost as much surprised himself.

"Is it too far for you to jump?" he asked.

"Too far!" they replied.

He swung, then, head downward through the opening, catching the edge of the trap in the hollow of his knees. At the gallery door the knocking was becoming insistent and now at that leading into the quarters of Hamadalban a man's voice had supplanted that of the woman. The fellow was demanding entrance, angrily.

"Open!" he shouted. "In the name of the king, open!"

"Open yourself!" shouted the fellow who had been hammering at the opposite door, thinking that the demand to open came from the interior of the chamber to which he sought admission.

"How can I open?" screamed back the other. "The door is locked upon your side!"

"It is not locked upon my side. It is locked upon yours," cried the other, angrily.

"You lie!" shouted he who sought entrance from Hamadalban's quarters, "and you will pay well when this is reported to the king."

Tarzan swung, head downward, into the chamber, his hands extended toward his companions. "Lift Talaskar to me," he directed Komodoflorensal, and as the other did so he grasped the girl's wrists and raised her as far as he could until she could seize upon a part of his leather harness and support herself alone without falling. Then he took another hold upon her, lower down, and lifted still higher, and in this way she managed to clamber into the chamber above.

The angry warriors at the two doors were now evidently engaged in an attempt to batter their way into the chamber. Heavy blows were falling upon the substantial panels that threatened to splinter them at any moment.

"Fill your pouch with candles, Komodoflorensal," said Tarzan, "and then jump for my hands."

"I took all the candles I could carry while we were in the

storeroom," replied the other. "Brace yourself! I am going to jump."

A panel splintered and bits of wood flew to the center of the floor from the door at the gallery just as Tarzan seized the outstretched hands of Komodoflorensal and an instant later, as both men kneeled in the darkness of the loft and looked down into the chamber below the opposite door flew open and the ten warriors who composed the ental burst in at the heels of their Vental.

For an instant they looked about in blank surprise and then their attention was attracted by the pounding upon the other door. A smile crossed the face of the Vental as he stepped quickly to the gallery door and unlocked it. Angry warriors rushed in upon him, but when he had explained the misapprehension under which both parties had been striving for entrance to the chamber they all joined in the laughter, albeit a trifle shamefacedly.

"But who was in here?" demanded the Vental who had brought the soldiers from the quarry.

"Kalfastoban and the green slave Caraftap," proffered a woman belonging to Hamadalban.

"They must be hiding!" said a warrior.

"Search the quarters!" commanded the Vental.

"It will not take long to find one," said another warrior, pointing at the floor just inside the storeroom doorway.

The others looked and there they saw a human hand resting upon the floor. The fingers seemed frozen into the semblance of clutching claws. Mutely they proclaimed death. One of the warriors stepped quickly to the storeroom, opened the door and dragged forth the body of Caraftap, to which the head was clinging by a shred of flesh. Even the warriors stepped back, aghast. They looked quickly around the chamber.

"Both doors were barred upon the inside," said the Vental. "Whatever did this must still be here."

"It could have been nothing human," whispered a woman who had followed them from the adjoining quarters.

"Search carefully," said the Vental, and as he was a brave man, he went first into one chamber and then another. In the last one they found Kalfastoban, run through the heart.

"It is time we got out of here if there is any way out," whispered Tarzan to Komodoflorensal. "One of them will espy this hole directly."

Very cautiously the two men felt their way in opposite direction around the walls of the dark, stuffy loft. Deep dust, the dust of ages, rose about them, chokingly, evidencing the fact that the room had not been used for years, perhaps for ages. Presently Komodoflorensal heard a "H-s-s-t!" from the ape-man who called them to him. "Come here, both of you. I have found something."

"What have you found?" asked Talaskar, coming close.

"An opening near the bottom of the wall," replied Tarzan. "It is large enough for a man to crawl through. Think you, Komodoflorensal, that it would be safe to light a candle?"

"No, not now," replied the prince.

"I will go without it, then," announced the ape-man, "for we must see where this tunnel leads, if anywhere."

He dropped upon his hands and knees, then, and Talaskar, who had been standing next him, felt him move away. She could not see him—it was too dark in the gloomy loft.

The two waited, but Zuanthrol did not return. They heard voices in the room below. They wondered if the searchers would soon investigate the loft, but really there was no need for apprehension. The searchers had determined to invest the place—it would be safer than crawling into that dark hole after an unknown thing that could tear the head from a man's body. When it came down, as come down it would have to, they would be prepared to destroy or capture it; but in the meantime they were content to wait.

"What has become of him?" whispered Talaskar, anxiously.

"You care very much for him, do you not?" asked Komodoflorensal.

"Why should I not?" asked the girl. "You do, too, do you not?"

"Yes," replied Komodoflorensal.

"He is very wonderful," said the girl.

"Yes," said Komodoflorensal.

As though in answer to their wish they heard a low whistle from the depths of the tunnel into which Tarzan had crawled. "Come!" whispered the ape-man.

Talaskar first, they followed him, crawling upon hands and knees through a winding tunnel, feeling their way through the darkness, until at last a light flared before them and they saw Zuanthrol lighting a candle in a small chamber that was only just high enough to permit a tall man to sit erect within it.

"I got this far," he said to them, "and as it offered a fair hiding place where we might have light without fear of discovery I came back after you. Here we can stop a while in comparative comfort and safety until I can explore the tunnel further. From what I have been able to judge it has never been used during the lifetime of any living Veltopismakusian, so there is little likelihood that anyone will think of looking here for us."

"Do you think they will follow us?" asked Talaskar.

"I think they will," replied Komodoflorensal, "and as we cannot go back it will be better if we push on at once, as it is reasonable to assume that the opposite end of this tunnel opens into another chamber. Possibly there we shall find an avenue of escape."

"You are right, Komodoflorensal," agreed Tarzan. "Nothing can be gained by remaining here. I will go ahead. Let Talaskar follow me, and you bring up the rear. If the place proves a blind alley we shall be no worse off for having investigated it."

Lighting their way this time with candles the three crawled laboriously and painfully over the uneven, rock floor of the tunnel, which turned often, this way and that, as though passing around chambers, until, to their relief, the passageway abruptly enlarged, both in width and height, so that now they could proceed in an erect position. The tunnel now dropped in a steep declivity to a lower level and a moment later the three emerged into a small chamber, where Talaskar suddenly placed a hand upon Tarzan's arm, with a little intaking of her breath in a half gasp.

"What is that, Zuanthrol!" she whispered, pointing into the darkness ahead.

Upon the floor at one side of the room a crouching figure was barely discernible close to the wall.

"And that!" exclaimed the girl, pointing to another portion of the room.

The ape-man shook her hand from his arm and stepped quickly forward, his candle held high in his left hand, his right upon his sword. He came close to the crouching figure and bent to examine it. He laid his hand upon it and it fell into a heap of dust.

"What is it?" demanded the girl.

"It *was* a man," replied Tarzan; "but it has been dead many years. It was chained to this wall. Even the chain has rusted away."

"And the other, too?" asked Talaskar.

"There are several of them," said Komodoflorensal. "See? There and there."

"At least they cannot detain us," said Tarzan, and moved on again across the chamber toward a doorway on the opposite side.

"But they tell us something, possibly," ventured Komodoflorensal.

"What do they say?" asked the ape-man.

"That this corridor connected with the quarters of a very powerful Veltopismakusian," replied the prince. "So powerful was he that he might dispose of his enemies thus, without question; and it also tells us that all this happened long years ago."

"The condition of the bodies told us that," said Tarzan.

"Not entirely," replied Komodoflorensal. "The ants would have reduced them to that state in a short time. In past ages the dead were left within the domes, and the ants, who were then our scavengers, soon disposed of them, but the ants sometimes attacked the living. They grew from a nuisance to a menace, and then every precaution had to be taken to keep from attracting them. Also we fought them. There were great battles waged in Trohanadalmakus between the Minunians and the ants and thousands of our warriors were devoured alive, and though we slew billions of ants their queens could propagate faster than we could kill the sexless workers who attacked us with their soldiers. But at last we turned our attention to their nests. There the carnage was terrific, but we succeeded in slaying their queens and since then no ants have come into our domes. They live about us, but they fear us. However, we do not risk attracting them again by leaving our dead within the domes."

"Then you believe that this corridor leads to the quarters of some great noble?" inquired Tarzan.

"I believe that it once did. The ages bring change. Its end

may now be walled up. The chamber to which it leads may have housed a king's son when these bones were quick; today it may be a barrack-room for soldiers, or a stable for diadets. About all that we know definitely about it," concluded Komodoflorensal, "is that it has not been used by man for a long time, and probably, therefore, is unknown to present-day Veltopismakusians."

Beyond the chamber of death the tunnel dropped rapidly to lower levels, entering, at last, a third chamber larger than either of the others. Upon the floor lay the bodies of many men.

"These were not chained to the walls," remarked Tarzan.

"No, they died fighting, as one may see by their naked swords and the position of their bones."

As the three paused a moment to look about the chamber there fell upon their ears the sound of a human voice.

19

As THE DAYS passed and Tarzan did not return to his home his son became more and more apprehensive. Runners were sent to nearby villages, but each returned with the same report. No one had seen The Big Bwana. Korak dispatched messages, then, to the nearest telegraph inquiring from all the principal points in Africa, where the ape-man might have made a landing, if aught had been seen or heard of him; but always again were the answers in the negative.

And at last, stripped to G-string and carrying naught but his primitive weapons, Korak the Killer took the trail with a score of the swiftest and bravest of the Waziri in search of his father. Long and diligently they searched the jungle and the forest, often enlisting the friendly services of the villages near which they chanced to be carrying on their quest, until they had covered as with a fine-toothed comb a vast area of country, covered it as could have no other body of men; but for all their care and all their diligence they uncovered no single clue as to the fate or whereabouts of Tarzan of the Apes, and so, disheartened yet indefatigable, they searched on and on through tangled miles of steaming jungle or across rocky uplands as inhospitable as the stunted thorns that dotted them.

And in the Royal Dome of Elkomoelhago, Thagosto of Veltopismakus, three people halted in a rock-walled, hidden chamber and listened to a human voice that appeared to come to them out of the very rock of the walls surrounding them. Upon the floor about them lay the bones of long-dead men. About them rose the impalpable dust of ages.

The girl pressed closer to Tarzan. "Who is it?" she whispered.

Tarzan shook his head.

"It is a woman's voice," said Komodoflorensal.

The ape-man raised his candle high above his head and took a step closer to the left-hand wall; then he stopped and pointed. The others looked in the direction indicated by Tarzan's finger and saw an opening in the wall a hual or two above his head. Tarzan handed his candle to Komodoflorensal, removed his sword and laid it on the floor, and then sprang lightly for the opening. For a moment he clung to its edge, listening, and then he dropped back into the chamber.

"It is pitch-black beyond," he said. "Whoever owns that voice is in another chamber beyond that into which I was just looking. There was no human being in the next apartment."

"If it was absolutely dark, how could you know that?" demanded Komodoflorensal.

"Had there been anyone there I should have smelled him," replied the ape-man.

The others looked at him in astonishment. "I am sure of it," said Tarzan, "because I could plainly feel a draught sucking up from the chamber, through the aperture, and into this chamber. Had there been a human being there his effluvium would have been carried directly to my nostrils."

"And you could have detected it?" demanded Komodoflorensal. "My friend, I can believe much of you, but not that."

Tarzan smiled. "I at least have the courage of my convictions," he said, "for I am going over there and investigate. From the clearness with which the voice comes to us I am certain that it comes through no solid wall. There must be an opening into the chamber where the woman is and as we should investigate every possible avenue of escape, I shall investigate this." He stepped again toward the wall below the aperture.

"Oh, let us not separate," cried the girl. "Where one goes, let us all go!"

"Two swords are better than one," said Komodoflorensal, though his tone was only halfhearted.

"Very well," replied Tarzan. "I will go first, and then you can pass Talaskar up to me."

Komodoflorensal nodded. A minute or two later the three stood upon the opposite side of the wall. Their candle revealed a narrow passage that showed indications of much more recent use than those through which they had passed from the quarters of Kalfastoban. The wall they had passed through to reach it was of stone, but that upon the opposite side was of studding and rough boards.

"This is a passage built along the side of a paneled room," whispered Komodoflorensal.

"The other side of these rough boards supports beautifully polished panels of brilliant woods or burnished metals."

"Then there should be a door, you think, opening from this passage into the adjoining chamber?" asked Tarzan.

"A secret panel, more likely," he replied.

They walked along the passage, listening intently. At first they had just been able to distinguish that the voice they heard was that of a woman; but now they heard the words.

"—had they let me have him," were the first that they distinguished.

"Most glorious mistress, this would not have happened then," replied another female voice.

"Zoanthrohago is a fool and deserves to die; but my illustrious father, the king, is a bigger fool," spoke the first voice. "He will kill Zoanthrohago and with him the chance of discovering the secret of making our warriors giants. Had they let me buy this Zuanthrol he would not have escaped. They thought that I would have killed him, but that was farthest from my intentions."

"What would you have done with him, wondrous Princess?"

"That is not for a slave to ask or know," snapped the mistress.

For a time there was silence.

"That is the Princess Janzara speaking," whispered Tarzan to Komodoflorensal. "It is the daughter of Elkomoelhago whom you would have captured and made your princess; but you would have had a handful."

"Is she as beautiful as they say?" asked Komodoflorensal.

"She is very beautiful, but she is a devil."

"It would have been my duty to take her," said Komodoflorensal.

Tarzan was silent. A plan was unfolding itself within his mind. The voice from beyond the partition spoke again.

"He was very wonderful," it said. "Much more wonderful than our warriors," and then, after a silence, "You may go, slave, and see to it that I am not disturbed before the sun stands midway between the Women's Corridor and the King's Corridor."

"May your candles burn as deathlessly as your beauty, Princess," said the slave, as she backed across the apartment.

An instant later the three behind the paneling heard a door close.

Tarzan crept stealthily along the passage, seeking the secret panel that connected the apartment where the Princess Janzara lay composed for the night; but it was Talaskar who found it.

"Here!" she whispered and together the three examined the fastening. It was simple and could evidently be opened from the opposite side by pressure upon a certain spot in the panel.

"Wait here!" said Tarzan to his companions. "I am going to fetch the Princess Janzara. If we cannot escape with her we should be able to buy our liberty with such a hostage."

Without waiting to discuss the advisability of his action with the others, Tarzan gently slid back the catch that held the panel and pushed it slightly ajar. Before him was the apartment of Janzara—a creation of gorgeous barbarity in the center of which, upon a marble slab, the princess lay upon her back, a gigantic candle burning at her head and another at her feet.

Regardless of the luxuriousness of their surroundings, of their wealth, or their positions in life, the Minunians never sleep upon a substance softer than a single thickness of fabric, which they throw upon the ground, or upon wooden, stone, or marble sleeping slabs, depending upon their caste and their wealth.

Leaving the panel open the ape-man stepped quietly into the apartment and moved directly toward the princess, who lay with closed eyes, either already asleep, or assiduously wooing Morpheus. He had crossed halfway to her cold couch when a sudden draught closed the panel with a noise that might well have awakened the dead.

Instantly the princess was on her feet and facing him. For a moment she stood in silence gazing at him and then she moved slowly toward him, the sinuous undulations of her graceful carriage suggesting to the Lord of the Jungle a similarity to the savage majesty of Sabor, the lioness.

"It is you, Zuanthrol!" breathed the princess. "You have come for me?"

"I have come for you, Princess," replied the ape-man. "Make no outcry and no harm will befall you."

"I will make no outcry," whispered Janzara as with half-closed lids she glided to him and threw her arms about his neck.

Tarzan drew back and gently disengaged himself. "You do not understand, Princess," he told her. "You are my prisoner. You are coming with me."

"Yes," she breathed, "I am your prisoner, but it is you who do not understand. I love you. It is my right to choose whatever slave I will to be my prince. I have chosen you."

Tarzan shook his head impatiently. "You do not love me," he said. "I am sorry that you think you do, for I do not love you. I have no time to waste. Come!" and he stepped closer to take her by the wrist.

Her eyes narrowed. "Are you mad?" she demanded. "Or can it be that you do not know who I am?"

"You are Janzara, daughter of Elkomoelhago," replied Tarzan. "I know well who you are."

"And you dare to spurn my love!" She was breathing heavily, her breasts rising and falling to the tumultuous urge of her emotions.

"It is no question of love between us," replied the ape-man. "To me it is only a question of liberty and life for myself and my companions."

"You love another?" questioned Janzara.

"Yes," Tarzan told her.

"Who is she?" demanded the princess.

"Will you come quietly, or shall I be compelled to carry you away by force?" asked the ape-man, ignoring her question.

For a moment the woman stood silently before him, her every muscle tensed, her dark eyes two blazing wells of fire, and then slowly her expression changed. Her face softened and she stretched one hand toward him.

"I will help you, Zuanthrol," she said. "I will help you to escape. Because I love you I shall do this. Come! Follow me!" She turned and moved swiftly across the apartment.

"But my companions," said the ape-man. "I cannot go without them."

"Where are they?"

He did not tell her, for as yet he was none too sure of her motives.

"Show me the way," he said, "and I can return for them."

"Yes," she replied, "I will show you and then perhaps you will love me better than you love the other."

In the passage behind the paneling Talaskar and Komodoflorensal awaited the outcome of Tarzan's venture. Distinctly to their ears came every word of the conversation between the ape-man and the princess.

"He loves you," said Komodoflorensal. "You see, he loves you."

"I see nothing of the kind," returned Talaskar. "Because he does not love the Princess Janzara is no proof that he loves me."

"But he does love you—and you love him! I have seen it since first he came. Would that he were not my friend, for then I might run him through."

"Why would you run him through because he loves me—if he does?" demanded the girl. "Am I so low that you would rather see your friend dead than mated with me?"

"I—" he hesitated. "I cannot tell you what I mean."

The girl laughed, and then suddenly sobered. "She is leading him from her apartment. We had better follow."

As Talaskar laid her fingers upon the spring that actuated the lock holding the panel in place, Janzara led Tarzan across her chamber toward a doorway in one of the side walls—not the doorway through which her slave had departed.

"Follow me," whispered the princess, "and you will see what the love of Janzara means."

Tarzan, not entirely assured of her intentions, followed her warily.

"You are afraid," she said. "You do not trust me! Well, come here then and look, yourself, into this chamber before you enter."

Komodoflorensal and Talaskar had but just stepped into the apartment when Tarzan approached the door to one side of which Janzara stood. They saw the floor give suddenly beneath his feet and an instant later Zuanthrol had disappeared. As he shot down a polished chute he heard a wild laugh from Janzara following him into the darkness of the unknown.

Komodoflorensal and Talaskar leaped quickly across the chamber, but too late. The floor that had given beneath Tarzan's feet had slipped quietly back into place. Janzara stood above the spot trembling with anger and staring down at the place where the ape-man had disappeared. She shook as an aspen shakes in the breeze—shook in the mad tempest of her own passions.

"If you will not come to me you shall never go to another!" she screamed, and then she turned and saw Komodoflorensal and Talaskar running toward her. What followed occurred so quickly that it would be impossible to record the facts in the brief time that they actually consumed. It was over almost before Tarzan reached the bottom of the chute and picked himself from the earthen floor upon which he had been deposited.

The room in which he found himself was lighted by several candles burning in iron-barred niches. Opposite him was a heavy gate of iron bars through which he could see another lighted apartment in which a man, his chin sagging directly upon his breast, was seated upon a low bench. At the sound of

Tarzan's precipitate entrance into the adjoining chamber the man looked up and at sight of Zuanthrol, leaped to his feet.

"Quick! To your left!" he cried, and Tarzan, turning, saw two huge, green-eyed beasts crouching to spring.

His first impulse was to rub his eyes as one might to erase the phantom figures of a disquieting dream, for what he saw were two ordinary African wildcats—ordinary in contour and markings, but in size gigantic. For an instant the ape-man forgot that he was but one-fourth his normal size, and that the cats, that appeared to him as large as full-grown lions, were in reality but average specimens of their kind.

As they came toward him he whipped out his sword, prepared to battle for his life with these great felines as he had so often before with their mighty cousins of his own jungle.

"If you can hold them off until you reach this gate," cried the man in the next chamber, "I can let you through. The bolt is upon this side," but even as he spoke one of the cats charged.

Komodoflorensal, brushing past Janzara, leaped for the spot upon the floor at which Tarzan had disappeared and as it gave beneath him he heard a savage cry break from the lips of the Princess of Veltopismakus.

"So it is you he loves?" she screamed. "But he shall not have you—no! not even in death!" and that was all that Komodoflorensal heard as the black chute swallowed him.

Talaskar, confronted by the infuriated Janzara, halted, and then stepped back, for the princess was rushing upon her with drawn dagger.

"Die, slave!" she screamed, as she lunged for the white breast of Talaskar, but the slave girl caught the other's wrist and a moment later they went down, locked in one another's embrace. Together they rolled about the floor, the daughter of Elkomoel-hago seeking to drive her slim blade into the breast of the slave girl, while Talaskar fought to hold off the menacing steel and to close with her fingers upon the throat of her antagonist.

As the first cat charged the other followed, not to be robbed of its share of the flesh of the kill, for both were half-starved and ravenous, and as the ape-man met the charge of the first, sidestepping its rush and springing in again to thrust at its side, Komodoflorensal, who had drawn his sword as he entered the apartment of Janzara, shot into the subterranean den almost into the teeth of the second beast, which was so disconcerted by the sudden appearance of this second human that it wheeled and sprang to the far end of the den before it could gather its courage for another attack.

In the chamber above, Talaskar and Janzara fought savagely, two she-tigers in human form. They rolled to and fro about the room, straining and striking; Janzara screaming: "Die, slave! You shall not have him!" But Talaskar held her peace and saved her breath, so that slowly she was overcoming the other when they chanced to roll upon the very spot that had let Tarzan and Komodoflorensal to the pit beneath.

As Janzara realized what had happened she uttered a scream of terror. "The cats! The cats!" she cried, and then the two disappeared into the black shaft.

Komodoflorensal did not follow the cat that had retreated to the far end of the pit; but sprang at once to Tarzan's aid, and together they drove off the first beast as they backed toward the gate where the man in the adjoining chamber stood ready to admit them to the safety of his own apartment.

The two cats charged and then retreated, springing in quickly and away again as quickly, for they had learned the taste of the sharp steel with which the humans were defending themselves. The two men were almost at the gate, another instant and they could spring through. The cats charged again and again were driven to the far corner of the pit. The man in the next chamber swung open the gate.

"Quick!" he cried, and at the same instant two figures shot from the mouth of the shaft and, locked tightly in one another's embrace, rolled to the floor of the pit directly in the path of the charging carnivores.

20

As Tarzan and Komodoflorensal realized that Talaskar
and Janzara lay exposed to the savage assault of the hungry
beasts they both sprang quickly toward the two girls. As had
been the case when Komodoflorensal had shot into the pit, the
cats were startled by the sudden appearance of these two new
humans, and in the first instant of their surprise had leaped
again to the far end of the chamber.

Janzara had lost her dagger as the two girls had fallen into
the shaft and now Talaskar saw it lying on the floor beside her.
Releasing her hold upon the princess she seized the weapon
and leaped to her feet. Already Tarzan and Komodoflorensal
were at her side and the cats were returning to the attack.

Janzara arose slowly and half-bewildered. She looked
about, terror disfiguring her marvelous beauty, and as she did
so the man in the adjoining chamber saw her.

"Janzara!" he cried. "My Princess, I come!" and seizing the
bench upon which he had been sitting, and the only thing
within the chamber that might be converted into a weapon, he
swung wide the gate and leaped into the chamber where the
four were now facing the thoroughly infuriated beasts.

Both animals, bleeding from many wounds, were mad with
pain, rage, and hunger. Screaming and growling they threw
themselves upon the swords of the two men, who had pushed
the girls behind them and were backing slowly toward the
gate, and then the man with the bench joined Tarzan and

Komodoflorensal and the three fought back the charges of the infuriated carnivores.

The bench proved fully as good a weapon of defense as the swords and so together the five drew slowly back, until, quite suddenly and without the slightest warning both cats leaped quickly to one side and darted behind the party as though sensing that the women would prove easier prey. One of them came near to closing upon Janzara had not the man with the bench, imbued apparently with demoniacal fury, leaped upon it with his strange weapon and beaten it back so desperately that it was forced to abandon the princess.

Even then the man did not cease to follow it but, brandishing the bench, pursued it and its fellow with such terrifying cries and prodigious blows that, to escape him, both cats suddenly dodged into the chamber that the man had occupied, and before they could return to the attack he with the bench had slammed the gate and fastened them upon its opposite side. Then he wheeled and faced the four.

"Zoanthrohago!" cried the princess.

"Your slave!" replied the noble, dropping to one knee and leaning far back, with outstretched arms.

"You have saved my life, Zoanthrohago," said Janzara, "and after all the indignities that I have heaped upon you! How can I reward you?"

"I love you, Princess, as you have long known," replied the man; "but now it is too late, for tomorrow I die by the king's will. Elkomoelhago has spoken, and even though you be his daughter, I do not hesitate to say his very ignorance prevents him ever changing a decision once reached."

"I know," said Janzara. "He is my sire but I love him not. He killed my mother in a fit of unreasoning jealousy. He is a fool—the fool of fools."

Suddenly she turned upon the others. "These slaves would escape, Zoanthrohago," she cried. "With my aid they might accomplish it. With their company we might succeed in escaping, too, and in finding an asylum in their own land."

"If any of them is of sufficient power in his native city," replied Zoanthrohago.

"This one," said Tarzan, seeing a miraculous opportunity for

freedom, "is the son of Adendrohahkis, King of Trohanadalmakus—the oldest son, and Zertolosto."

Janzara looked at Tarzan a moment after he had done
speaking. "I was wicked, Zuanthrol," she said; "but I thought
that I wanted you and being the daughter of a king I have
seldom been denied aught that I craved," and then to Talaskar:
"Take your man, my girl, and may you be happy with him,"
and she pushed Talaskar gently toward the ape-man; but
Talaskar drew back.

"You are mistaken, Janzara," she said, "I do not love Zuanthrol, nor does he love me."

Komodoflorensal looked quickly at Tarzan as though
expecting that he would quickly deny the truth of Talaskar's
statement, but the ape-man only nodded his head in assent.

"Do you mean," demanded Komodoflorensal, "that you do
not love Talaskar?" and he looked straight into the eyes of his
friend.

"On the contrary, I love her very much," replied Tarzan;
"but not in the way that you have believed, or should I say
feared? I love her because she is a good girl and a kind girl and
a loyal friend, and also because she was in trouble and needed
the love and protection which you and I alone could give her;
but as a man loves his mate, I do not love her, for I have a mate
of my own in my country beyond the thorns."

Komodoflorensal said no more, but he thought a great deal.
He thought of what it would mean to return to his own city
where he was the Zertolosto, and where, by all the customs of
ages, he would be supposed to marry a princess from another
city. But he did not want a princess—he wanted Talaskar, the
little slave girl of Veltopismakus, who scarcely knew her own
mother and most probably had never heard that of her father, if
her mother knew it.

He wanted Talaskar, but he could only have her in Trohanadalmakus as a slave. His love for her was real and so he
would not insult her by thinking such a thing as that. If he could
not make her his princess he would not have her at all, and so
Komodoflorensal, the son of Adendrohahkis, was sad.

But he had none too much time to dwell upon his sorrow
now, for the others were planning the best means for escape.

"The keepers come down to feed the cats upon this side,"

said Zoanthrohago, indicating a small door in the wall of the pit opposite that which led into the chamber in which he had been incarcerated.

"Doubtless it is not locked, either," said Janzara, "for a prisoner could not reach it without crossing through this chamber where the cats were kept."

"We will see," said Tarzan, and crossed to the door.

A moment sufficed to force it open, revealing a narrow corridor beyond. One after another the five crawled through the small aperture and following the corridor ascended an acclivity, lighting their way with candles taken from the den of the carnivores. At the top a door opened into a wide corridor, a short distance down which stood a warrior, evidently on guard before a door.

Janzara looked through the tiny crack that Tarzan had opened the door and saw the corridor and the man. "Good!" she exclaimed. "It is my own corridor and the warrior is on guard before my door. I know him well. Through me he has escaped payment of his taxes for the past thirty moons. He would die for me. Come! we have nothing to fear," and stepping boldly into the corridor she approached the sentry, the others following behind her.

Until he recognized her there was danger that the fellow would raise an alarm, but the moment he saw who it was he was as wax in her hands.

"You are blind," she told him.

"If the Princess Janzara wishes it," he replied.

She told him what she wished—five diadets and some heavy, warriors' wraps. He eyed those who were with her, and evidently recognized Zoanthrohago and guessed who the two other men were.

"Not only shall I be blind for my princess," he said, "but tomorrow I shall be dead for her."

"Fetch six diadets, then," said the princess.

Then she turned to Komodoflorensal. "You are Prince Royal of Trohanadalmakus?" she asked.

"I am," he replied.

"And if we show you the way to liberty you will not enslave us?"

"I shall take you to the city as my own slaves and then liberate you," he replied.

"It is something that has seldom if ever been done," she mused; "not in the memory of living man in Veltopismakus. I wonder if your sire will permit it."

"The thing is not without precedent," replied Komodoflorensal. "It has been done but rarely, yet it *has* been done. I think you may feel assured of a friendly welcome at the court of Adendrohahkis, where the wisdom of Zoanthrohago will not go unappreciated or unrewarded."

It was a long time before the warrior returned with the diadets. His face was covered with perspiration and his hands with blood.

"I had to fight for them," he said, "and we shall have to fight to use them if we do not hurry. Here, Prince, I brought you weapons," and he handed a sword and dagger to Zoanthrohago.

They mounted quickly. It was Tarzan's first experience upon one of the wiry, active, little mounts of the Minunians; but he found the saddle well designed and the diadet easily controlled.

"They will be following me from the King's Corridor," explained Oratharc, the warrior who had fetched the diadets. "It would be best, then, to leave by one of the others."

"Trohanadalmakus is east of Veltopismakus," said Zoanthrohago, "and if we leave by the Women's Corridor with two slaves from Trohanadalmakus they will assume that we are going there; but if we leave by another corridor they will not be sure and if they lose even a little time in starting the pursuit it will give us just that much of an advantage. If we go straight toward Trohanadalmakus we shall almost certainly be overtaken as the swiftest of diadets will be used in our pursuit. Our only hope lies in deceiving them as to our route or destination, and to accomplish this I believe that we should leave either by the Warriors' Corridor or the Slaves' Corridor, cross the hills north of the city, circle far out to the north and east, not turning south until we are well past Trohanadalmakus. In this way we can approach that city from the east while our pursuers are patrolling the country west of Trohanadalmakus to Veltopismakus."

"Let us leave by the Warriors' Corridor then," suggested Janzara.

"The trees and shrubbery will conceal us while we pass around to the north of the city," said Komodoflorensal.

"We should leave at once," urged Oratharc.

"Go first then, with the princess," said Zoanthrohago, "for there is a possibility that the guard at the entrance will let her pass with her party. We will muffle ourselves well with our warriors' cloaks. Come, lead the way!"

With Janzara and Oratharc ahead and the others following closely they moved at a steady trot along the circular corridor toward the Warriors' Corridor, and it was not until they had turned into the latter that any sign of pursuit developed. Even then, though they heard the voices of men behind them, they hesitated to break into a faster gait lest they arouse the suspicions of the warriors in the guard room which they must pass near the mouth of the corridor.

Never had the Warriors' Corridor seemed so long to any of the Veltopismakusians in the party as it did this night; never had they so wished to race their diadets as now; but they held their mounts to an even pace that would never have suggested to the most suspicious that here were six people seeking escape, most of them from death.

They had come almost to the exit when they were aware that the pursuit had turned into the Warriors' Corridor behind them and that their pursuers were advancing at a rapid gait.

Janzara and Oratharc drew up beside the sentry at the mouth of the corridor as he stepped out to bar their progress.

"The Princess Janzara!" announced Oratharc. "Aside for the Princess Janzara!"

The princess threw back the hood of the warrior's cloak she wore, revealing her features, well known to every warrior in the Royal Dome—and well feared. The fellow hesitated.

"Aside, man!" cried the princess, "or I ride you down."

A great shout arose behind them. Warriors on swiftly galloping diadets leaped along the corridor toward them. The warriors were shouting something, the sense of which was hidden by the noise; but the sentry was suspicious.

"Wait until I call the Novand of the guard, Princess," he cried. "Something is amiss and I dare let no one pass without authority; but wait! here he is!" and the party turned in their saddles to see a Novand emerging from the door of the guard room, followed by a number of warriors.

"Ride!" cried Janzara and spurred her diadet straight for the single sentry in their path.

The others lifted their mounts quickly in pursuit. The sentry went down, striking valiantly with his rapier at the legs and bellies of flying diadets. The Novand and his men rushed from the guard room just in time to collide with the pursuers, whom they immediately assumed were belated members of the fleeing party. The brief minutes that these fought, before explanations could be made and understood, gave the fugitives time to pass among the trees to the west side of the city, and, turning north, make for the hills that were dimly visible in the light of a clear but moonless night.

Oratharc, who said that he knew the hill trails perfectly, led the way, the others following as closely as they could; Komodoflorensal and Tarzan bringing up the rear. Thus they moved on in silence through the night, winding along precipitous mountain trails, leaping now and again from rock to rock where the trail itself had been able to find no footing; sliding into dark ravines, clambering through heavy brush and timber along tunnel-like trails that followed their windings, or crept up their opposite sides to narrow ridge or broad plateau; and all night long no sign of pursuit developed.

Came the morning at last and with it, from the summit of a lofty ridge, a panorama of broad plain stretching to the north, of distant hills, of forests, and of streams. They decided then to descend to one of the numerous parklike glades that they could see nestling in the hills below them, and there rest their mounts and permit them to feed, for the work of the night had been hard upon them.

They knew that in the hills they might hide almost indefinitely, so wild and so little traveled were they and so they went into camp an hour after sunrise in a tiny cuplike valley surrounded by great trees, and watered and fed their mounts with a sense of security greater than they had felt since they left Veltopismakus.

Oratharc went out on foot and killed a number of quail and Tarzan speared a couple of fish in the stream. These they prepared and ate, and then, the men taking turns on guard, they slept until afternoon, for none had had sleep the night before.

Taking up their flight again in the midafternoon they were well out upon the plain when darkness overtook them. Komodoflorensal and Zoanthrohago were riding far out upon the flanks and all were searching for a suitable camping place. It was Zoanthrohago who found it and when they all gathered about him Tarzan saw nothing in the waning light of day that appeared any more like a good camping place than any other spot on the open plain. There was a little clump of trees, but they had passed many such clumps, and there was nothing about this one that seemed to offer any greater security than another. As a matter of fact, to Tarzan it appeared anything but a desirable campsite. There was no water, there was little shelter from the wind and none from an enemy; but perhaps they were going into the trees. That would be better. He looked up at the lofty branches lovingly. How enormous these trees seemed! He knew them for what they were and that they were trees of but average size, yet to him now they reared their heads aloft like veritable giants.

"I will go in first," he heard Komodoflorensal say, and turned to learn what he referred to.

The other three men were standing at the mouth of a large hole, into which they were looking. Tarzan knew that the opening was the mouth of the burrow of a ratel, the African member of the badger family, and he wondered why any of them wished to enter it. Tarzan had never cared for the flesh of the ratel. He stepped over and joined the others, and as he did so he saw Komodoflorensal crawl into the opening, his drawn sword in his hand.

"Why is he doing that?" he asked Zoanthrohago.

"To drive out, or kill the cambon, if he is there," replied the prince, giving the ratel its Minunian name.

"And why?" asked Tarzan. "Surely, you do not eat its flesh!"

"No, but we want his home for the night," replied Zoanthrohago. "I had forgotten that you are not a Minunian. We will spend the night in the underground chambers of the cambon, safe from the attacks of the cat or the lion. It would be better were we there now—this is a bad hour of the night for Minunians to be abroad on the plain or in the forest, for it is at this hour that the lion hunts."

A few minutes later Komodoflorensal emerged from the hole. "The cambon is not there," he said. "The burrow is deserted. I found only a snake, which I killed. Go in, Oratharc, and Janzara and Talaskar will follow you. You have candles?"

They had, and one by one they disappeared into the mouth of the hole, until Tarzan, who had asked to remain until last, stood alone in the gathering night gazing at the mouth of the ratel's burrow, a smile upon his lips. It seemed ridiculous to him that Tarzan of the Apes should ever be contemplating hiding from Numa in the hole of a ratel, or, worse still, hiding from little Skree, the wildcat, and as he stood there smiling a bulk loomed dimly among the trees; the diadets, standing near, untethered, snorted and leaped away; and Tarzan wheeled to face the largest lion he ever had seen—a lion that towered over twice the ape-man's height above him.

How tremendous, how awe-inspiring Numa appeared to one the size of a Minunian!

The lion crouched, its tail extended, the tip moving ever so gently; but the ape-man was not deceived. He guessed what was coming and even as the great cat sprang he turned and dove headforemost down the hole of the ratel and behind him rattled the loose earth pushed into the burrow's mouth by Numa as he alighted upon the spot where Tarzan had stood.

21

FOR THREE DAYS the six traveled toward the east, and then, upon the fourth, they turned south. A great forest loomed upon the distant southern horizon, sweeping also wide upon the east. To the southwest lay Trohanadalmakus, a good two-days' journey for their tired diadets. Tarzan often wondered what rest the little creatures obtained. At night they were turned loose to graze; but his knowledge of the habits of the carnivores assured him that the tiny antelope must spend the greater part of each night in terrified watching or in flight; yet every morning they were back at the camp awaiting the pleasure of their masters. That they did not escape, never to return, is doubtless due to two facts. One is that they have been for ages bred in the domes of the Minunians—they know no other life than with their masters, to whom they look for food and care—and the other is the extreme kindness and affection which the Minunians accord their beautiful beasts of burden, and which have won the love and confidence of the little animals to such an extent that the diadet is most contented when in the company of man.

It was during the afternoon of the fourth day of their flight that Talaskar suddenly called their attention to a small cloud of dust far to their rear. For a long time all six watched it intently as it increased in size and drew nearer.

"It may be the long-awaited pursuit," said Zoanthrohago.

"Or some of my own people from Trohanadalmakus," suggested Komodoflorensal.

"Whoever they are, they greatly outnumber us," said Janzara, "and I think we should find shelter until we know their identity."

"We can reach the forest before they overtake us," said Oratharc, "and in the forest we may elude them if it is necessary."

"I fear the forest," said Janzara.

"We have no alternative," said Zoanthrohago; "but even now I doubt that we can reach it ahead of them. Come! we must be quick!"

Never before had Tarzan of the Apes covered ground so rapidly upon the back of an animal. The diadets flew through the air in great bounds. Behind them the nucleus of the dust cloud had resolved itself into a dozen mounted warriors, against whom their four blades would be helpless. Their one hope, therefore, lay in reaching the forest ahead of their pursuers, and now it seemed that they would be successful and now it seemed that they would not.

The recently distant wood seemed rushing toward him as Tarzan watched ahead between the tiny horns of his graceful mount, and, behind, the enemy was gaining. They were Veltopismakusian—they were close enough now for the devices upon their helmets to be seen—and they had recognized their quarry, for they cried aloud upon them to stop, calling several of them by name.

One of the pursuers forged farther ahead than the others. He came now close behind Zoanthrohago, who rode neck and neck with Tarzan, in the rear of their party. A half-length ahead of Zoanthrohago, was Janzara. The fellow called aloud to her.

"Princess!" he cried. "The king's pardon for you all if you return the slaves to us. Surrender and all will be forgiven."

Tarzan of the Apes heard and he wondered what the Veltopismakusians would do. It must have been a great temptation and he knew it. Had it not been for Talaskar he would have advised them to fall back among their friends; but he would not see the slave girl sacrificed. He drew his sword then and dropped back beside Zoanthrohago, though the other never guessed his purpose.

"Surrender, and all will be forgiven!" shouted the pursuer again.

"Never!" cried Zoanthrohago.

"Never!" echoed Janzara.

"The consequences are yours," cried the messenger, and on they rushed, pursuers and pursued, toward the dark forest, while from just within its rim savage eyes watched the mad race and red tongues licked hungry lips in anticipation.

Tarzan had been glad to hear the reply given by both Zoan-throhago and Janzara whom he had found likeable companions and good comrades. Janzara's whole attitude had changed since the very instant she had joined them in their attempted escape. No longer was she the spoiled daughter of a despot, but a woman seeking happiness through the new love that she had found, or the old love that she had just discovered, for she often told Zoanthrohago that she knew now that she always had loved him. And this new thing in her life made her more considerate and loving of others. She seemed now to be trying to make up to Talaskar for the cruelty of her attack upon her when she had first seen her. Her mad infatuation for Tarzan she now knew in its true light—because she had been refused him she wanted him, and she would have taken him as her prince to spite her father, whom she hated.

Komodoflorensal and Talaskar always rode together, but no words of love did the Trohanadalmakusian speak in the ear of the little slave girl. A great resolve was crystallizing in his mind, but it had as yet taken on no definite form. And Talaskar, seemingly happy just to be near him, rode blissfully through the first days of the only freedom she had ever known; but now all was forgotten except the instant danger of capture and its alternative concomitants, death and slavery.

The six urged their straining mounts ahead. The forest was so near now. Ah, if they could but reach it! There one warrior might be as good as three and the odds against them would be reduced, for in the forest the whole twelve could not engage them at once and by careful maneuvering they doubtless could separate them.

They were going to succeed! A great shout rose to the lips of Oratharc as his diadet leaped into the shadows of the first trees, and the others took it up, for a brief instant, and then it died upon their lips as they saw a giant hand reach down and snatch Oratharc from his saddle. They tried to stop and wheel their mounts, but it was too late. Already they were in the forest and all about them was a horde of the hideous Zertalacolols. One by one they were snatched from their diadets, while their pursuers, who must have seen what was taking place just inside the forest, wheeled and galloped away.

Talaskar, writhing in the grip of a she-Alali, turned toward Komodoflorensal.

"Good-bye!" she cried. "This, at last, is the end; but I can die near you and so I am happier dying than I have been living until you came to Veltopismakus."

"Good-bye, Talaskar!" he replied. "Living, I dared not tell you; but dying, I can proclaim my love. Tell me that you loved me."

"With all my heart, Komodoflorensal!" They seemed to have forgotten that another existed but themselves. In death they were alone with their love.

Tarzan found himself in the hand of a male and he also found himself wondering, even as he faced certain death, how it occurred that this great band of male and female Alali should be hunting together, and then he noticed the weapons of the males. They were not the crude bludgeon and the slinging-stones that they had formerly carried, but long, trim spears, and bows and arrows.

And now the creature that held him had lifted him even with his face and was scrutinizing him and Tarzan saw a look of recognition and amazement cross the bestial features, and he, in turn, recognized his captor. It was the son of The First Woman. Tarzan did not wait to learn the temper of his old acquaintance. Possibly their relations were altered now. Possibly they were not. He recalled the doglike devotion of the creature when last he had seen him and he put him to the test at once.

"Put me down!" he signed, peremptorily; "and tell your people to put down all of my people. Harm them not!"

Instantly the great creature set Tarzan gently upon the ground and immediately signaled his fellows to do the same with their captives. The men did immediately as they were bid, and all of the women but one. She hesitated. The son of The First Woman leaped toward her, his spear raised like a whip, and the female cowered and set Talaskar down upon the ground.

Very proud, the son of The First Woman explained to Tarzan as best he could the great change that had come upon the Alali since the ape-man had given the men weapons and the son of The First Woman had discovered what a proper use of them would mean to the males of his kind. Now each male had a woman cooking for him—at least one, and some of them—the stronger—had more than one.

To entertain Tarzan and to show him what great strides civilization had taken in the land of the Zertalacolols, the son of The First Woman seized a female by the hair and dragging her to him struck her heavily about the head and face with his clenched fist, and the woman fell upon her knees and fondled his legs, looking wistfully into his face, her own glowing with love and admiration.

That night the six slept in the open surrounded by the great Zertalacolols and the next day they started across the plain toward Trohanadalmakus where Tarzan had resolved to remain until he regained his normal size, when he would make a determined effort to cut his way through the thorn forest to his own country.

The Zertalacolols went a short distance out into the plain with them, and both men and women tried in their crude, savage way to show Tarzan their gratitude for the change that he had wrought among them, and the new happiness he had given them.

Two days later the six fugitives approached the domes of Trohanadalmakus. They had been seen by sentries when they were still a long way off, and a body of warriors rode forth to meet them, for it is always well to learn the nature of a visitor's business in Minuni before he gets too close to your home.

When the warriors discovered that Komodoflorensal and Tarzan had returned they shouted for joy and a number of them galloped swiftly back to the city to spread the news.

The fugitives were conducted at once to the throne room of Adendrohahkis and there that great ruler took his son in his arms and wept, so great was his happiness at having him returned safely to him. Nor did he forget Tarzan, though it was some time before he or the other Trohanadalmakusians could accustom themselves to the fact that this man, no bigger than they, was the great giant who had dwelt among them a few moons since.

Adendrohahkis called Tarzan to the foot of the throne and

there, before the nobles and warriors of Trohanadalmakus, he made him a Zertol, or prince, and he gave him diadets and riches and allotted him quarters fitted to his rank, begging him to stay among them always.

Janzara, Zoanthrohago, and Oratharc he gave their liberty and permission to remain in Trohanadalmakus, and then Komodoflorensal drew Talaskar to the foot of the throne.

"And now for myself I ask a boon, Adendrohahkis," he said. "As Zertolosto I am bound by custom to wed a prisoner princess taken from another city; but in this slave girl have I found the one I love. Let me renounce my rights to the throne and have her instead."

Talaskar raised her hand as though to demur, but Komodoflorensal would not let her speak, and then Adendrohahkis rose and descended the steps at the foot of which Talaskar stood and taking her by the hand led her to a place beside the throne.

"You are bound by custom only, Komodoflorensal," he said, "to wed a princess; but custom is not law. A Trohanadalmakusian may wed whom he pleases."

"And even though he were bound by law," said Talaskar, "to wed a princess, still might he wed me, for I am the daughter of Talaskhago, king of Mandalamakus. My mother was captured by the Veltopismakusians but a few moons before my birth, which took place in the very chamber in which Komodoflorensal found me. She taught me to take my life before mating with anyone less than a prince; but I would have forgotten her teachings had Komodoflorensal been but the son of a slave. That he was the son of a king I did not dream until the night we left Veltopismakus, and I had already given him my heart long before, though he did not know it."

Weeks passed and still no change came to Tarzan of the Apes. He was happy in his life with the Minunians, but he longed for his own people and the mate who would be grieving for him, and so he determined to set forth as he was, pass through the thorn forest and make his way toward home, trusting to chance that he might escape the countless dangers that would infest his way, and perhaps come to his normal size somewhere during the long journey.

His friends sought to dissuade him, but he was determined,

and at last, brooking no further delay, he set out toward the southeast in the direction that he thought lay the point where he had entered the land of the Minuni. A kamak, a body consisting of one thousand mounted warriors, accompanied him to the great forest and there, after some days' delay, the son of The First Woman found him. The Minunians bid him good-bye, and as he watched them ride away upon their graceful mounts, something rose in his throat that only came upon those few occasions in his life that Tarzan of the Apes knew the meaning of homesickness.

The son of The First Woman and his savage band escorted Tarzan to the edge of the thorn forest. Further than that they could not go. A moment later they saw him disappear among the thorns, with a wave of farewell to them. For two days Tarzan, no larger than a Minunian, made his way through the thorn forest. He met small animals that were now large enough to be dangerous to him, but he met nothing that he could not cope with. By night he slept in the burrows of the larger burrowing animals. Birds and eggs formed his food supply.

During the second night he awoke with a feeling of nausea suffusing him. A premonition of danger assailed him. It was dark as the grave in the burrow he had selected for the night. Suddenly the thought smote him that he might be about to pass through the ordeal of regaining his normal stature. To have this thing happen while he lay buried in this tiny burrow would mean death, for he would be crushed, strangled, or suffocated before he regained consciousness.

Already he felt dizzy, as one might feel who was upon the verge of unconsciousness. He stumbled to his knees and clawed his way up the steep acclivity that led to the surface. Would he reach it in time? He stumbled on and then, suddenly, a burst of fresh night air smote his nostrils. He staggered to his feet. He was out! He was free!

Behind him he heard a low growl. Grasping his sword, he lunged forward among the thorn trees. How far he went, or in what direction he did not know. It was still dark when he stumbled and fell unconscious to the ground.

22

A Waziri, returning from the village of Obebe the cannibal, saw a bone lying beside the trail. This, in itself, was nothing remarkable. Many bones lie along savage trails in Africa. But this bone caused him to pause. It was the bone of a child. Nor was that alone enough to give pause to a warrior hastening through an unfriendly country back toward his own people.

But Usula had heard strange tales in the village of Obebe the cannibal where rumor had brought him in search of his beloved master. The Big Bwana. Obebe had not seen nor heard anything of Tarzan of the Apes. Not for years had he seen the giant white. He assured Usula of this fact many times; but from other members of the tribe the Waziri learned that a white man had been kept a prisoner by Obebe for a year or more and that some time since he had escaped. At first Usula thought this white man might have been Tarzan but when he verified the statement of the time that had elapsed since the man was captured he knew that it could not have been his master, and so he turned back along the trail toward home; but when he saw the child's bone along the trail several days out he recalled the story of the missing Uhha and he paused, just for a moment, to look at the bone. And as he looked he saw something else—a small skin bag, lying among some more bones a few feet off the trail. Usula stooped and picked up the bag. He opened it and poured some of the contents into his palm. He knew what the things were and he knew that they had belonged to his

411

master, for Usula was a head man who knew much about his master's affairs. These were the diamonds that had been stolen from The Big Bwana many moons before by the white men who had found Opar. He would take them back to The Big Bwana's lady.

Three days later as he moved silently along the trail close to The Great Thorn Forest he came suddenly to a halt, the hand grasping his heavy spear tensing in readiness. In a little open place he saw a man, an almost naked man, lying upon the ground. The man was alive—he saw him move—but what was he doing? Usula crept closer, making no noise. He moved around until he could observe the man from another angle and then he saw a horrid sight. The man was white and he lay beside the carcass of a long-dead buffalo, greedily devouring the remnants of hide that clung to the bleaching bones.

The man raised his head a little and Usula, catching a better view of his face, gave a cry of horror. Then the man looked up and grinned. It was The Big Bwana!

Usula ran to him and raised him upon his knees, but the man only laughed and babbled like a child. At his side, caught over one of the horns of the buffalo, was The Big Bwana's golden locket with the great diamonds set in it. Usula replaced it about the man's neck. He built a strong shelter for him nearby and hunted food, and for many days he remained until the man's strength came back; but his mind did not come back. And thus, in this condition, the faithful Usula led home his master.

They found many wounds and bruises upon his body and his head, some old, some new, some trivial, some serious; and they sent to England for a great surgeon to come out to Africa and seek to mend the poor thing that once had been Tarzan of the Apes.

The dogs that had once loved Lord Greystoke slunk from this brainless creature. Jad-bal-ja, the Golden Lion, growled when the man was wheeled near his cage.

Korak The Killer paced the floor in dumb despair, for his mother was on her way from England, and what would be the effect upon her of this awful blow? He hesitated even to contemplate it.

Khamis, the witch doctor, had searched untiringly for Uhha, his daughter, since The River Devil had stolen her from the village of Obebe the cannibal. He had made pilgrimages to other villages, some of them remote from his own country, but he had found no trace of her or her abductor.

He was returning from another fruitless search that had extended far to the east of the village of Obebe, skirting The Great Thorn Forest a few miles north of the Ugogo. It was early morning. He had just broken his lonely camp and set out upon the last leg of his homeward journey when his keen old eyes discovered something lying at the edge of a small open space a hundred yards to his right. He had just a glimpse of something that was not of the surrounding vegetation. He did not know what it was; but instinct bade him investigate. Moving cautiously nearer he presently identified the thing as a human knee just showing above the low grass that covered the clearing. He crept closer and suddenly his eyes narrowed and his breath made a single, odd little sound as it sucked rapidly between his lips in mechanical reaction to surprise, for what he saw was the body of The River Devil lying upon its back, one knee flexed—the knee that he had seen above the grasses.

His spear advanced and ready he approached until he stood above the motionless body. Was The River Devil dead, or was he asleep? Placing the point of his spear against the brown breast Khamis prodded. The Devil did not awaken. He was not asleep, then! nor did he appear to be dead. Khamis knelt and placed an ear above the other's heart. He was not dead!

The witch doctor thought quickly. In his heart he did not believe in River Devils, yet there was a chance that there might be such things and perhaps this one was shamming unconsciousness, or temporarily absent from the flesh it assumed as a disguise that it might go among men without arousing suspicion. But, too, it was the abductor of his daughter. That thought filled him with rage and with courage. He must force the truth from those lips even though the creature were a Devil.

He unwound a bit of fiber rope from about his waist and, turning the body over upon its back, quickly bound the wrists behind it. Then he sat down beside it to wait. It was an hour before signs of returning consciousness appeared, then The River Devil opened his eyes.

"Where is Uhha, my daughter?" demanded the witch doctor. The River Devil tried to free his arms, but they were too tightly bound. He made no reply to Khamis's question. It was as though he had not heard it. He ceased struggling and lay back again, resting. After a while he opened his eyes once more and lay looking at Khamis, but he did not speak.

"Get up!" commanded the witch doctor and prodded him with a spear.

The River Devil rolled over on his side, flexed his right knee, raised on one elbow and finally got to his feet. Khamis prodded him in the direction of the trail. Toward dusk they arrived at the village of Obebe.

When the warriors and the women and the children saw who it was that Khamis was bringing to the village they became very much excited, and had it not been for the witch doctor, of whom they were afraid, they would have knifed and stoned the prisoner to death before he was fairly inside the village gates; but Khamis did not want The River Devil killed—not yet. He wanted first to force from him the truth concerning Uhha. So far he had been unable to get a word out of his prisoner. Incessant questioning, emphasized by many prods of the spear point had elicited nothing.

Khamis threw his prisoner into the same hut from which The River Devil had escaped; but he bound him securely and placed two warriors on guard. He had no mind to lose him again. Obebe came to see him. He, too, questioned him; but The River Devil only looked blankly in the face of the chief.

"I will make him speak," said Obebe. "After we have finished eating we will have him out and make him speak. I know many ways."

"You must not kill him," said the witch doctor. "He knows what became of Uhha, and until he tells me no one shall kill him."

"He will speak before he dies," said Obebe.

"He is a River Devil and will never die," said Khamis, reverting to the old controversy.

"He is Tarzan," cried Obebe, and the two were still arguing after they had passed out of hearing of the prisoner lying in the filth of the hut.

After they had eaten he saw them heating irons in a fire near the hut of the witch doctor, who was squatting before the entrance working rapidly with numerous charms—bits of wood wrapped in leaves, pieces of stone, some pebbles, a zebra's tail.

Villagers were congregating about Khamis until presently the prisoner could no longer see him. A little later a black boy came and spoke to his guards, and he was taken out and pushed roughly toward the hut of the witch doctor.

Obebe was there, as he saw after the guards had opened a way through the throng and he stood beside the fire in the center of the circle. It was only a small fire; just enough to keep a couple of irons hot.

"Where is Uhha, my daughter?" demanded Khamis.

The River Devil did not answer. Not once had he spoken since Khamis had captured him.

"Burn out one of his eyes," said Obebe. "That will make him speak!"

"Cut out his tongue!" screamed a woman. "Cut out his tongue."

"Then he cannot speak at all, you fool," cried Khamis.

The witch doctor arose and put the question again, but received no reply. Then he struck The River Devil a heavy blow in the face. Khamis had lost his temper, so that he did not fear even a River Devil.

"You will answer me now!" he screamed, and stooping he seized a red-hot iron.

"The right eye first!" shrilled Obebe.

The doctor came to the bungalow of the ape-man—Lady Greystoke brought him with her. They were three tired and dusty travelers as they dismounted at last before the rose-embowered entrance—the famous London surgeon, Lady Greystoke, and Flora Hawkes, her maid. The surgeon and Lady Greystoke went immediately to the room where Tarzan sat in an improvised wheelchair. He looked up at them blankly as they entered.

"Don't you know me, John?" asked the woman.

Her son took her by the shoulders and led her away, weeping.

"He does not know any of us," he said. "Wait until after the operation, mother, before you see him again. You can do him no good and to see him this way is too hard upon you."

The great surgeon made his examination. There was pressure on the brain from a recent fracture of the skull. An operation would relieve the pressure and might restore the patient's mind and memory. It was worth attempting.

Nurses and two doctors from Nairobi, engaged the day they arrived there, followed Lady Greystoke and the London surgeon, reaching the bungalow the day after their arrival. The operation took place the following morning.

Lady Greystoke, Korak, and Meriem were awaiting, in an adjoining room, the verdict of the surgeon. Was the operation a failure or a success? They sat mutely staring at the door leading into the improvised operating room. At last it opened, after what seemed ages, but was only perhaps an hour. The surgeon entered the room where they sat. Their eyes, dumbly pleading, asked him the question that their lips dared not voice.

"I cannot tell you anything as yet," he said, "other than that the operation, as an operation, was successful. What the result of it will be only time will tell. I have given orders that no one is to enter his room, other than the nurses for ten days. They are instructed not to speak to him or allow him to speak for the same length of time; but he will not wish to speak, for I shall keep him in a semiconscious condition, by means of drugs, until the ten days have elapsed. Until then, Lady Greystoke, we may only hope for the best; but I can assure you that your husband has every chance for complete recovery. I think you may safely hope for the best."

The witch doctor laid his left hand upon the shoulder of The River Devil; in his right hand was clutched a red-hot iron.

"The right eye first," shrilled Obebe again.

Suddenly the muscles upon the back and shoulders of the prisoner leaped into action, rolling beneath his brown hide. For just an instant he appeared to exert terrific physical force, there was a snapping sound at his back as the strands about his wrists parted, and an instant later steel-thewed fingers fell upon the right wrist of the witch doctor. Blazing eyes burned into his. He dropped the red-hot rod, his fingers paralyzed by the pressure upon his wrist, and he screamed, for he saw death in the angry face of the god.

Obebe leaped to his feet. Warriors pressed forward, but not near enough to be within reach of The River Devil. They had never been certain of the safety of tempting Providence in any such manner as Khamis and Obebe had been about to do. Now here was the result! The wrath of The River Devil would fall upon them all. They fell back, some of them, and that was a cue for others to fall back. In the minds of all was the same thought—if I have no hand in this The River Devil will not be angry with me. Then they turned and fled to their huts, stumbling over their women and their children who were trying to outdistance their lords and masters.

Obebe turned now to flee also, and The River Devil picked Khamis up, and held him in two hands high above his head, and ran after Obebe the chief. The latter dodged into his own hut. He had scarce reached the center of it when there came a terrific crash upon the light, thatched roof, which gave way beneath a heavy weight. A body descending upon the chief filled him with terror. The River Devil had leaped in through the roof of his hut to destroy him! The instinct of self-preservation rose momentarily above his fear of the supernatural, for now he was convinced that Khamis had been right and the creature they had so long held prisoner was indeed The River Devil. And Obebe drew the knife at his side and plunged it again and again into the body of the creature that had leaped upon him, and when he knew that life was extinct he rose and dragging the body after him stepped out of his hut into the light of the moon and the fires.

"Come, my people!" he cried. "You have nothing to fear, for I, Obebe, your chief, have slain The River Devil with my own hands," and then he looked down at the thing trailing behind him, and gave a gasp, and sat down suddenly in the dirt of the village street, for the body at his heels was that of Khamis, the witch doctor.

His people came and when they saw what had happened they said nothing, but looked terrified. Obebe examined his hut and the ground around it. He took several warriors and searched the village. The stranger had departed. He went to the gates. They were closed; but in the dust before them was the imprint of naked feet—the naked feet of a white man. Then he came back to his hut, where his frightened people stood waiting him.

"Obebe was right," he said. "The creature was not The River Devil—it was Tarzan of the Apes, for only he could hurl Khamis so high above his head that he would fall through the roof of a hut, and only he could pass unaided over our gates."

The tenth day had come. The great surgeon was still at the Greystoke bungalow awaiting the outcome of the operation. The patient was slowly emerging from under the influence of the last dose of drugs that had been given him during the preceding night, but he was regaining his consciousness more slowly than the surgeon had hoped. The long hours dragged by, morning ran into afternoon, and evening came, and still there was no word from the sickroom.

It was dark. The lamps were lighted. The family were congregated in the big living room. Suddenly the door opened and a nurse appeared. Behind her was the patient. There was a puzzled look upon his face; but the face of the nurse was wreathed in smiles. The surgeon came behind, assisting the man, who was weak from long inactivity.

"I think Lord Greystoke will recover rapidly now," he said. "There are many things that you may have to tell him. He did not know who he was, when he regained consciousness; but that is not unusual in such cases."

The patient took a few steps into the room, looking wonderingly about.

"There is your wife, Greystoke," said the surgeon, kindly.

Lady Greystoke rose and crossed the room toward her husband, her arms outstretched. A smile crossed the face of the invalid, as he stepped forward to meet her and take her in his arms; but suddenly someone was between them, holding them apart. It was Flora Hawkes.

"My Gawd, Lady Greystoke!" she cried. "He ain't your husband. It's Miranda, Esteban Miranda! Don't you suppose I'd know him in a million? I ain't seen him since we came back, never havin' been in the sick chamber, but I suspicioned something the minute he stepped into this room and when he smiled, I knew."

"Flora!" cried the distracted wife. "Are you sure? No! no! you must be wrong! God has not given me back my husband only to steal him away again. John! tell me, is it you? You would not lie to me?"

For a moment the man before them was silent. He swayed to and fro, as in weakness. The surgeon stepped forward and supported him.

"I have been very sick," he said. "Possibly I have changed; but I am Lord Greystoke. I do not remember this woman," and he indicated Flora Hawkes.

"He lies!" cried the girl.

"Yes, he lies," said a quiet voice behind them, and they all turned to see the figure of a giant white standing in the open French windows leading to the veranda.

"John!" cried Lady Greystoke, running toward him, "how could I have been mistaken? I—" but the rest of the sentence was lost as Tarzan of the Apes sprang into the room and taking his mate in his arms covered her lips with kisses.

THIS IS IT!

The much-awaited Edgar Rice Burroughs manuscript that spent 50 years in a vault, waiting for the right collaborator and the right moment!

Read on for a glimpse into . . .

TARZAN: THE LOST ADVENTURE
by Edgar Rice Burroughs
and award-winning novelist Joe R. Lansdale

NUMA THE LION padded silently along the trail of the man-thing he was stalking. Numa was getting old. Resiliency had gone from his muscles. When he sprang to seize his prey, he was too slow now, and often he went hungry. Pacco the zebra eluded him with ease, and so did Bara the deer. Only the slowest and weakest of creatures fell prey to his charges. And thus Numa became a man-eater. But he was still a powerful engine of destruction.

The man, naked but for a loincloth and his weapons—spear, bow and arrow, knife, and rope—moved as silently through the forest as did the maneater behind him. He was moving upwind, and the scent spoor of the carnivore was carried away from him. But he had another keen sense always on guard to warn him of approaching danger, and when one of Numa's padded paws snapped a little twig, the man wheeled and faced the lion. He dropped the rope, bow, and quiver from his shoulder, let go of the spear he was carrying, and drew his great knife.

With only a knife, the man faced the king of beasts, and at this close range, that was the way he preferred it.

Discovered, Numa roared and charged. As he rose upon his hind feet to seize his prey, the man leapt to one side, turned and sprang upon Numa's back. The man's right arm encircled the beast's neck, and his legs locked around the small of its body, all with the speed of light.

Roaring in rage, Numa reared erect as the long-bladed knife sank to the hilt behind his left shoulder. Again and again the man struck, and Numa's rich red blood leapt in the sunlight. The lion threw himself from side to side, leaping and bounding in futile efforts to dislodge the creature from its back. And constantly the knife rose and fell, the man clinging to Numa as tight as an entwined ivy vine.

The lion hurled itself on its side and rolled about the jungle floor, tossing up dried leaves and leaf mold, trying to press its attacker into the dirt and dislodge him, but the man held and the knife struck repeatedly.

Suddenly, the lion went limp and sank lifeless to the ground. The man, gore-covered from the spray of Numa's life's blood, leapt erect, and, placing a foot on the body of his kill, lifted his face to the heavens and voiced a long and hideous scream that sent monkeys chattering in fear through the treetops. After five years, Tarzan of the Apes had returned to his jungle.

He was ranging the vast domain that had been his stamping ground since childhood. Here he had foraged with the tribe of Kerchak the king ape. Here the she-ape Kala, his foster mother, had been killed by Kulonga the warrior-son of Mbonga the chief. And here Tarzan had slain Kulonga.

These and many other memories, sweet and bitter-sweet, passed through Tarzan's mind as he paused to wipe the blood from his body and blade with leaves.

In most of this area, far off the beaten track, there were only the animals and the native tribes—savage and primitive, living as their forebears had for ages. The wilderness teemed with game. On the plains, the herbivores grazed; and there the carnivores hunted them by night, which was according to the laws of Nature.

But Tarzan had caught the scent spoor of creatures

notorious as destroyers of peace and tranquility, the one thing that stupidly upsets the balance of Nature. To his sensitive nostrils, Usha the wind carried the effluvium of humanity. And Tarzan was going to investigate.

Tarzan was always suspicious of humans in this district, as there were far more accessible hunting grounds elsewhere; and, too, several of the native tribes here were dangerous, having learned from past experience that outsiders, or at least those they had encountered, had little or no respect for their way of life or for the natural laws of the jungle.

Tarzan could not imagine any reputable guide leading a safari into such dangers; any reliable guide or hunter would know that outsiders had not earned the respect of the natives here, and that to bring foreigners into this realm was to court death.

As the scent of the intruders grew stronger, indicating that he was approaching his quarry, Tarzan took to the trees, swinging through the middle terrace. So gently and naturally did he move amongst the limbs and vines of the great forest, the birds remained undisturbed. This silent, arboreal approach gave him an advantage when his quarry was man, as man is far less likely to detect danger approaching from above than at his own level.

Presently, he reached a point from which he could see those he sought. He looked down on a small, poor safari encamped in a jungle clearing. Tarzan's quick eyes and keen mind took in every important detail of the camp and its occupants.

Four tough-looking men moved about the camp with an assurance that told Tarzan they were the bwanas of this safari. Two of the men were white, two were black. All four looked as hard as tree bark and had the appearance of men accustomed to harshness. They wore .45s on their hips. Each of them wore a battered military uniform, probably the French Foreign Legion, though they were in such bad condition, it was impossible to tell at a glance. From that fact, Tarzan deduced that they were probably deserters. They seemed an impoverished and ill-equipped company, probably straggling through the jungle on their way to the coast.

Besides the four uniformed men, there were ten bearers, and two askaris—head bearers. Tarzan noted particularly that there was no ivory in the camp. That exonerated them from any suspicion of ivory poaching, which, with the needless slaughter of game, was a crime he constantly sought to prevent by any means or measure.

He watched them trudge along for a moment, then left them, but with the intention of keeping an eye on them from time to time until they were out of his domain.

Unaware that Tarzan had hovered above them and passed on, the four bwanas, who were preparing to break camp, uncorked a canteen and passed it around. The askaris and bearers behind them watched them intently, ready to take up their packs at a moment's notice.

When the canteen had made two rounds, one of the white men, a small, wiry man with a face that had seen it all and not liked any of it, turned to the large black man walking beside him, said, "There's only two of 'em, Wilson. And they're picture-takers, and one's a girl. They got lots of food, and we ain't got none."

The other white man, large and sweaty, great moons of sweat swelling beneath his armpits and where his shirt fit tight over the mound of his belly, nodded, said, "Gromvitch is right, Wilson. Another thing. They got plenty of ammunition. We ain't got none. We could use it."

Wilson Jones, whose black face looked to have been at one time a great and avid collector of blows, said, "Yeah, they got food, and they got ammunition, Cannon, but they also got what shoots the ammunition. Get my drift?"

"I get it," said Cannon, "but we don't get what they got, well, we're meat for the worms out here. We got to have ammunition and food to survive."

Wilson looked to the other Negro, Charles Talent. He was a tall man in a ragged uniform with too-short sleeves and too-short pants. The sides of his boots were starting to burst. He was leaning just off the trail against a tree. He didn't look like much, but Wilson knew he was amazingly fast and much stronger than his leanness suggested.

As always, Talent wouldn't look directly at Wilson, or anyone for that matter. He once confided to Wilson it was because his old man had beat him with sticks of sugar cane when he was young; he beat him every day and made Charles look him in the eye and say what the beating was for, even if he didn't know what it was for, other than the fact his old man enjoyed doing it.

Old man Talent had gone through a number of canes when Charles was growing up, but the last one he cut was the last time he did anything. Charles put a cane knife in him, spilled his guts in the cane field, happily kicked his innards around in the dirt, and departed and never looked back.

From that time on, Charles had never been able to look a man directly in the eye. Unless he was killing him.

Wilson studied Charles's slumped posture, his bowed head, and said, "You got somethin' to say, Charles?"

It was slow in coming, but finally, "I ain't got nothin' against doin' what needs to be done. We should have done it then, when we come up on 'em. But then or now, it's all the same. That's all I got to say."

Wilson knew what that meant. Charles loved killing. For Charles, that was what always needed to be done. It was the only time he felt strong, in control.

The other two, they weren't much better. Gromvitch, though a bully, maybe didn't enjoy killing as much as Talent, didn't accept it as quickly as Cannon, but he didn't mind it. And Wilson knew he himself was only a hair's breadth better than any of them. He liked to think that difference made him slightly superior, but in fact he felt bad about how he lived, the choices he had made.

Cannon said, "We got ammunition, we don't need the food so bad. We can hunt game then. We don't get it, we won't last long. Anyone finds us, ever, there won't be enough left to pack a snuff box. Some chewed bones. I say we got to do something, even if it's wrong."

Wilson grinned some damaged teeth. "Hell, boys, wrong is all we ever done, ain't it?"

"That's the truth," said Cannon, "but now we got to do some right for ourselves, even if it is wrong for them pilgrims."

"They've talked to us and gone on," Gromvitch said. "I don't think they suspect nothin', and if they do, they don't care. They're just glad to be shed of us. See how nervous they was? 'Specially that gal."

"I figure if they thought we was gonna do somethin' we'd have done it," Cannon said. "This way, we can surprise 'em. Swoop down on 'em like hawks . . . 'sides, I'd like to have me a little visit with that gal. See she's put together right."

"That's good by me too," Gromvitch said, and he shook the canteen. "And they might have some whiskey somewheres. I'm sick of water."

Wilson thought a moment, studied his companions, and hated them as never before. He couldn't figure how he had ever got himself into such a mess. He wished he'd never left the boxing game. Throwing that fight had changed his life. He shouldn't have done it. Not for money. Not for any reason. He should have fought his best. He should have gone on to be a manager, even a cut man. He should have done a lot of things, but he hadn't done any of them.

425

Wilson thought, if I had it to do over ... He caught himself. Yeah, *if*. And if wishes were horses, beggars would ride.

Wilson turned to Gromvitch. "You stay here, we'll go."

"Me?" Gromvitch said. "Why me?"

"Because I said so," Wilson said. "That isn't good enough, maybe I ought to remind you who's boss here. Without me, you'd still be a Legionnaire eatin' desert."

"No," Gromvitch said. "I don't need no remindin'. But that girl—"

"Get it out of your mind," Wilson said. "I'm not in for that. We have to kill them, we do it quick, and we're out of there. We do what we got to do, not what's fun for you."

"Well," Gromvitch said. "Whiskey then."

"Just mind the camp," Wilson said, then turned to his confederates. "Come on, let's get goin'."

TARZAN: THE LOST ADVENTURE
by Edgar Rice Burroughs
and Joe R. Lansdale

First time in paperback!

Available in June 1997.
Published by Del Rey® Books